Growth and Development in Early Childhood

Eilis Flood

BORU

PRESS

Boru Press Ltd.
The Farmyard
Birdhill
Co. Tipperary
www.borupress.ie

© Eilis Flood 2021

ISBN 978-1-8384134-5-3
Design by Sarah McCoy
Print origination by Liz White Designs
Illustrations by Andriy Yankovskyy
Index by Jane Rogers
Printed by Grafo, S.A. (Spain)

The paper used in this book is made from wood pulp
of managed forests. For every tree felled, at least one tree is planted, thereby
renewing natural resources.

A CIP catalogue record for this book is available from the British Library.

For permission to reproduce photographs and artworks, the author and publisher
gratefully acknowledge the following:
© Alamy: 8, 11, 14, 38, 69, 70, 79, 82, 84, 85, 86, 93, 117, 119, 150, 163, 168, 171, 202,
217, 218, 222, 227, 229, 260 © CF Ireland: 153 © Eilis Flood: 107, 178, 181 © iStock 4,
6, 29, 44, 65, 72, 94, 208, 242 © Shutterstock 2, 3, 18, 19, 21, 22, 23, 24, 25, 26, 27, 30,
31, 33, 37, 42, 44, 45, 47, 49, 51, 52, 54, 59, 70, 71, 72, 77, 94, 118, 120, 128, 142, 146,
148, 154, 160, 166, 167, 173, 175, 187, 195, 199, 205, 206, 207, 208, 214, 215, 223, 224,
225, 226, 230, 236, 239, 244, 246, 249, 250, 253, 256, 257, 258, 259, 261, 268, 273, 278.

The author and publisher have made every effort to trace all copyright holders, but if
any has been inadvertently overlooked we would be pleased to make the necessary
arrangement at the first opportunity.

Boru Press is an independent publisher and is not associated with any education and
training board.

Contents

Acknowledgements

I wish to express my deepest appreciation to everyone who contributed, both professionally and personally, to the writing of this book.

To Marion O'Brien, publishing director. I have worked with you for over fifteen years now and you always approach any new project with such calm efficiency. Thank you.

To Anna Carroll for managing the production of this book, editors Jane Rogers and Tess Tattersall and to designer Liz White and typesetter Jen Patton. Thank you for all your hard work and attention to detail.

Finally, to my three men – Paddy, Luke and Mark – for all your support and encouragement.

Section 1

Child Development 0–6 years

Key Concepts in Child Development

1.1 HISTORICAL VIEWS OF THE CHILD

Childhood is now considered such a distinct and important stage in life that it is difficult to imagine a time when little or no distinction was made between childhood and adulthood. As recently as the end of the 1800s children in Europe, particularly the children of the poor, were treated as miniature adults and were afforded no special status. This is still the case in many parts of the developing world today, with children as young as six or seven years old working to care for younger children and supplement their family's income.

Young child working in poor conditions

Did you know?

Worldwide today 152 million children are victims of child labour, with 73 million of them working in areas defined as hazardous.

Source: International Labour Organization (2017), *Global Estimates of Child Labour: Results and Trends, 2012–2017*. Geneva: ILO.

Throughout history, scholars and philosophers have theorised about the length and nature of childhood and about how children should be raised. Three broad philosophical views of the nature of childhood emerged: original sin; tabula rasa; and innate goodness.

ORIGINAL SIN

Children were thought to be born with the original sin of Adam and Eve. Baptism can remove this sin, but the soul is still susceptible to choosing evil over good. The principal goal of childrearing was to rid the child of this sin, thus creating a decent, law-abiding adult. Childrearing practices were therefore harsh, and punishments were severe.

Did you know?

Corporal punishment was not banned in Irish schools until 1982.

TABULA RASA

This view was originally put forward by the Ancient Greek philosopher Aristotle (384–322 BC), who believed that children were born as 'blank slates'. Later, the English philosopher John Locke (1632–1704) argued that children were not innately sinful, but like a 'blank slate' or 'tabula rasa'. Locke believed that experiences in childhood were important in determining adult characteristics. He advised parents to spend time with their children (something that was not commonplace) so that they could help them to become contributing members of society. Locke and others believed that an adult's personality is largely determined by their upbringing or environment.

John Locke

Extend your learning

The 2003 novel by Lionel Shriver, *We Need to Talk about Kevin*, later adapted into a film, tells the story of a boy who is responsible for a fictional high school massacre. Both the book and film are written in the first person by Kevin's mother, Eva, who documents her attempt to find an explanation for her son's unspeakable actions.

Children Learn What They Live

If children live with criticism, they learn to condemn.

If children live with hostility, they learn to fight.

If children live with fear, they learn to be apprehensive.

If children live with pity, they learn to feel sorry for themselves.

If children live with ridicule, they learn to feel shy.

If children live with jealousy, they learn to feel envy.

If children live with shame, they learn to feel guilty.

If children live with encouragement, they learn confidence.

If children live with tolerance, they learn patience.

If children live with praise, they learn appreciation.

If children live with acceptance, they learn to love.

If children live with approval, they learn to like themselves.

If children live with recognition, they learn it is good to have a goal.

If children live with sharing, they learn generosity.

If children live with honesty, they learn truthfulness.

If children live with fairness, they learn justice.

If children live with kindness and consideration, they learn respect.

If children live with security, they learn to have faith in themselves and in those about them.

If children live with friendliness, they learn the world is a nice place in which to live.

Dorothy Law Nolte

INNATE GOODNESS

This view, put forward by the Swiss-born philosopher Jean-Jacques Rousseau (1712–1778) during the eighteenth century, stressed the inherent goodness of children. He believed that children should be allowed to grow naturally without too much parental monitoring or constraint. He thought that it was important for children to be given opportunities to be close to nature. In his later life he himself is said to have led a very simple life, close to nature – something that is said to have been fostered by his father.

Jean-Jacques Rousseau

Today, Western society views childhood as a highly eventful and unique period during which children master specific skills in preparation for adult life. We believe that experiences in childhood lay important foundations for adult personality and behaviour. Childhood is no longer considered an inconvenient waiting period during which children should be seen and not heard. Today, we protect children from adult stresses and responsibilities, we have strict child labour laws, we handle juvenile crime through a special system of juvenile justice, we have systems of child protection when families require it and we spend considerable resources researching, caring for and educating children.

Collaborate

Below are two extracts from the book *A 1950s Irish Childhood: From Catapults to Communion Medals* by Ruth Illingworth. Read the extract and discuss in groups the ways in which experiences of childhood in Ireland have changed during the intervening years.

Popular playground games included 'Red Rover'. This involved six to ten, or more, children forming two opposing lines, with those in each line all clasping hands. One team would send a runner towards the opposing team, who would try to crash in between the other team's players where their hands met. The defending team tried to stop the attack and capture the runner. If the runner broke though, they grabbed a player from the other team and took them to join their team. If he didn't break through, he was captured by the other team. As the game proceeded, the players would chant 'Red Rover, Red Rover, send someone over'. A variation of this game was 'Bulldog', in which two lines of children would face each other and then charge fast and hard against the opposite line, seeking to break through it. (Illingworth 2018: 98)

Playing conkers was a popular game in the Autumn. Hours would be spent collecting them, and in some areas, there were conker championships, the object being 'to smash your rivals' conkers with your own' as Deirdre Purcell recalls it. The matches tended to be 'short and brutal'. Conkers on strings were a familiar sight in school play yards and streets around the country. No one worried too much about eye injuries. (Illingworth 2018: 112)

1.2 WHAT IS MEANT BY THE TERM 'CHILD DEVELOPMENT'?

Child development refers to the sequence of physical, intellectual, language, social and emotional changes that occur in a child from conception to the beginning of adulthood. During this process a child progresses from dependency on their parent/guardian to increasing independence.

Child development incorporates physical growth as well as intellectual, language, emotional and social development. While these aspects are often considered separately, each is very much connected to and influences the other. For example, as the brain develops physically, intellectual abilities also increase. This increased intellectual ability allows the child to explore their social world more, to develop their emotional responses to it, and it stimulates the language needed to describe it. This exploration directly impacts on further physical brain development – and so on.

Several factors affect the course and progression of an individual child's development. These include the innate or the biological makeup of the child themselves and external factors such as family, society, economics, health and culture. Thus, growth and development are directly related to the child's nutrition, socioeconomic status, parenting styles, education and interaction with peers.

1.3 WHY STUDY CHILD DEVELOPMENT?

Over the years, the nature of childhood and child development has been the subject of much research. Why?

IMPROVING CHILDREN'S HEALTH AND WELLBEING

What effects does smoking, alcohol or drug use have on the unborn foetus? How does a poor diet affect a child's ability to learn effectively? Are computer games making today's children more violent? More overweight? It is important to understand how environmental influences such as these affect children's mental, emotional and physical health in order to work towards improvement. This is one of the primary reasons for studying child development.

PARENTING

What effect does two parents working outside the home have on children? What difficulties may be experienced by children reared in one-parent households? Do adopted and fostered children fare as well as children raised by their biological parents? How damaging is separation and divorce to a child's development? How should children be guided and disciplined? Understanding the nature of child development can help people to become better parents. It encourages people to reflect on their own experiences as children and sort through which practices they feel were good and that they should continue, and which they feel they should adapt or abandon.

Collaborate

The Irish psychotherapist Stella O'Malley in her book *Cotton Wool Kids – What's Making Irish Parents Paranoid?* (2015) asks why modern parents are keeping their children indoors for fear of predators lurking around every corner and children are spending their days in front of screens or in supervised activities, over-controlled and growing steadily fatter and more unhappy and anxious. She contends that  commercial interests ensure that parents feel anxious and filled with fear simply to sell them more stuff. While in fact childhood has never been safer; the rates of childhood mortality, injury and sexual abuse are lower today that at any time since records began.

In groups, discuss the concept of 'cotton wool kids' described by Stella O' Malley.

EDUCATION

How can children's overall development be best encouraged in the education setting? What methods are most effective in facilitating children to learn to read and do mathematics? Should we be concentrating on a broad all-round education rather than focusing narrowly on academic outcomes? How can children falling behind be best identified and what interventions are most effective? How does a child's home environment affect their ability to learn effectively? What forms of behavioural management are most effective in care and educational settings? These are some of the questions that concern professionals working with children in a care and educational capacity and are some of the reasons for much research in the area of child development.

EARLY IDENTIFICATION OF ADDITIONAL NEEDS

It is important to be aware that while a child's development has a predictable sequence, all children are unique in their developmental journey and the timeframes at which they meet their developmental milestones. Having said this, checking a child's developmental progress at particular age markers helps to ensure that the child is roughly on track for their age. Early detection of developmental challenges and additional needs means that positive interventions and supports can be put in place in a timely manner. Early intervention and support can help minimise the impact these developmental challenges have on a child's skill development and subsequently their confidence. Early, appropriate interventions can have a very strong positive impact on future developmental progress.

1.4 THE DEVELOPMENTAL PROCESS

We all develop similarly in some ways. For example, most full-term babies smile at six weeks, walk at about a year and say their first words at about 13 months. In other ways, however, we can develop very differently from each other. For example, some children begin reading as early as three years, whereas others may never learn to read fluently; some children develop great sporting talent, whereas others may show no such talent; some children show huge musical ability, whereas others do not. Child development studies the process of human development. It tries to identify its milestones and tries to understand what best shapes and promotes it. The pattern of human development results from an interplay between three different processes – biological, cognitive and socio-emotional.

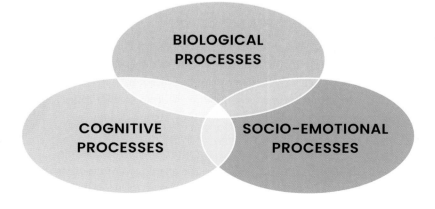

1.5 PERSPECTIVES AND THEORIES OF CHILD DEVELOPMENT

Over the years developmental theorists have proposed several different theories about why people develop and behave the way they do. Theorists gather data and try to come up with possible explanations for that data, thus forming a theory. Child development is a complex and multifaceted area of study. There is no one theory that covers it all. Each theory contributes a part to the overall puzzle, and while some theories seem to disagree, most complement each other in our overall understanding of how children develop and learn. Some theories lend more weight to innate factors (heredity); others place more importance on environment and the experiences a child has. Some theorists believe that development is continuous over the lifespan; others believe it occurs in distinctive stages.

Human development theory can be loosely classified under **five** different headings or perspectives. Each of these is introduced below and is dealt with in more detail in later chapters.

1. **Psychoanalytic perspective** – focuses on emotions
2. **Learning perspective** – focuses on observable behaviours (this is sometimes called a behaviourist perspective)
3. **Ethological perspective** – focuses on evolutionary underpinning of behaviour (sometimes called the maturationalist perspective)
4. **Cognitive perspective** – focuses on the importance of thought processes (sometimes called the constructivist perspective)
5. **Contextual or social constructionist perspective** – focuses on the importance of culture and social relationships

PSYCHOANALYTIC PERSPECTIVE

The psychoanalytic perspective is concerned with the unconscious forces that motivate human behaviour. This perspective was introduced at the beginning of the twentieth century in the work of Sigmund Freud (1856–1939). Psychoanalytic theory emphasises that observable behaviour is merely a surface characteristic or manifestation of the inner workings of the mind. Psychoanalytic theorists stress the importance of early life experiences and relationships with parents in the formation of the adult personality. The psychoanalytic perspective has been expanded and modified over the years by other influential theorists, including Anna Freud, Melanie Klein, Erik Erikson and D.W. Winnicott. These theorists are discussed in later chapters, particularly in Chapter 7.

LEARNING OR BEHAVIOURIST PERSPECTIVE

The learning or behaviourist perspective, unlike the psychoanalytic perspective, is not concerned with unconscious forces but with behaviour that can be observed and objectively studied in a scientific manner. Learning theorists believe that development results from learning rather than the other way round. Learning occurs when there is a long-lasting change in behaviour as a result of the individual responding and adapting to their environment. Classical and operant conditioning are important concepts in this perspective. Ivan Pavlov, B.F. Skinner and J.B. Watson are all important theorists of this perspective. These theorists are discussed in later chapters, particularly in Chapter 5.

B.F. Skinner

ETHOLOGICAL OR MATURATIONALIST PERSPECTIVE

The ethological or maturationalist perspective focuses on the biological or evolutionary basis of behaviour. This perspective originated with the famous English naturalist Charles Darwin (1809–1892). In 1859 Darwin published his famous (and at the time hugely controversial) book *On the Origin of Species*. His main thesis was that all species have descended over time from the same ancestors and that species-specific characteristics have evolved over time through a process of natural selection. Characteristics that are advantageous to a species' survival tend to be passed down from generation to generation. Those that are not advantageous tend not to be passed down and die out. The Austrian ethnologists Konrad Lorenz and Karl von Frisch, together with Dutch colleague Nikolaas Tinbergen, received the Nobel Prize in Physiology and Medicine in 1973 for their observations of different species of animals both in their natural environment and in the laboratory setting. Their belief was that for each species, a variety of innate, species-specific behaviours has evolved to increase their odds of survival. In the 1950s John Bowlby extended these ethnological principles to human development with his theories on infant attachment (see Chapter 7).

COGNITIVE PERSPECTIVE

The cognitive perspective emphasises the importance of conscious thoughts and how the way we think changes as we mature. It proposes that, much like a scientist, children actively 'construct' understandings for themselves by studying the world around them. Cognitivists or constructivists do not believe that children are mere vessels to be filled with ready-made knowledge and understanding, but instead that children take in information and knowledge from the world around them, process this information and arrive at their own understandings. Jean Piaget (1896–1980) is seen as the founder of cognitive theory. His theories are dealt with in more detail in Chapters 5 and 7.

CONTEXTUAL OR SOCIAL CONSTRUCTIONIST PERSPECTIVE

Like Piaget, the Russian psychologist Lev Vygotsky (1896–1934) argued that children actively construct their own knowledge. Unlike Piaget, however, he emphasised the importance of social interactions and culture in this construction. This is why Vygotsky's theories are sometimes classified under a separate heading from Piaget's, namely social constructionism. Vygotsky's and Piaget's theories are dealt with in more detail in Chapters 5 and 7.

1.6 THE NATURE VS. NURTURE DEBATE

The nature vs. nurture debate has long been the subject of discussion among developmental psychologists. The debate centres on the question of whether development is primarily influenced by **nature** – genetic and hereditary factors that influence who we are, from our physical appearance to our intellectual ability to our personality traits – or by **nurture** – all the environmental variables that impact on who we are, e.g. early childhood experiences, parenting practices, social relationships and our culture. Almost nobody argues today that development can be explained by either nature or nurture alone. However, which is more important? This is where disagreement arises.

Nativist philosophers such as Plato and Descartes take the position that all or most behaviours and characteristics are the result of inheritance. **Empiricists** such as John Locke, as mentioned above, believe that children are born as blank slates or tabula rasa and therefore place most importance on the environment a child is raised in. Behaviourism is a good example of a theory rooted in empiricism. Behaviourists such as JB Watson (1878–1954) believed that people could be trained to do and become anything, regardless of their genetic background.

In the middle between nativists and empiricists were psychologists such as Jack Tizard (1919–1979). He believed that while genetic inheritance can strongly influence developmental potential, environment has an important part to play in optimising that potential. Jack Tizard's Brooklands experiment involved moving 16 children with severe learning disabilities from the Fountain Hospital in London, a large institution for children and adults with learning disabilities, to a smaller, more homely house called Brooklands in Surrey, England. The children had an average age of seven years and an average IQ of 25. The group was matched with 16 children of a similar age and IQ, who remained at the large Fountain Hospital. The children in Brooklands were divided into two 'families' of eight, each with two housemothers who worked primarily with the same group of eight children. In this way intimate relationships between the children and the adults who cared for them could be fostered. There was no formal instruction and much of the children's day was spent communicating with staff and at play, with interest being the motivating factor. After three years, the children living in Brooklands showed greater development, particularly in the areas of speech and social intelligence.

Extend your learning

The short film 'Mentally Handicapped Children Growing Up' (22 minutes) was made in 1969 about the Brooklands experiment. While the film uses outdated terms that would not be acceptable today to describe children with disabilities, it does give a good insight into Tizard's work. It is available to download from Vimeo.

TWIN STUDIES

Studies of identical twins have been used to investigate the nature vs. nurture debate further. For example, in 1979, Thomas Bouchard began to study identical twins who had been separated at birth and raised in different families. He found that an identical twin reared away from his or her co-twin has the same chance of being similar to the co-twin in terms of personality, interests and attitudes as one who has been reared with his or her co-twin. This led to the conclusion that the similarities between identical twins are due to genes, not environment, and that the differences between identical twins reared apart must be due totally to the environment.

THREE IDENTICAL STRANGERS

Three Identical Strangers is a 2018 documentary, directed by Tim Wardle, about the lives of Edward Galland, David Kellman and Robert Shafran, identical triplets adopted as six-month-old infants by separate families. The documentary describes how Robert (Bobby) discovered he had a twin brother by chance when he arrived on the campus of a New York community college and was greeted by fellow students who

Edward Galland, David Kellman and Robert Shafran

incorrectly thought he was Edward (Eddy). Months later the publicity surrounding this human-interest story reached David, whose resemblance to the other two boys and the similarities around their adoption status suggested that the three were triplets.

The brothers, despite being reared apart, realised that they were remarkably alike and they celebrated their newfound brotherhood. They soon appeared in the print media and on talk shows. They moved in together and opened their own restaurant. Over time, however, differences between the three men became apparent and they began to experience difficulties in their relationships with each other and others. All three brothers experienced mental health problems for years and Edward Galland tragically took his own life in 1995.

Following the revelation that the boys were triplets, their adoptive parents sought more information from the Louise Wise adoption agency, which claimed that they separated the boys because of the difficulty of placing triplets in a single household. On further investigation, however, the brothers and their adoptive parents discovered that they had been unknowingly involved in a study by Austrian-born psychiatrist Peter B. Neubauer, under the auspices of the Jewish Board of Guardians. The study was never published because Neubauer, a survivor of the Nazi regime, feared that public opinion would be strongly against it. Full records of the study are sealed at the Yale University Library until 25 October 2065.

Neubauer and his research associates intentionally separated and placed his twin and triplet subjects with families who had different parenting styles and economic statuses. In the case of the triplets, one was placed with a very well-off family, one with a middle-class family and one with a working-class family. Throughout their childhood, the triplets (and another five sets of twins who were also part of the study) were visited and their development studied and evaluated.

1.7 CRITICAL/SENSITIVE PERIOD OF CHILDREN'S DEVELOPMENT

There are times in the life of a child (both before and after birth) during which certain environmental conditions are deemed vital or important to normal development. These are called critical or sensitive periods. The difference between 'critical' periods and 'sensitive' periods is subtle. Indeed, in many research reports both terms are taken to mean the same thing.

A **critical period** is a short period of time during which it is vital that the embryo, foetus, baby or child is exposed to the correct environmental conditions. If this does not happen, there can be irreversible consequences in terms of the child's development.

Sensitive periods occur over a longer period of time. During this time, it is important that the foetus, infant or child is exposed to the correct environmental conditions. If this does not happen, there will be developmental delays that will require targeted interventions to overcome.

Critical and sensitive periods in human development are very difficult to study scientifically because it is unethical to perform experiments on humans to prove or disprove the presence of critical and/ or sensitive periods. Much of the theory on critical and sensitive periods has been based on findings from cases of naturally occurring instances of malnutrition, neglect or abuse. However, because these cases are not under strict experimental controls these studies often provide correlational evidence only.

EVIDENCE SUPPORTING CRITICAL PERIOD THEORY

THE CASE OF GENIE

Genie (not her real name) was a child who spent nearly all the first 13 years of her life locked inside a bedroom strapped naked to a potty chair. She was a victim of one of the most severe cases of social isolation and abuse in history. Genie was discovered by American authorities on 4 November 1970 when her mother, who was almost completely blind, took her with her to claim disability benefits. Genie was born in 1957, to a mother and father who were both mentally unstable. Genie had three older siblings, only one of whom survived, a brother. When Genie was between 14 and 20 months of age and just beginning to learn speech, a doctor told her family that she seemed to be developmentally delayed. Her father took the opinion more seriously than it was expressed by the doctor, apparently deciding that she was profoundly mentally disabled, and subjected her to severe confinement and ritual ill treatment in an attempt to 'protect' her.

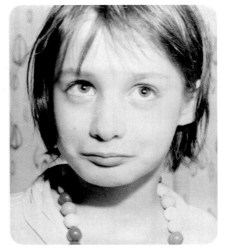

Genie

Genie spent the next 11 years of her life locked in a room at the back of the house. During the day, she was tied naked to a child's potty chair, while at night, she was bound in a sleeping bag and placed in a cot that was covered with wire mesh. It is believed that Genie's father beat her if she vocalised and barked and growled at her like a dog in order to keep her quiet. He also rarely allowed his wife and son to leave the house or even to speak, and he absolutely forbade them to speak to Genie. By the age of 13, Genie was almost entirely mute, with a vocabulary of about 20 words and a few short phrases (nearly all negative), such as 'stop it' and 'no more'.

After Genie was discovered, she began a programme of extensive rehabilitation at Children's Hospital Los Angeles. On occasion, Genie lived with the psychologists working with her and also in a series of foster homes. Genie never learned to speak fluently and incorrectly constructed sentences, e.g. 'Applesauce buy store.' Her failure to master language completely is taken as evidence of the critical period theory in relation to language development.

Genie's mother successfully sued the Californian health authorities for their treatment of Genie, arguing that they treated Genie like a medical experiment and ignored her welfare as a human being. Genie is still alive today and lives in an undisclosed sheltered home in southern California for adults who cannot live independently.

HOW THIS CASE SUPPORTS THE CRITICAL PERIOD THEORY

During the first years of life children have many more neural connections in their brain than adults, e.g. a three-year-old has twice as many connections as an adult. These connections, however, are quite disorganised. As the brain develops, these neural connections are 'tested and organised' and those that are not being used are 'cut'. In this way the brain develops using a 'use it or lose it' mechanism. In Genie's case, because she was not exposed to normal speech during her early years the parts of the brain responsible for grammar were not developed and were therefore irreversibly 'cut'. Genie was able to learn many words, but was never able to learn question words such as who, what, when, where and why or pronouns such as he, she, it, they, him or her. Such words and a knowledge of how to use them is necessary for forming grammatically correct sentences. This case therefore supports the critical period theory in relation to child development.

Extend your learning

A film about Genie's case, *Mockingbird Don't Sing*, made in 2001, is available to watch on YouTube (1 hour 40 mins). A shorter but very interesting clip about the case is also available on YouTube: 'Genie Wiley TLC Documentary 2003' (12.27).

Collaborate

In groups, discuss the implications that the critical period theory might have for the learning of a second language.

EVIDENCE SUPPORTING SENSITIVE PERIOD THEORY

In child development terminology an **attachment** is a close emotional bond between a child and his or her primary carer. Strong or secure attachments are considered vital to healthy emotional development and the formation of secure relationships in childhood and later in life. Attachment theory indicates that the sensitive period for these primary attachments is between birth and two years of age. In the past, and even today, in some countries infants are reared together in orphanages with a large numbers of babies and not enough staff members to take care of their attachment needs. Many of these children go through their first years with hardly any touch or affection that would teach them to trust and form strong securely attached relationships.

In 1966 Nicolae Ceauşescu came to power in Romania. He was a communist dictator and believed in the 1930s' Stalinist dogma that population growth would fuel economic growth. Government policy at this time was for women to bear as many children as possible. Romania was still a very poor country, and this meant that many parents were encouraged to place their children in state-run institutions.

When the Ceauşescu regime in Romania fell in 1989, there was widespread media coverage of the plight of approximately 170,000 children being reared in profoundly deprived institutions. The concern raised over their suffering led to a humanitarian response that involved a substantial number of children being adopted. From a scientific and theoretical perspective, the extreme circumstances that these children were reared in created a valuable 'natural experiment'.

Romanian orphanage

For example, in 2000 three colleagues, Nathan Fox, Charles Nelson and Charles Zeanah, launched the Bucharest Project. This project began by assessing 136 children ranging in age from six months to nearly three years (average age 22 months) who had been living in Bucharest's institutions from birth. They randomly assigned half of the children to move into Romanian foster families, whom the researchers recruited and assisted financially. The other half remained in institutions. A third, control, group had never been in an institution.

Over the next 14 years, the researchers returned to assess the development of the children in all three settings. They found many profound problems among the children who remained in institutions. These children had delays in cognitive function, motor development and language. They showed deficits in socio-emotional behaviours and experienced more psychiatric disorders. They also showed changes in the patterns of electrical activity in their brain, as measured by EEG.

For the children who were moved into foster care, the situation was better. These children showed improvements in language, IQ and social-emotional functioning. They were able to form secure attachment relationships with their caregivers and made significant gains in their ability to express emotions.

While children in foster care showed significant improvements when compared with those remaining in institutions, they still remained behind the control group of children who had never been institutionalised. Most important, some foster children fared much better than others. The most predictable indicator of this was the age at which the child was moved to foster care. Children who were removed from the institutions before the age of two made the biggest gains, thus supporting the idea that there is a sensitive period for forming emotional attachments.

REFLECTIVE PRACTICE

Read the case study below. In groups, make some suggestions as to how a quality early learning and care (ELC) setting can help nurture this child's environment and help improve his developmental outcomes.

CASE STUDY

David was adopted from Thailand a year ago by Abigale and Benny Lynch. David had been in a Thai institution from birth until he came to Ireland aged two and a half. David is now three and a half and in terms of his overall development those who care for him have noticed that he does not seem to be as advanced as other children of the same age in the setting. He cannot run as confidently as the other children, often falling or bumping into objects; he cannot yet ride a tricycle; and unlike the other children finds it difficult to catch or kick a large ball. In terms of his vocabulary he still speaks in two- or three-word sentences and unlike the other children does not generally ask questions. He tends not to play with other children but rather plays alongside them. While he has been attending the setting each day for the past six months, David still gets very upset each morning when his mum drops him off so she can go to work.

SHOW YOU KNOW

1. Name and briefly describe the three broad philosophical views of the nature of childhood that have emerged throughout history.

2. Describe what is meant by the term 'child development'.

3. Outline four reasons why it is important to study child development.

4. Name and describe two perspectives of child development.

5. Explain what is meant by the 'nature vs. nurture' debate.

6. Do you believe that there are critical or sensitive periods in children's development? Please give reasons for your answer.

Promoting Children's Holistic Development in Line with Aistear and Síolta

What I will learn

* The concept of holistic development

* The pattern of holistic development from simple to complex, from head to toe, from inner to outer and from general to specific

* The difference between 'growth' and 'development'

* How the rate and sequence of children's development can vary from child to child

* How studying normative patterns of development in children can assist practitioners with child observation and curriculum/programme planning

* How Aistear and Síolta promote children's holistic development

2.1 HOLISTIC DEVELOPMENT

Holistic approaches to children's development and learning recognise the connectedness of a child's mind, body and spirit. When early learning and childcare professionals take a holistic approach, they pay attention to children's physical, social, emotional and spiritual wellbeing as well as cognitive and linguistic aspects of learning. If different aspects of a child's development are seen in isolation, the child is not being seen in a holistic way or as a 'whole' person.

On the other hand, it can be useful to observe particular areas of development closely, e.g. to check a child's progress, celebrate success, plan next steps or give special help where needed. However, even when focusing on one aspect of development it is important to continue to see the child as a 'whole person' with a body, thoughts and ideas, emotions and social relationships all developing and functioning simultaneously. When we think of the child in this way, we are taking a 'holistic approach'.

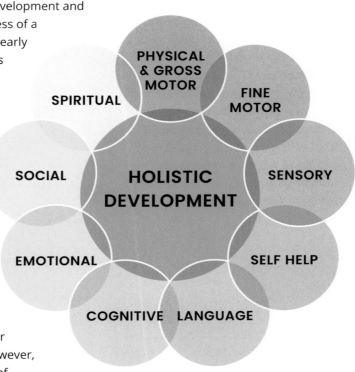

A holistic approach is important when planning and assessing the needs of young children. It allows you to see the child as an individual and understand how they are progressing and developing. It enables you to see how all the developmental areas link up and how progress in one area may promote progress in another area. For example, a child is learning how to eat independently with a spoon (physical). This can also impact on other aspects of development. If the child is given plenty of time and encouraged and praised for their efforts, this will lead to greater independence and increased self-esteem (emotional) and the child is learning about spatial awareness (cognitive).

In order to use a holistic approach to child development we need to examine each of the areas of development in order to understand how each area links to the others. For example, when a child begins to walk independently and steadily this gives them the opportunity to explore and offers them increased opportunities for learning. Understanding children's development holistically helps ensure that no aspect of a child's development is neglected or hampered in some way that could prevent or challenge the child reaching their full potential.

Collaborate

Read the case study below and discuss in groups how aspects of Adrian's development could be impacted as a result of his home environment. Imagine that Adrian has recently joined your pre-school. Make some suggestions about how the setting could help attend to Adrian's needs in a holistic way. Consider especially Adrian's social development.

CASE STUDY

Ellen and Peter Greenan are both 46 years old. They have been married for over 20 years and Adrian is their miracle baby. They had been trying for years to have a baby and had given up just after Ellen's 40th birthday after having had many rounds of fertility treatment. Adrian was conceived naturally. Ellen was ultra-careful during the pregnancy, terrified that something would go wrong, as it had so many times before. Peter is a science lecturer and Ellen a music teacher. Ellen took a career break to care for Adrian, returning to work when Adrian turned four years old. Since Adrian was born both Ellen and Peter have spent lots of time with him, reading to him, introducing him to music and bringing him on interesting trips to places like the zoo. Adrian does have cousins, all of whom are much older than him, so he spends a lot of his time in the company of adults. The family live in a rural area, so there are no children Adrian's age living close to him. Adrian has now just turned four and is very advanced in many ways. He can read, he has started to play the piano and is very interested in inventions and anything to do with science and nature. He feels comfortable talking with adults but can be very shy around children his own age. He finds it difficult to relate to them, especially if they are engaging in rough and tumble play, kicking a ball or generally involved in unstructured activities.

2.2 PATTERNS OF HOLISTIC DEVELOPMENT

There is a set of principles that characterise the pattern and process of growth and development. These principles or characteristics describe typical development as a predictable and orderly process; that is, we can predict how most children will develop and that they will develop at the same rate and at about the same time as other children. Although there are individual differences in children's personalities, activity levels and timing of developmental milestones, such as ages and stages, the principles and characteristics of development follow universal patterns.

FROM SIMPLE (CONCRETE) TO COMPLEX

Development progresses from simple actions to increasingly more complex ones. For example, children sit unaided before they can crawl and stand before they can walk. Likewise, children use their cognitive and language skills to reason and solve problems. These skills also progress from the simple to the more complex. For example, learning the relationship between things (how things are different or similar) is termed classification. In the beginning children are not able to classify effectively at all and may for example call all four-legged furry creatures 'doggy', a concept they are familiar with. A three- or four-year-old will classify objects according to some concrete reason, for example an apple and an orange are similar because they are round, or you can eat them. Later, children will understand the more abstract concept of fruit.

FROM HEAD TO TOE

This principle of development is also called the **cephalocaudal principle**. Children's development progresses downwards from head to toe. Physical control begins with the baby being able to hold their head upright and control their facial movements. Development then progresses down the body to the arms and hands, e.g. at 4–6 months the baby will transfer an object from head to hand. Development then progresses down the back, with the child being able to sit unaided from approximately 6–7 months, and finally to the legs and feet, with most babies walking at approximately 13 months.

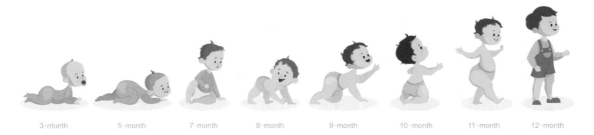

| 3-month | 5-month | 7-month | 8-month | 9-month | 10-month | 11-month | 12-month |

FROM INNER TO OUTER

This is the principal of **proximodistal development**. This means that the spinal cord develops before the outer parts of the body. The child's arms develop before the hands, and the hands and feet develop before the fingers and toes.

FROM GENERAL TO SPECIFIC

Development progresses from general to more specific. In motor development, the infant will grasp objects with the whole hand before they can use only their thumb and forefinger. In terms of emotional development, a young baby will show pleasure by a massive general response, e.g. they give a broad smile, their eyes widen and they wave their arms and kick their legs vigorously. An older child, in contrast, exhibits a much more specific response, e.g. they may smile or give a gesture like a thumbs-up.

2.3 DIFFERENCES BETWEEN GROWTH AND DEVELOPMENT

Growth refers to a physical increase over time. It includes changes in height, weight, body proportions and general physical appearance. Growth involves structural and physiological changes that take place in an individual during the process of maturation. During childhood, growth means an increase in height, weight and the size of the child's organs.

Development refers to changes in the individual as a whole. Development is a continuous process during which physical, intellectual, language, social and emotional changes occur. Development is also possible without growth. Growth does not continue throughout life, whereas development does. Growth occurs due to the multiplication of body cells, whereas development occurs due to maturation and interaction with the environment. Growth is cellular whereas development is organisational, involving cells, tissues, organs and whole systems, e.g. the nervous system.

2.4 SEQUENCE AND RATE OF DEVELOPMENT

Children throughout the world seem to pass through similar sequences of development. In 1973 Mary Sheridan first published her book *From Birth to Five Years*, in which she suggested that children pass through various stages linked to the child's age, e.g. the child sits, then crawls, then stands holding on to furniture, then walks. However, not all children go through this exact sequence. Some children never crawl, preferring to bottom shuffle and walk much earlier or later than indicated. A traditional approach to child development has placed an emphasis on normative measurement and with children reaching various 'milestones' at certain ages. In reality, however, there is a wide range of normal development, which is influenced by many factors such as genetics, family, society and culture. For example, babies in rural African communities tend to walk earlier than European or American babies. Studies have found that this is because African mothers tend to actively 'teach' the child to sit alone, stand and then walk. A study of the babies born into the Kokwet farming community in Kenya found that babies were taught to sit starting at five months old. The baby is set down into a special hole in the ground that has been made to support their back. The babies spent on average 60% of their waking time sitting like this and quickly learned to sit alone. When Western babies are sitting in baby bouncers, etc., they do not have to support their own torso (Super 1976). While this study was done many years ago, the findings still stand today. Normal development does not occur at predetermined age-defined stages but is influenced by many factors.

2.5 NORMATIVE PATTERNS OF DEVELOPMENT

However, while normative patterns of development should not be used prescriptively in the early learning and care (ELC) setting, they are useful. They can help those caring and working with young children to observe children in a structured way and plan activities that will promote their holistic development. The mnemonic **PILES** can be used to make sure that practitioners remember to look at every aspect of a child's development, thus considering the child holistically. PILES stands for **P**hysical, **I**ntellectual (also called cognitive), **L**anguage, **E**motional and **S**ocial. These areas of development are very well recognised and promoted by all four themes of Aistear, the Irish curriculum framework for children from birth to six years. Aistear recognises these areas of development and also adds creative, moral and spiritual development. Aistear's themes are:

1. Wellbeing
2. Identity and Belonging
3. Communicating
4. Exploring and Thinking

Holistic Development in the First Month

Normative Physical Development

Gross motor skills:

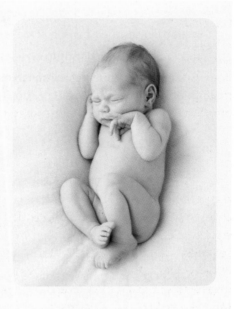

* When lying in the supine position (on their back), lies with head to one side, knees bent towards the body with soles of the feet touching.

* When placed in the prone position (on their front) there is complete flexion, i.e. legs and arms are curled up under the body.

* When held in a sitting position, complete head lag and the back is curved.

* Will startle if they hear loud noises.

* Arms and legs (left and right) move in unison – not one arm or one leg at a time.

Fine motor skills:

* Fists are clenched.

* Turns their head towards the light or bright shiny objects and stares.

* Gazes at their carer's face while being fed or held.

Normative Intellectual or Cognitive Development

* Demonstrates innate reflexes, e.g. sucking, grasping, crying.

* Explores their environment through their senses:

    * **Touch:** from the beginning babies feel pain. Their face, abdomen, hands and the soles of their feet are very sensitive to touch. If a baby is moved suddenly, they will 'startle' – this is called the Moro reflex.

    * **Sound:** even a newborn baby will turn to sound. The baby may become still and 'listen' to the sound or quicken their movement to a louder, higher-pitched sound. They show a preference for familiar human voices.

    * **Taste:** babies like sweet tastes, e.g. breastmilk.

    * **Sight:** babies are sensitive to light. They can focus on objects up to 20 cm away and show a preference for human faces.

* Will imitate facial expressions, e.g. they will put their tongue out if you do.

Normative Communication and Language Development

* Responds to sounds, particularly familiar voices.
* Cries to indicate need, e.g. hungry, cold or dirty nappy and quietens when picked up.
* Makes eye contact.

Normative Emotional and Social Development:

* Recognises their parent's/carer's voice.
* When upset, responds to cuddles, voice and affection.
* Uses whole-body responses to express pleasure, e.g. while being fed or bathed.
* Becomes alert when hearing a pleasant sound, like music.

Holistic Development: One to Three Months

Normative Physical Development

Gross motor skills:

* When lying in the supine position, lies with head to one side, can move head to change position, arm and leg on side head is facing will be held out. By three months head can be held in a central position and baby will kick legs strongly, sometimes together, sometimes separately. Will wave arms symmetrically before bringing them in over the body.
* When placed in the prone position, lies on one side but can now move head to change position, legs and arms are no longer bent and tucked under the body. By three months the baby will be able to lift head and chest, supporting themselves on their elbows and forearms.
* When held in a sitting position, head may stay steady for a moment before falling onto chest. By three months back will be straight, except for curve at bottom of lumbar region.

Fine motor skills:

* Will follow moving objects close to their face.
* Gazes at their carer's face while being fed or held.
* By three months finger play starts; the baby will move their hands around and watch them. They will wave their arms in excitement and can hold an object such as a rattle in their hand for a short time before dropping it. May hit themselves on the head with it.

Normative Intellectual or Cognitive Development

* Will begin to repeat actions first encountered by chance, e.g. infant sucks their thumb and will begin to do so intentionally. All actions are self-directed.
* Recognises breast or bottle – will wave arms in excitement.
* Will be able to differentiate the smell of their mother from others.

Normative Communication and Language Development

* Begins to coo and gurgle when happy and content.
* Cries become more expressive.

Normative Emotional and Social Development

* Social smile emerges from five to six weeks. Babies will smile at anyone who smiles at them.
* Enjoys being hugged or cuddled.
* May stop crying when they hear, see or feel their carer close.

Holistic Development: Three to Six Months

Normative Physical Development

Gross motor skills:

* Will move head around to follow people or other things, e.g. family dog.
* Good head control and is beginning to sit with support.
* Can roll over from back to side.
* Is beginning to reach for objects.
* Plays with own feet when in supine position.
* Will hold their head up when pulled to sitting position.

Fine motor skills:

* Begins to use palmar grasp and can transfer objects, e.g. a block, from hand to hand.
* Puts everything towards their mouth.

Normative Intellectual or Cognitive Development

* Enjoys looking at bright colours and complicated objects.
* Begins to reach for things so is starting to gain some spatial awareness.
* Knows who their carers are and will begin to 'make strange' when approached by unfamiliar people.
* Co-ordination improves, e.g. can pick up an object and put it into their mouth.
* Can differentiate between the taste of different foods and may begin to show preferences.

Normative Communication and Language Development

* Will react to the tone of someone's voice, e.g. may laugh at a happy tone or get upset by an angry one.
* Begins to make vowel sounds, e.g. 'ee', 'ah'.
* Begins to laugh or squeal with pleasure.

»

Normative Emotional and Social Development

* Begins to 'make strange' at between four and six months. They show a preference for their familiar carer.
* Begins to have a regular and predictable sleep pattern.

Holistic Development: Six to Nine Months

Normative Physical Development

Gross motor skills:

* Can roll from front to back but not from back to front.
* May grasp feet and put them in their mouth.
* May attempt to crawl, but sometimes legs will slide backwards.
* Can sit without support for longer periods of time.
* May begin to stand up holding furniture, or 'cruise', i.e. walk along holding on to furniture.

Fine motor skills:

* May pick up objects using pincer grasp with thumb and index finger.
* Will transfer objects from hand to hand.
* Continues to put objects in their mouth.

Normative Intellectual or Cognitive Development

* From 8–9 months will look for a fallen object. This is called the object permanence, i.e. they know that objects continue to exist even when we can't see them.
* Can now make simple associations, e.g. when carer puts on their bib, they know food is coming.

Normative Communication and Language Development

* Babbling becomes tuneful (this does not happen in deaf babies).
* Begins to understand words like 'up', e.g. may lift up arms to be lifted when this word is said.
* Repeats sounds.

Normative Emotional and Social Development

* Can feed themselves with finger foods.
* May show distress when their carer leaves and may continue crying for some time.
* Shows fear of 'strangers' and will cry if a non-familiar adult interacts with them.
* Crawling allows babies to do more for themselves and reach for objects or crawl to preferred people.
* Recognition of emotion emerges – will laugh or cry with others, e.g. siblings.

Holistic Development: Nine to Twelve Months

Normative Physical Development

Gross motor skills:

* Increased mobility – may be crawling, bottom shuffling, bear walking or even walking.
* Can sit steadily on their own and bend forward to pick up objects.
* May crawl upstairs or onto furniture – will find it difficult to climb down safely, though.
* May bounce to the rhythm of music.

Fine motor skills:

* Mature pincer grasp and can pick up even small objects.
* Will use index finger to point to interesting or desired objects.
* Can imitate adult actions, e.g. clapping hands and peek-a-boo.
* Can spoonfeed themselves; however, sometimes turns spoon upside down when feeding.
* Can throw toys deliberately.

Normative Intellectual or Cognitive Development

* Memory of past events begins to develop, e.g. if they enjoyed going to a grandparent's house will show excitement when they see that is where they are.
* Begins to be able to anticipate the future, e.g. will have some understanding of daily routines e.g. bath, change, feed and then sleep.

Normative Communication and Language Development

* Engages in tuneful babbling that rises and lowers in pitch, just as conversation does.
* Can follow simple instructions, e.g. wave bye-bye.
* Word approximations appear, e.g. ask what the horsey says and they will make a 'clip clop' sound with their tongue.
* First words (active vocabulary) may emerge and will usually include the names of familiar people, e.g. Mama, Dada, Nana; familiar objects, e.g. ball, car, doggy; body parts, e.g. eyes; foods, e.g. juice; or greetings, e.g. day-day.
* Passive or receptive vocabulary is much greater than active vocabulary (will understand much more than they can say).

Normative Emotional and Social Development

* Can drink from a cup with help.

* Still likes to be close to familiar adult.

* Will play alone for extended periods.

* Enjoys songs, action rhymes and games like peek-a-boo.

* Co-operates when getting dressed.

* Will like to look at themselves in a plastic safety mirror.

* Will imitate other people, e.g. wave bye-bye – there is often a time lapse between the person going and them responding.

Holistic Development: Twelve to Fifteen Months

Normative Physical Development

Gross motor skills:

* May walk alone feet wide apart with arms raised to help keep balance.

* Falls easily, especially when stopping.

* Cannot avoid obstacles and will bump into them.

* Can sit from standing but is likely to land heavily on their bottom.

* May get from sitting to standing without the help of furniture.

* May kneel without support.

* May climb forwards onto an adult chair and then turn around.

* Can throw a ball weakly but may fall over.

Fine motor skills:

* Enjoys playing with small blocks or bricks, often spending time putting them in and out of a container.

* Turns several pages of a book at once.

* Holds crayons in a palmer grasp, but finds it difficult to make marks on a page

* Shows a preference for one hand but will use either one.

Normative Intellectual or Cognitive Development

* Explores objects in different ways e.g. banging, shaking, throwing, dropping.
* Can point at an object in a book or reality when it is named.
* Begins to use objects correctly e.g. pretending to talk on the phone.
* Imitates activities e.g. sweeping the floor.
* Begins to engage in simple problem-solving activities e.g. puzzles.

Normative Communication and Language Development

* Makes increasingly speech-like sounds.
* May commonly use six or more words but will demonstrate by their actions that they know many more, e.g. give Mammy the brush.
* Will look at picture books for a few minutes at a time.
* Extensive use of pointing to have needs met.

Normative Emotional and Social Development

* Begins to show preference for certain activities and will resist napping if engaged in desired activity.
* Uses transitional objects (such as a blanket or soft toy) to self-comfort.
* May show strong dislikes, e.g. for bathtime, loud noises (e.g. vacuum cleaner).
* Shows affection to carers with hugs and kisses.

Holistic Development: Fifteen Months to Two Years

Normative Physical Development

Gross motor skills from 15 months:

* Walks alone, feet wide apart, with arms raised to help keep balance.
* Falls easily, especially when stopping.
* Cannot avoid obstacles and will bump into them.
* Can sit from standing.
* Can get from sitting to standing without the help of furniture.
* Can kneel without support.
* May climb forwards onto an adult chair and then turn around.
* Can throw a ball weakly but may fall over.

Gross motor skills from 18 months:

* Can walk confidently without arms out for balance.
* Can stop without falling.
* Can squat to pick up objects.
* Tries to kick a ball, often with success.
* Can walk upstairs with hand held.
* Can run, but often falls, bumping into objects.
* Likes push-pull toys but will get frustrated if they get stuck.
* Can walk downstairs if hand is held.

Fine motor skills:

* Can thread large beads.
* Uses pincer grasp to pick up small objects.
* Can build a tower of several blocks.
* Can scribble to and fro on paper.

Normative Intellectual or Cognitive Development

* Can follow simple instructions e.g. go and get your coat.
* Learns through trial and error.
* Begins to engage in imaginative play, e.g. pretending that a cardboard box is a car.
* Talks to themselves while at play.
* From approximately 18 months 'theory of mind' begins to develop. The baby begins to realise that others may think or feel differently from them, e.g. Dad is tired so he doesn't want to play at the moment.

Normative Communication and Language Development

* By 18 months most babies speak between 20 and 50 words.
* Enjoys rhymes and action songs, e.g. 'Roly Poly'.
* Loves picture books and often points and names objects and animals in books.
* Echolalia is a feature at this age – the baby will echo the last part of what others say.

Normative Emotional and Social Development

* Memory increases.
* Expresses their feelings in words and gestures.
* Begins to enjoy being able to do things for themselves, e.g. will try to dress themselves.
* Can interpret others' emotions, e.g. when a parent is worried about them climbing.

Holistic Development: Two to Three Years

Normative Physical Development

Gross motor skills:

* Very mobile and can run safely.

* Can walk up and down stairs, two feet to a step.

* Can kick a ball, but not catch.

Fine motor skills:

* Can draw circles, lines and dots.

* Enjoys picture books and turns pages singly.

* Can build a tower of six or more blocks.

Normative Intellectual or Cognitive Development

* Improved memory skills – can name two or three colours, usually yellow, red and blue or green.

* Begins to understand cause and effect, e.g. if I drop this it might break.

* Can remember an absent object when reminded of it, e.g. they might see their dog's empty bowl and ask 'Where Max?'

Normative Communication and Language Development

* Begins to rapidly learn new words; this is often called the vocabulary spurt.

* 'Overextends' words, e.g. call all men daddies.

* Begins to use 'telegraphese' e.g. 'Mammy gone?'

* Constantly names items they see and also actions, e.g. if climbing up onto a chair they might say 'up'.

* Loves to share songs, rhymes, dances and conversations.

Normative Emotional and Social Development

* Self-care skills develop, e.g. can toilet independently.

* Begins to be able to express feelings but may become frustrated when language inhibits expression.

* Begins to play with other children but may not like to share possessions.

Holistic Development: Three to Four Years

Normative Physical Development

Gross motor skills:

* Walks upstairs with alternating feet, one foot to a step (adult style).
* Walks downstairs two feet to a step, jumping from the bottom step.
* Climbs pre-school apparatus with agility.
* Can turn around obstacles and corners while running and also while pushing and pulling large toys.
* Walks forwards, backwards and sideways.
* Can ride a tricycle, using pedals, and can steer around wide corners.
* Can stand and walk on tiptoe.
* Stands momentarily on preferred foot, when shown.
* Sits with feet crossed at the ankles.
* Can throw a ball overhead and catch a large ball between extended arms. Kicks a ball forcefully.

Fine motor skills:

* Can pick up very small objects, e.g. thread.
* Uses hands co-operatively while building blocks or other similar activities.
* Can thread large wooden beads onto a shoelace.
* Can close fist and wriggle thumb in imitation, right and left.
* Holds pencil in preferred hand, near the point, with first two fingers and thumb. Uses it with control.
* Copies circles, V, H, T, and can imitate a cross.
* Draws man with head and usually indication of one or more features or parts.
* Enjoys painting with a large brush. Will usually cover whole page with paint or may paint primitive pictures, which are named after production.
* Cuts with child scissors.

Normative Intellectual or Cognitive Development

* Symbolic behaviour develops further; child will engage in a lot of pretend play, often talking to themselves while doing so.
* Represents events or people in drawings, etc.
* Will 'pretend' to write.
* Becomes fascinated by cause and effect and will continually ask Why questions.

Normative Communication and Language Development

* Language develops very rapidly during this period – often called vocabulary spurt.

* Begins to use plurals, pronouns, adjectives, words related to time, tenses and sentences.

* Uses virtuous errors, e.g. may say 'My feets are wet.' In English we normally add an 's' to make a word plural – the child will do this even with irregular plurals.

* Asks many questions, e.g. who, what, when, where and why.

* It is not unusual for a child to stutter at this age, when trying hard to explain something as thoughts can often occur more quickly than child can articulate.

* Enjoys more complicated stories and will ask for favourites time and time again.

Normative Emotional and Social Development

* Pretend play helps the child to decentre and understand things from another's perspective.

* Begins to see themselves and being male or female. This can result in stereotypical play.

* Makes friends and is interested in having friends.

* Begins to be able to negotiate and will begin to share toys or other possessions.

* As imagination develops, may become afraid of things, e.g. the dark.

Holistic Development: Four to Five Years

Normative Physical Development

Gross motor skills:

* Balance is developing well. Some children begin to learn to ride a two-wheeled bicycle.

* Can walk quickly up and down stairs, one foot to a step.

* Can catch, kick and throw a ball.

* Bends from the waist to pick up objects.

* Can stand on preferred foot for three to five seconds and hop on preferred foot.

Fine motor skills:

* Can thread small beads to make a necklace if adult threads the needle first.

* Holds pencil with good control in adult fashion.

* Draws a person with head, legs, trunk and usually arms and fingers.

* Draws a recognisable house.

Normative Intellectual or Cognitive Development

* By age four can normally count up to 20, but does not yet understand the concept of numbers. If counting out sweets, is unlikely to count accurately.

* Understands concepts such as more, fewer, big and small.

* Begins to be able to see things from another's perspective and will empathise with others, e.g. if a child fell and was hurt.

Normative Communication and Language Development

* Continues to be fascinated by 'cause and effect' and will continue to ask many questions.

* Begins to problem solve and hypothesise, wondering 'What would happen if …?'

* Can think of the past and future more than before and will begin to use past and future tense more often in speech.

* Can learn to say their name, age and address.

* Enjoys nonsense words, both hearing them and making them up.

* If the child hears swearing, they too will swear.

Normative Emotional and Social Development

* Likes to be independent and can be very strong-willed.

* Shows a sense of humour and enjoys funny stories and jokes.

* Can dress and undress him or herself (except for laces).

* Can take care of themselves – washing and drying hands and brushing teeth.

* Begins to see themselves as being male or female. This can result in stereotypical play.

* Becomes very interested in making friends.

* Will willingly share toys and other possessions.

* As imagination develops further, will engage in elaborate pretend play.

Holistic Development: Five to Six Years

Normative Physical Development

Gross motor skills:

* Balance is well developed. Many children can ride a two-wheeled bicycle.

* Enjoys using a variety of play equipment – swings, slides, climbing frames, etc.

* Can play ball games.

* Can skip.

Fine motor skills:

* Can draw a person with head, legs, eyes, mouth and nose.

* Good pencil control – can copy shapes well.

Normative Intellectual or Cognitive Development

* May begin to read and write.

* Personal symbols still dominate, e.g. will draw their own family, house or dog.

* Starts to understand the concept of time.

* Understands the meaning of numbers, e.g. can count out ten sweets.

Normative Communication and Language Development

* Will ask the meaning of new words they hear.

* Will use adverbs and prepositions.

* Talks confidently and with more fluency.

* The child is still learning new vocabulary very rapidly.

* Begins to realise that different situations require different ways of talking, e.g. will understand that they have to speak quietly while in the doctor's surgery.

Normative Emotional and Social Development

* Continues to have fears, such as fear of monsters.

* While the child still predominantly wants their parents to play with them, there is a gradual shift and a greater need for other children.

* Plays in ways that include a lot of fantasy and imagination.

* Usually likes to play with friends of the same gender.

* Continues to develop an understanding of the feelings of others but still most focused on their own needs.

2.6 INTRODUCTION TO AISTEAR

Just as you probably followed the Junior Cycle or Leaving Certificate Curriculum frameworks, Aistear is the National Curriculum Framework for children from birth to six years. 'It provides information for adults to help them plan for and provide enjoyable and challenging learning experiences, so that all children can grow and develop as competent and confident learners within loving relationships with others' (Aistear 2009: 6).

Aistear is based on 12 principles of early learning and development. These are presented in three groups. As you can see, Principle 7 below is specifically concerned with holistic learning and development.

* Group 1: Children and their lives in early childhood:
    * the child's uniqueness
    * equality and diversity
    * children as citizens
* Group 2: Children's connections with others:
    * relationships
    * parents, family and community
    * the adult's role
* Group 3: How children learn and develop:
    * holistic learning and development
    * active learning
    * play and hands-on experiences
    * relevant and meaningful experiences
    * communication and language
    * the learning environment

Each principle is presented using a short statement, followed by an explanation of the principle from the child's perspective. This explanation highlights the adult's role in supporting children's early learning and development.

The promotion of children's holistic learning and development is a very important principle of the Aistear curriculum framework and is a concept that features throughout the entire framework. In addition, as stated above, Principle 7 specifically addresses holistic learning and development. The following is an extract from the Aistear framework document.

Holistic learning and development

> Children learn many different things at the same time. What they learn is connected to where, how and with whom they learn.

- I learn lots of things at the same time. Think about all areas of my learning and development — cognitive, creative, emotional, linguistic, moral, physical, social, and spiritual, and provide me with opportunities in all of these areas.

- When supporting me to learn and develop, remember that what I learn in my early childhood setting is shaped by previous learning and experiences with my family and my community and as part of a wider society.

- Take time to observe me and to talk to me regularly. Use this time to identify moments when you can help me connect my new learning and development with past experiences and plan for my future learning.

(Aistear, 2009)

2.7 INTRODUCTION TO SÍOLTA

Síolta is the name given to the Irish National Quality Framework for Early Childhood Education in Ireland. Síolta has been designed to assist those working in ELC settings to understand the components of a **quality** service, i.e. what does a quality service look like in reality? Síolta and Aistear complement each other: Síolta is concerned specifically with quality, while Aistear is concerned specifically with curriculum provision. Together, the two frameworks in a very practical way offer suggestions and ideas of how ELC practitioners can develop a curriculum that helps all children to enjoy and progress in their early learning and development.

The Síolta framework includes principles, standards and components as seen in the graphic below.

12 PRINCIPLES ▶ **16 STANDARDS OF QUALITY** ▶ **75 COMPONENTS OF QUALITY**

Nine Síolta standards and their related components relate very closely to Aistear because they are concerned with standards relating to curriculum provision. Síolta's Standard 7: Curriculum, is particularly important to the concept of holistic development.

This standard requires that any curriculum offered in an ELC setting must be 'encouraging of each child's holistic development, and learning requires the implementation of a verifiable, broad-based, documented and flexible curriculum or programme' (DES 2017: 55).

But what does this standard mean in practical terms for ELC practitioners? The standard has six components of quality, meaning that a quality ELC setting should be able to demonstrate the following for all age groups.

Component 7.1
It is evident that the child's learning and development are holistic experiences and processes, that play is central to integrated learning and development and to curriculum/programme implementation.

Component 7.2
There is a well-referenced curriculum or programme in operation, based on established and verifiable principles of child development.

Component 7.3
The curriculum/programme is reflected in and implemented through the child's daily routine, spontaneous learning opportunities, structured activities and activities initiated by the child.

Component 7.4
Curriculum/programme is achieved through a variety of adults' strategies, close and supportive relationships in the setting and a wide range of experiences which are made available to the child.

Component 7.5
The curriculum or programme of activities being implemented is documented and the documentation is available and in use.

Component 7.6
Planning for curriculum or programme implementation is based on the child's individual profile, which is established through systematic observation and assessment for learning.

(DES 2017: 56)

SIGNPOSTS FOR REFLECTION

Síolta's 'Signposts for Reflection' ask practitioners to reflect on and think about practices in their setting. Some are general and are applicable to all age groups, i.e. 0–6 years. Others are more specific, e.g. they ask questions about practice in relation to 0–18-month-old babies.

In relation to Component 7.1, practitioners need to understand:

* What is meant by holistic development

* That when a child is engaged in a particular activity, this activity should be holistic in nature, engaging and promoting all aspects of development

* That even when an activity is more focused on one aspect of development, effort should be made to bring in other areas

* That **play** is the only way to implement a holistic curriculum.

In terms of younger children (0–36 months), the major emphasis is on the importance of forming secure, trusting relationships with adults in the ELC environment. This is vital in providing a quality curriculum. During daily routines babies should be provided with opportunities to use their skills and knowledge in different contexts.

In relation to Component 7.2, practitioners must ask themselves:

* How does the curriculum/programme on offer in the setting support the setting's aims and objectives for development and learning?

* What theories and principles of child development are influencing the curriculum offered?

Collaborate

Aisling recently visited a forest school in County Donegal and was amazed by what she saw. Children spend most of their day outside in a large, forested area. The forest school follows the Aistear curriculum but in a very different way. Children are given great freedom to play and explore, surrounded by nature. They are given lots of opportunity for risky play. Aisling would like to bring  some of what she learned back to her own setting, which is located in an urban area. It does have a reasonably big garden, but the garden does not contain many items from the natural world and children generally do not spend very much time there, except in fine weather.

In groups, come up with ideas as to how Aisling could bring some of what she learned on her visit to the forest school to her setting.

In relation to Component 7.3, practitioners must ask themselves:

* How are daily routines, including care routines, used to implement the setting's curriculum/ programme?

* Do aspects of the curriculum/programme lend themselves to spontaneous learning opportunities and child-initiated activity?

* How can the curriculum/programme be adapted to support the needs of all children, including those with additional needs?

REFLECTIVE PRACTICE 🍃

In Patrick's setting (pre-school) the children have a routine of setting the table each day for lunch using placemats, napkins, drinking glasses, adult cutlery and delph crockery. Each table has a central small floral arrangement. The children love this routine and always set the table very carefully and nicely.

What learning and development opportunities does this routine bring?

In relation to Component 7.4, practitioners must ask themselves:

* What strategies do practitioners in the setting use to implement the curriculum/programme, e.g. modelling, facilitating, enabling, playing, observing and listening? What language/body language do practitioners use?

* How are practitioners proactive in becoming involved in children's learning and development, e.g. by giving individual attention, being emotionally present at all times, sharing interests and engaging in joint projects?

* What type of relationship do you have with the children in the setting? Is it caring, responsive, sensitive and supportive?

* What type of relationship do adults in the setting have, i.e. management, staff and parents? How might this impact on children's learning and development?

REFLECTIVE PRACTICE

Andrea, an early years practitioner, was setting up the pre-school room in which she works. She was looking forward to the day, as the team were implementing an idea she had found online – making sea creatures from a variety of natural and other art materials. She had spent most of the week after work sourcing a lovely variety of materials and had planned to take the children outside for the activity. As she was almost finished with her preparations, another practitioner appeared at the door with a message from the manager to say that Andrea was needed to cover in the 'wobbler' room as they were short-staffed. This happens all too frequently.

In groups, discuss how you feel Andrea might be feeling for the rest of the day. How do you think this could impact on her interactions with the children she was working with that day?

In relation to Component 7.5, practitioners must ask themselves:

* What types of planning documentation does the setting maintain in order to effectively implement the curriculum/programme?

* Is the documentation up to date? Is it available to all who require it?

* How often do practitioners document their curriculum planning – do they have long-term yearly plans and/or session/term plans? Do practitioners make weekly and daily plans based on their longer-term plans?

Collaborate

In groups, discuss the types of documentation that are used to plan and evaluate the curriculum/programmes offered in your work placement settings. Using a large sheet of paper and a marker, ask one member of the group to record the methods that are spoken about. Ask another member of the group to share your group's findings with the rest of the class.

In relation to Component 7.6, practitioners must ask themselves:

* What systems of observation and assessment does the setting use, e.g. observations, parental inputs, children's self-assessments, informal assessments and consultation with colleagues?

* Do children have individual education plans (IEPs)?

* How are observations and assessments recorded by the setting, e.g. daily observation notebooks, use of observation templates, child portfolios, photos and videos?

* Are cultural experiences and knowledge validated in the curriculum/programme?

Collaborate

In groups, discuss the ways children's learning and development is observed and assessed in your work placement settings. Using a large sheet of paper and a marker, ask one member of the group to record the methods that are spoken about. Ask another member of the group to share your group's findings with the rest of the class.

SHOW YOU KNOW

1. Explain what is meant by the term 'holistic development'.
2. Explain why taking a holistic approach to children's development is considered good practice.
3. Describe one of the following patterns of holistic development: from simple to complex; from head to toe; from inner to outer; from general to specific.
4. Differentiate between the terms 'growth' and 'development'.
5. 'Studying normative patterns of development is useful for ELC practitioners.' Discuss.
6. What is Aistear?
7. Explain how Aistear promotes holistic learning and development in children aged 0–6 years.
8. What is Síolta?
9. Explain how Síolta promotes holistic learning and development in children aged 0–6 years.
10. Read the case study below. Do you feel children's holistic learning and development is promoted by this activity? Explain your answer.

CASE STUDY

Sarah works in an urban pre-school. She grew up on a farm and would like to share some of what she learned growing up with the children in her class. There are eight children in the class, all aged between four years and four years six months. She has decided to have the children in her class grow their own potatoes in large 'bag for life' shopping bags. For this activity she gathers the following for each child:

* A 'bag for life' shopping bag (each child brought in their own) – Sarah punches four marble-sized holes in the bottom of each
* Four seed potatoes (which she bought online)
* Compost (which she bought in the local garden centre)
* A garden trowel (one shared between two children)

It is the beginning of April and Sarah brings the children out to the sunniest part of the garden. All the children fill their bags half full of compost using their trowel. They then place four seed potatoes, sprouts facing up, into their bags. Sarah tells them to place the potatoes about 14 cm apart (she shows them what 14 cm looks like using a strip of card). The children then cover the potatoes until the bag is three-quarters full. Then they water the potatoes. Over the next 14 weeks the children go out and water their potatoes each day. Occasionally they add extra compost to their bags. When the potatoes flower and then the flowers and stems begin to die off, the children harvest their potatoes. Sarah takes pictures of her class with their crops. They are all thrilled to bring their potatoes home for dinner!

3

Child Development from Conception to Birth

What I will learn

* The genetic foundations of human development
* What occurs during each of the following stages of pre-natal development: germinal, embryonic and foetal
* The three stages of childbirth
* Why and how pregnant mothers may require an assisted delivery
* The challenges that can be faced by babies born prematurely
* The antenatal and post-natal care services available to pregnant women in Ireland
* How a newborn baby is assessed after birth and during their six-week check-up
* The factors that can adversely affect a baby's development during pregnancy and childbirth

3.1 GENETIC FOUNDATIONS OF DEVELOPMENT

Each of us begins life as a single cell weighing about one-millionth of a gram. This tiny cell contains our entire genetic code, or blueprint, reproducing itself many millions of times in order to create the person we are. The nucleus of each human cell contains chromosomes, which are thread-like structures made up of deoxyribonucleic acid (DNA). Genes are short segments or pieces of DNA that contain all the hereditary information about an individual, e.g. eye and hair colour, height, intelligence. In addition, some life-threatening conditions are genetically transmitted, e.g. cystic fibrosis (see Chapter 9).

Each cell in the human body contains 23 pairs of chromosomes, i.e. 46 chromosomes in total. The exception to this is the sperm and ova, which have only 23 in all. When fertilisation occurs the sperm and ova join together to form a new cell, called a zygote, which has the full 23 pairs of chromosomes. The gender of a baby is determined by the male sperm. Each sperm cell contains either an X **or** a Y chromosome, whereas egg cells contain X chromosomes only. If a sperm cell containing an X chromosome fertilises the egg, the baby will be female. If a sperm cell containing a Y chromosome fertilises the egg, the baby will be male.

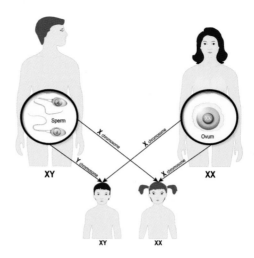

3.2 PRENATAL DEVELOPMENT

Prenatal development lasts approximately 40 weeks, beginning with fertilisation and ending with birth. It can generally be divided into three different stages – germinal, embryonic and foetal.

GERMINAL STAGE

Conception occurs in the Fallopian tube when a male sperm meets the female egg or ovum and fertilises it and a new life begins.

During sexual intercourse sperm cells travel in semen from the penis to the area at the top of the vagina called the cervix. From here the sperm travel to the fallopian tubes. If the woman is ovulating at that time and there is an egg or ovum present, fertilisation may occur. Fertilisation occurs when an egg cell meets with a sperm cell and joins with it. Once fertilised, the ovum or egg cell contains genetic material from both the mother and the father. The ovum is now called a zygote and it travels from the fallopian tube to the uterus.

> ### Did you know?
>
> In approximately 2% of cases a fertilised egg implants itself in the wall of the fallopian tube, resulting in an ectopic pregnancy. Such pregnancies cannot be sustained and may rupture the fallopian tube, resulting in serious internal bleeding (Reece *et al.* 2015).

The **germinal** stage takes place during the first two weeks after conception. During this stage, the cells of the zygote (the fertilised egg) divide continuously, attaching to the uterine wall. This process of cell division is called cleavage. Approximately one week after conception, a group of cells, called the blastocyst, has formed. The inner mass of these cells will become the embryo. The outer layer, called the trophoblast, becomes the placenta and umbilical cord. Ten to 14 days after conception, the zygote attaches itself to the wall of the uterus; this is called implantation. Once implantation begins, a hormone called human chorionic gonadotropin (HCG) is released. This is the hormone detected by pregnancy test kits.

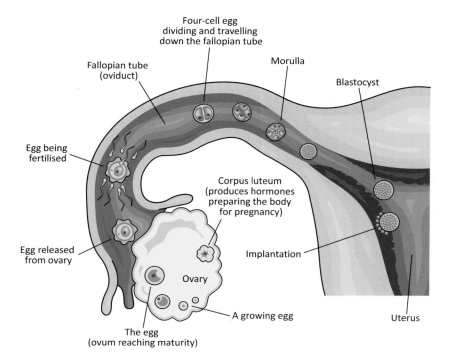

Ovulation, conception and implantation

EMBRYONIC STAGE

The embryonic stage is the period from two to eight weeks after conception. The zygote is called an embryo from two weeks. During this time, the cells of the embryo differentiate or organise themselves into three different layers – the endoderm, mesoderm and ectoderm.

The **endoderm** is the innermost layer and will become the innermost organs of the body – the digestive and respiratory systems. The middle layer or **mesoderm** will form the circulatory, excretory and reproductive systems, along with the bones and muscles. The outer **ectoderm** will form the nervous system, ears, nose, eyes, skin, hair and nails.

This process of organ formation is called **organogenesis**. It is a critical period of development, during which the embryo can be seriously harmed by teratogens (harmful substances such as alcohol).

Did you know?

Occasionally, an embryo splits during the first month of development, resulting in identical or monozygotic twins or triplets. Fraternal, or dizygotic, twins or triplets arise in a very different way. Two or three follicles mature in a single menstrual cycle, followed by independent fertilisation and implantation of two or three genetically distinct embryos. Identical twins occur in about three in 1,000 births.

As the embryo's cells begin to differentiate, its life support system also develops. This life support system includes the amniotic sac (amnion), umbilical cord and placenta. The **amniotic sac** is a bag filled with fluid (amniotic fluid) that provides a constant temperature and shockproof environment for the developing embryo. The **umbilical cord** contains two arteries and one vein and connects the embryo to the placenta. The **placenta** consists of a disc-shaped mass of tissue, in which tiny blood vessels (capillaries) of the mother and

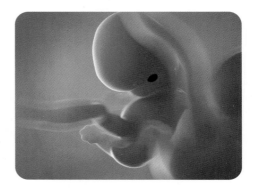

embryo intertwine but do not mix. Because the blood vessels of the mother and embryo lie so close to each other, food and oxygen can pass from mother to embryo and waste products from embryo to mother. This continues throughout the pregnancy. Unfortunately, some harmful substances, e.g. heroin, are also small enough to pass across.

At the end of this stage, the embryo is about 2.5 cm (1 inch) long. Legs and arms have appeared, with toes and fingers beginning to form. Major internal body organs (brain, lungs, kidneys, liver and intestines) are all developing rapidly.

FOETAL STAGE

This stage begins two months after conception and ends at birth. The embryo is now called a foetus.

During this time, the foetus continues to grow and develop rapidly.

* By 12 weeks, the foetus has tripled in size and now weighs about 75 g.

* By 16 weeks, the lower body begins to grow, and the mother begins to feel movements as the foetus kicks and moves its arms and legs.

* By 20 weeks, the foetus is approximately 20 cm long. This requires the adoption of the foetal position (head and knees together) due to the limited space available. The skin and nails form. The foetus is very active at this stage and normally shows a preference for a particular position in the womb.

* By 24 weeks, the foetus will be approximately 35 cm (14 inches) long and will have gained another 250 to 500 g (½–1 lb). The eyes and eyelids will have fully formed and there will be a covering of fine hair over the head and parts of the body. This is called lanugo.

* From 28 weeks, the foetus would have a good chance of survival if born prematurely, although babies born at this stage will need help breathing and may suffer long-term physical, intellectual and emotional effects. By this time, the foetus is approximately 40 cm (16 inches) long and weighs 1,500 g (3 lb). The lanugo begins to disappear, and the foetus is covered by vernix, which is a white creamy substance that protects its skin.

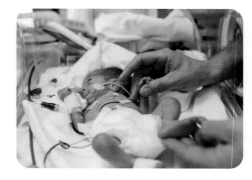

* During the last 12 weeks in the womb, the foetus puts on fatty tissue, and organs such as the kidneys, heart and lungs develop more fully. The vernix disappears and the foetus usually settles into the head-down position ready to be born. When the head moves down into the pelvis, it is said to be 'engaged', but this may not happen until labour begins.

* At birth, the average baby weighs 3.4 kg (7½ lb) and is 50 cm (20 inches) long.

Sometimes a pregnancy is divided into three trimesters – this is different from the three stages described above. Each trimester lasts three months and viability (the chance of surviving outside the womb) occurs at the beginning of the third trimester.

3.3 CHILDBIRTH

Childbirth, also known as labour, occurs at the end of pregnancy when the baby (or babies, in the case of multiple births) leaves the uterus by passing through the vagina or by caesarean section. The vast majority of births in Ireland occur in hospital maternity units and midwife-led units (MLUs). Only one per cent of births occur at home (HSE, 2020).

> ### Did you know?
>
> In 2018 there were 61,000 live births in Ireland, a fall of almost 20% from ten years previously (CSO). Why do you think there was such a significant fall in birth rate during these ten years?

The most common way for a mother to give birth is by vaginal delivery. Birth or labour occurs in three stages. During stage one the cervix dilates until it is 'fully dilated' at 10 cm, preparing for delivery. This is the longest stage of labour, lasting anywhere from 12 to 18 hours. During stage two the baby descends through the birth canal. This stage normally lasts between one and two hours. Finally, during stage three, the placenta and umbilical cord are delivered. This stage normally lasts around 15 minutes.

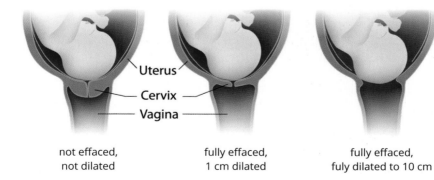

	Uterus	
	Cervix	
	Vagina	

not effaced,   fully effaced,   fully effaced,
not dilated   1 cm dilated   fuly dilated to 10 cm

ASSISTED DELIVERY

Assisted delivery (forceps or vacuum), occurs in about one in eight births. An assisted delivery may be required if:

* The mother has an underlying health condition, e.g. high blood pressure, and has been advised not to exert herself too much.

* There are concerns over the baby's heart rate.

* The baby is in an awkward position, e.g. breech or lying face upwards or on their side.

* The baby is getting tired and there are concerns that they are getting distressed.

* The baby is premature – forceps will form a 'protective cage' around the baby's head.

Forceps delivery: Forceps are used during the second stage of labour. The forceps fit around the baby's head and are designed to protect it.

Vacuum or **ventouse delivery:** A ventouse (vacuum cup) is attached to the baby's head by suction. During a contraction and with the help of the mother pushing, the obstetrician or midwife gently pulls to help deliver the baby.

Women having assisted vaginal deliveries are more likely to have:

* Vaginal tearing or an episiotomy – an episiotomy is when the obstetrician or midwife makes a cut in the area between the opening of the vagina and the anus (perineum). This makes the opening of the vagina wider, allowing the baby to pass through more easily. An episiotomy is carried out to prevent vaginal tearing, which can be slower to heal. After the birth the cut is stitched using dissolvable stitches.

* Higher risk of blood clots in the veins of the legs and pelvis area – mothers are advised to walk around as much as they can and may also be advised to wear special anti-clot stockings.

* Urinary incontinence – this is not unusual after childbirth but is more common after forceps or ventouse deliveries.

* Anal incontinence – this is not common but is more common after forceps or ventouse deliveries because of the increased risk of vaginal tears.

Assisted deliveries are carried out to protect both the mother and the baby. Babies may have marks on their head and face from the forceps or ventouse cup but these will normally disappear after 48 hours.

Many health organisations around the world advise that immediately following a vaginal birth, or as soon as the mother is alert and responsive after a caesarean section, the baby be placed on the mother's chest. This is termed skin-to-skin contact. It is recommended that routine procedures are delayed for at least an hour or two until after the baby has had its first breast feed.

While most babies are born head first, approximately 5% present feet or buttocks first – they are described as being in the breech position. Usually an attempt will be made by the obstetrician to turn the baby, but if this is not successful a caesarean delivery is likely to be recommended.

CAESAREAN BIRTH

A caesarean section (or C-section) is an operation performed to deliver the baby by making an incision in the mother's abdomen and uterus. The incision is usually made just below the bikini line. The operation normally lasts about 45 minutes. Some caesarean births are planned, while others are emergency procedures carried out when complications occur during labour. A planned or elective caesarean birth can be carried out for a number of reasons, for example: the mother has had previous C-sections which have weakened the muscles of the uterus; the baby has remained in the breech position; the baby is very big; or other complications such as placenta praevia, where the placenta is too low.

A spinal anaesthetic or epidural is used in most caesarean births. This means that the mother is awake and conscious during the operation but does not feel any pain, just some tugging and pulling. After the birth the mother will be given an injection of oxytocin to cause the womb to contract and reduce the risk of bleeding. The cut in the uterus will be closed using dissolvable stitches and the cut in the mother's skin will be closed using dissolvable stitches or regular stitches or staples that need to be removed 5–7 days later.

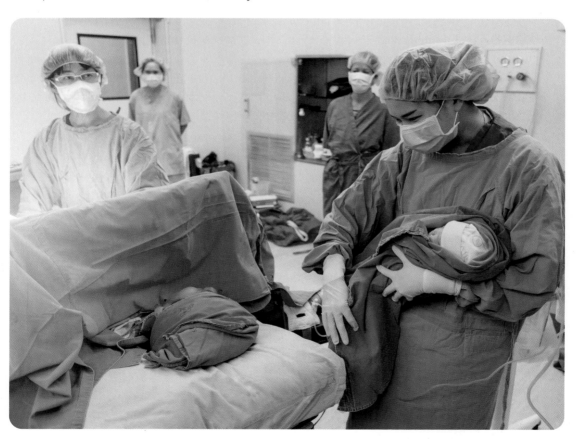

3.4 LOW BIRTH WEIGHT, PREMATURE, SMALL-FOR-DATE INFANTS AND POST-TERM BIRTHS

Low birth weight infants weigh less than 2.5 kg (5½ lb) at birth. **Very low birth weight infants** weigh less than 1.36 kg (3 lb), and **extremely low birth weight infants** weigh less than 900 g (2 lb). **Pre-term** or **premature** infants are infants born three weeks or more before their due date. **Small-for-date** infants weigh 10 per cent less than the average baby of the same gestational age.

Each year, approximately 4,500 babies are born in Ireland prematurely. This means that one in every 16 women will have a premature baby. Low birth weight is associated with a range of risk factors – multiple births, mothers aged under 17 or over 35, poor nutrition, smoking, alcohol or other drug use, women who have had previous miscarriages or abortions, and maternal stress (particularly relationship stress).

There has been a huge volume of research conducted on the effects of low birth weight on subsequent development. Severity and likelihood of effects relate directly to how low the birth weight was. Possible effects include:

* **Temperature control:** Babies born prematurely will have difficulty keeping warm. The surface area of the skin is high compared with the baby's weight and there will be little subcutaneous fat to insulate the baby against heat loss. Babies may spend some time in a heated incubator after birth because of this.

* **Breathing issues:** The baby's respiratory system is immature, and the baby may have difficulty breathing alone. This is called respiratory distress syndrome. Babies may have to be assisted with their breathing, using a ventilator.

* **Jaundice:** Premature babies often have jaundice, due to immaturity of their liver function.

* **Feeding:** Premature babies often have difficulty feeding by themselves and will need to have a nasal gastric tube inserted so that they can be fed in this way.

* **Hearing and sight problems:** Babies born very prematurely (before 30 weeks) have a significantly increased risk of hearing and sight problems.

* **Other:** Other possible long-term effects of prematurity and low birth weight include delayed language development, increased likelihood of learning disabilities, increased respiratory infections and asthma and increased incidence of ADHD and other emotional and behavioural disorders.

There have been huge advances in neonatal special care over the past number of decades. This has resulted in much better outcomes for low birth weight babies. In addition, practices such as kangaroo care (where the baby is held wearing just a nappy against his or her parent's bare chest for several hours per day) and infant massage therapy are now being used to counteract the effects on the baby of being cared for in incubators.

Did you know?

Sometimes doctors may try to delay labour by giving the mother drugs called **tocolytics**. The mother may also be given steroid injections to help the baby's lungs to develop while it is still in the uterus.

POST-TERM BIRTHS

Babies born after the expected due date (after 40 weeks) may also experience respiratory difficulties, feeding difficulties and difficulties keeping warm. This is because the placenta begins to stop functioning after 42 weeks, failing to provide the baby with enough oxygenated blood. Usually women are induced, using the drug oxytocin, which starts labour.

3.5 ANTENATAL CARE

Antenatal care is the care that a pregnant woman receives during pregnancy to help her deliver a healthy baby. All pregnant women in Ireland are entitled to free antenatal care under the maternity and infant care scheme. This scheme means that all pregnant women have access to:

* Appointments with their GP
* Appointments with their midwife or obstetrician if required
* Ultra-sound scans
* Blood tests to screen for a wide range of issues or conditions
* Medical care during labour and birth from midwives and an obstetrician, if required
* Appointment with their GP for the baby's two-week and six-week check-ups and the mother's six-week check-up

Once a pregnant woman registers with the maternity and infant care scheme, the first appointment she will have is with her GP. The GP will do some antenatal checks and discuss issues such as folic acid supplements (for the prevention of neural tube defects), healthy eating and exercise and also vaccinations such as flu and whooping cough. Pregnant women also attend their local maternity unit or hospital. The number of appointments will depend on the woman's and her baby's needs. Blood pressure and urine will be checked at each appointment.

The first appointment at the maternity unit or hospital is referred to as the 'booking visit'. This appointment is usually with a midwife and takes place between eight and 12 weeks. At this appointment a detailed medical history will be taken, which will include:

* Details of the menstrual cycle and the date of the last period. This date will be used to calculate the expected delivery date (EDD)
* Medical history, e.g. diabetes, high blood pressure or heart disease
* Family history, e.g. any inherited disorders or history of multiple births
* Details of any previous pregnancies or miscarriages
* Social history, e.g. supports at home, quality of housing

During this and subsequent visits several medical checks and screening tests will be carried out.

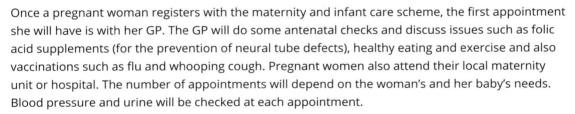

MEDICAL CHECKS

* **Height:** This will be used to calculate ideal weight. Also, small women (under 1.5 m or 5 ft) will be more carefully monitored as the pelvis may be too narrow for the baby to be delivered vaginally.

* **Weight:** This will be recorded at every visit as excessive weight gain during pregnancy can cause complications, e.g. increased risk of gestational diabetes and high blood pressure. Women who gain excess weight are also more likely to have a very big baby, which can contribute to delivery complications such as vaginal tears, excess bleeding and the need for a C-section. Normal weight gain during pregnancy is 12–15 kg.

* **Blood pressure:** Blood pressure is recorded at every appointment, as hypertension or high blood pressure during pregnancy can interfere with blood supply to the placenta and lead to a dangerous condition called pre-eclampsia.

* **Urine tests:** Urine is tested at each antenatal appointment:
  * Sugar (glucose) in the urine may indicate gestational diabetes
  * Protein (albumen) in the urine may indicate infection or be an early sign of pre-eclampsia
  * Ketones in the urine may indicate pre-eclampsia and associated kidney damage

* **Blood tests:** A blood sample will be taken and used to determine:
  * Blood group – A, AB, B or O
  * Rhesus factor – negative or positive
  * Iron levels – to detect possible anaemia
  * High blood sugar levels – to detect gestational diabetes
  * Conditions such as syphilis and sickle cell disease

Extend your learning

Gestational diabetes is diabetes that develops when a woman is pregnant. Sometimes there are no symptoms, but there might be extreme thirst, hunger or fatigue. Most women with gestational diabetes can control their blood sugar levels by following a strict eating and exercise plan recommended by their obstetrician. Some women, however, may need to take insulin to keep their blood sugar levels under control. If gestational diabetes is not well controlled there is an increased risk of pre-eclampsia (see page 51), premature delivery, having a very big baby (which can cause difficulties during birth) and the baby being born with low blood sugar levels, breathing difficulties and jaundice.

SCREENING

Screening tests are used to track the development of the baby and the health of the pregnancy. They can also be used to indicate a level of risk for certain conditions such as Down syndrome or spina bifida. These screens do not diagnose these conditions, but rather indicate increased risk.

* **Ultrasound scans** can be used at various stages during pregnancy for different reasons. In the early stages of pregnancy, they are used to check foetal size and heartbeat, to check if there is more than one baby or to check on foetal health if the woman is having symptoms of miscarriage. At around 12–13 weeks the scan can be used with the nuchal fold translucency test (see below). At around 18–20 weeks most women have a second, more detailed scan. This scan checks that there is enough amniotic fluid surrounding the baby. The baby's heart, head, spine and other internal organs are examined in detail. The position, size and functioning of the placenta are also checked. This scan can also identify possible physical issues such as spina bifida or cleft lip and palate.

* **Nuchal fold translucency test:** This is a screening test for Down syndrome that some pregnant women request. It is usually carried out between 12 and 14 weeks. The test involves an ultrasound scan to measure the amount of fluid at the back of the baby's neck. Babies with Down syndrome have a thicker layer of fluid. If the layer is found to be greater than average, the woman may opt for a diagnostic test, e.g. amniocentesis (see page 52).

* **Alpha-fetoprotein (AFP) test:** The pregnant woman undergoes a blood test, and if raised levels of the protein AFP are detected, this can indicate that her baby may have Down syndrome.

* **Maternal serum screening:** This is another blood test administered to assess the risk of Down syndrome. Like the other screening tests, a positive result does not mean that the baby will have Down syndrome but rather has an increased risk. The mother may then decide to go for a diagnostic test such as an amniocentesis.

Extend your learning

Pre-eclampsia is a condition that affects approximately 6% of pregnancies, usually during the second half of pregnancy or soon after the baby is delivered (post-partum pre-eclampsia). Early signs of pre-eclampsia are high blood pressure and protein in the urine. The pregnant woman and her baby will be closely monitored and will usually stay in hospital until the baby is delivered. Blood pressure and anti-epileptic medication may be administered. If pre-eclampsia is severe and not properly monitored it can cause stillbirth, failure of the baby to grow properly or premature delivery. In the mother, problems associated with pre-eclampsia include seizures, stroke and organ damage (liver and kidney).

DIAGNOSTIC TESTING DURING PREGNANCY

Diagnostic tests are tests carried out to confirm whether or not a baby has a certain condition. Unlike screening, these tests are invasive, so do carry with them a slight risk of miscarriage.

* **Amniocentesis** is a diagnostic test carried out between weeks 15 and 19 of pregnancy. A fine needle is inserted into the amniotic fluid surrounding the baby and a small quantity is extracted. Because the baby floats in the amniotic fluid, some of their body cells will be contained in it. The amniotic fluid is then analysed in a laboratory, and it can take up to a month for the results to come back, which can be a very anxious time for parents. This test can accurately diagnose genetic disorders such as cystic fibrosis or Down syndrome (see also Chapter 11).

* **Chorionic villus sampling (CVS)** is a diagnostic test carried out between week 10 and week 12 of pregnancy. A fine instrument is inserted through the cervix into the woman's uterus and a tiny sample of the chorionic villi (found in the placenta) is taken. These villi carry the same genetic material as the baby. Results are not as accurate as for amniocentesis, but they come back within a few days.

Collaborate

Diagnostic testing such as amniocentesis and chorionic villus sampling have long been considered controversial procedures in Ireland, whereas in other countries they are routinely offered. Discuss this in groups and feed back your group's opinions to the class.

3.6 POST-NATAL CARE

MOTHERS

Once the baby is born the mother will normally remain in hospital for two or three days if she has had a normal or assisted delivery and four or five days if she has had a caesarean section. During this time the mother will be examined ensure that the uterus is returning to its normal size and that there is no infection or excessive bleeding. Stitches will be checked to make sure that wounds are healing properly and that there is no

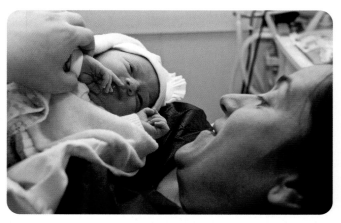

infection. Blood pressure will be monitored, and advice and assistance with infant feeding will be given. When the mother returns home, she will be visited by a public health nurse, who will support her with any difficulties she is experiencing.

After six weeks the mother and her new baby will attend their GP for their six-week check-up. The mother's weight and blood pressure will be checked. A urine test will be administered to ensure that the kidneys are functioning well and that there is no infection. The GP will ask if the mother has any concerns in relation to the healing of wounds, e.g. a caesarean scar. If the mother doesn't have rubella immunity, she will be offered it now. It is possible to become pregnant soon after birth so the GP may also discuss contraception if required. The new mother will be asked how she is feeling, e.g. if she is feeling overwhelmed, tired or depressed, and will be offered support if required.

Extend your learning

Post-natal depression is the term used for depression that some women feel during the first year after having a baby. Symptoms may start as baby blues (most women feel a little low and weepy during the first few days after birth) but get worse as time goes on. Post-natal depression occurs in 10–15% of women (O'Hara et al, 1996). Signs of postnatal depression include:

* Feelings of sadness, anxiousness or loneliness

* Loss of appetite

* Poor concentration

* Constant fatigue

* Problems sleeping

* Frequently tearful

* Feelings of inadequacy

Some mothers feel overwhelming fears, e.g. about their baby dying

Some mothers have recurring thoughts or fears about harming their baby. Very few mothers act on this.

The GP may refer the mother to primary care psychology or counselling services and/or prescribe medication such as an anti-depressant.

BABIES

Very shortly after birth, the newborn baby is weighed, cleaned up and assessed for any signs of developmental problems that may require urgent attention. The Apgar scale, which was developed by Dr Virginia Apgar in 1952, is widely used worldwide to assess infants in the first five minutes after birth. The scale measures five things: activity and muscle tone; pulse rate; grimace (response to catheter inserted into nostril); appearance (body colour); and respiratory effort. Babies are given a score of 0, 1 or 2 for each of the five measures (see table). Scores are then added up to give an overall indication of the newborn's health. A perfect Apgar score is a 10, but a baby who rates a 7 is considered healthy. A baby whose score ranges from 0 to 3 may need resuscitation and babies with scores in the middle, from 4 to 6, may require various interventions, including extra oxygen.

POINTS	0	1	2
Muscle tone	Limp	Some limb movement	Active movement
Pulse rate	Absent	Less than 100 beats per minute	More than 100 beats per minute
Reflex response	No response	Grimace	Sneeze/cough
Skin colour	Blue	Body oxygenated but hands and feet blue	Well oxygenated
Respiration	Absent	Slow and irregular	Regular, crying

The Apgar Scoring System

SCREENING TESTS

Four screening tests are routinely carried out on the newborn baby to check for specific disorders that can be treated successfully if detected at this stage.

1. **Barlow's test:** This is a test carried out after birth, at the six-week check-up and all other routine check-ups until the baby is walking. The test is used to detect congenital dislocation of the hips. There are varying degrees of this disorder and treatment involves splinting the baby's legs to keep them in a frog-like position until it is successfully treated.

2. **Heel prick test:** This test is carried out to detect phenylketonuria (PKU) and congenital hypothyroidism (CHT). PKU is a metabolic disorder (the person cannot metabolise the protein phenylalanine) which, if untreated, leads to brain damage and learning delay. It can be treated very successfully using a special formula protein diet that the person will have to follow for the rest of their life. In CHT the baby does not produce enough thyroxin. If it is untreated, the baby will develop serious permanent physical and mental disabilities. Early treatment (thyroxin supplements) is started as soon as possible after birth.

3. **Otoacoustic emissions test (OAE):** This is used to test the newborn's hearing. It involves placing a tiny earpiece into each of the baby's ears and playing clicking sounds through it. Reactions to these sounds are picked up by an attached computer.

4. **Vision checks:** These are carried out after birth while the baby is still in hospital, at the six-week check and early in primary school.

SIX-WEEK CHECK-UP

The baby's six-week check-up is normally carried out by their GP at the same time as the mother's check-up. This is a thorough examination of the baby's health and development and involves a number of checks:

* The baby's heart and lungs are checked using a stethoscope.

* Their weight, length and head circumference are measured and plotted on a centile or growth chart.

* General presentation is noted, e.g. are they smiling, reacting to movement and sound, etc.?

* The eyes are inspected using a light, and their ability to follow a small light beam with their head will be noted.

* Their hips will be checked again.

* The mother will be asked about how the baby is feeding and sleeping or if there are any issues with bowel motions or passing urine.

Collaborate

If there are any members of the group who have had a baby, perhaps they would be willing to share their experience of pregnancy, birth and post-natal care with the class.

3.7 FACTORS THAT CAN AFFECT DEVELOPMENT DURING THE PRE-NATAL STAGE AND BIRTH

TERATOLOGY

Teratology is the name given to the study of the causes of birth defects. A teratogen is anything that can potentially cause a birth defect or negatively affect any area of the child's development. Teratogens include drugs, infectious diseases, advanced maternal or paternal age, environmental pollutants, incompatible blood types and nutritional deficiencies.

Exposure to teratogens during the germinal period will normally prevent implantation, so pregnancy will frequently not occur. If the pregnancy does continue, teratogens generally have the most damaging effects if exposure occurs during the embryonic stage (two to eight weeks after conception). As stated earlier, this is when organogenesis occurs and therefore structural damage to the organs may occur. Exposure during the foetal stage normally causes stunted growth and problems with organ function.

1 EXPOSURE TO DRUGS

Prescription and non-prescription drugs: Prescription drugs such as the antibiotic Streptomycin, found to cause deafness, and Accutane, a drug given to treat acne and which has been found to cause brain, heart and facial defects, should be completely avoided during pregnancy. Non-prescription drugs that can be harmful include slimming tablets and aspirin. To be safe, women who suspect they may be pregnant should not take any form of medication without first consulting their doctor.

Psychoactive drugs: These are drugs that act on the nervous system, causing changes to the individual's physical and mental state. Examples include caffeine, alcohol, nicotine, marijuana, cocaine and heroin.

* **Caffeine:** Caffeine is found in tea, coffee, chocolate, cola and other soft drinks, e.g. Red Bull. Studies have found that caffeine intakes in excess of 200 mg (two cups of tea or coffee) increase the risk of miscarriage and low birth weight. Pregnant women should therefore avoid caffeine or consume very little.

* **Alcohol:** Alcohol consumption by women during pregnancy can have devastating effects on their children. Foetal alcohol spectrum disorders (FASDs), sometimes referred to as foetal alcohol syndrome (FAS), are a cluster of abnormalities and problems that appear in the offspring of mothers who drink alcohol during pregnancy. Effects of the condition vary from child to child but include:

  * Facial abnormalities such as wide-set eyes, thin upper lip, flat cheekbones and unevenly paired ears
  * Heart defects
  * Limb defects, particularly of the right hand and forearm
  * Learning problems – many have below-average IQ and a significant number have severe learning difficulties
  * Impaired memory functioning
  * Increased incidence of attention deficit hyperactivity disorder (ADHD)
  * A predisposition to addiction
  * Prone to depression and other psychiatric illnesses later in life
  * A large proportion grow up to become unemployed, with many unable to live independently (Spohr, Williams & Steinhausen 2007).

  It is recommended that no alcohol is consumed during pregnancy. While moderate drinking is unlikely to cause FASDs, some studies have shown that it increases the risk of premature birth. Other studies have found that the children of women who drink moderately during pregnancy are smaller and less attentive and alert than the children of women who do not drink at all (Pollard 2007).

* **Nicotine:** Smoking cigarettes during pregnancy increases the risk of the baby being pre-term and the risk of low birth weight, foetal death, respiratory problems and sudden infant death syndrome (SIDS). Studies also link smoking during pregnancy with increased irritability, lower scores on cognitive tests and increased inattention in children (Van Meurs 1999). Others argue that such differences could be due to other environmental factors as well as smoking. Women who quit smoking during early pregnancy can avoid these problems, thereby reducing the risk to their baby to that of the level of a non-smoker.

* **Marijuana:** There have been several longitudinal studies carried out into the effects of marijuana use during pregnancy. Effects include reduced intelligence, memory and information-processing skills as well as increased childhood depression and early marijuana use by the child themselves (Fried and Smith 2001). Marijuana should not be used in pregnancy.

* **Cocaine:** Cocaine use during pregnancy can cause a myriad of negative effects in children, such as low birth weight and head circumference, prematurity, higher excitability and irritability, slower motor development, slower growth rate, increased risk of ADHD and learning difficulties and impaired language development. Some researchers suggest that these results be viewed with caution, as it is also more likely that mothers who use cocaine also live in poverty, are badly nourished and use other harmful substances such as alcohol, nicotine, marijuana and other drugs.

✳ **Heroin:** Babies born to heroin users and users of the heroin substitute methadone are likely to experience withdrawal symptoms such as tremors, poor sleep patterns, irritability and shrill crying. 'Heroin babies' are more likely to have ADHD and experience behavioural problems as they get older. There is also the risk of HIV infection being passed on as a result of using dirty needles.

2 BLOOD INCOMPATIBILITY

Everyone is born with a specific blood type and Rhesus (Rh) factor. The four different blood groups are A, B, AB and O, and the Rhesus factor is either Rh-negative or Rh-positive. Most people are Rh-positive. Approximately 15% of white people are Rh-negative, and Rh-negative blood is much less common among black and Asian populations, at approximately 5%. Blood incompatibility can arise if the mother is Rh-negative and her baby is Rh-positive. This is because the mother's body may begin to produce anti-Rh-positive antibodies that can pass across the placenta and harm the baby. This does not usually happen in the first pregnancy, but if the baby's and mother's blood mix during labour and birth (which they are likely to do), the mother may then begin producing anti-Rh-positive antibodies that would attack any subsequent Rh-positive baby.

Immediately after birth, a sample of blood from the baby's umbilical cord will be tested to determine whether the baby is Rh-positive or negative. In addition, a sample of the mother's blood will be taken to determine the number of foetal blood cells present in her own blood. If foetal cells are found and the baby is Rh-positive, then the mother will be given an anti-D injection that will prevent her from developing anti-Rh-positive antibodies, which could harm subsequent Rh-positive babies.

If anti-D was not given, serious complications would arise – babies could be born with severe, life-threatening anaemia, liver damage, hearing loss or learning disability. They could also suffer seizures, cardiac failure and even death.

3 MATERNAL DISEASES AND INFECTIONS

Certain maternal diseases and infections can cause defects and complications in the newborn, either because they pass across the placenta to the foetus during pregnancy or are transmitted to the baby during the birthing process.

✳ **Rubella (German measles)**, while a mild disease in itself, causes prenatal and neonatal (just after birth) death, deafness, blindness, learning difficulties and heart defects. In Ireland in the past, many pregnant women who contracted rubella had babies who either died or were severely affected by the condition. Since 1971, the rubella vaccine has been administered to pre-pubertal girls, and to both boys and girls since 1988. Currently, the MMR (measles, mumps and rubella) vaccine is offered at 12 months with a booster at four to five years to all babies born in Ireland. Unfortunately, in part as a result of a much-criticised paper linking the MMR vaccine with autism, vaccine uptake for MMR dropped to 80%, thus putting the population again at risk of rubella (Deer 2009). Women who are thinking of becoming pregnant should have a blood test to confirm their immunity to the disease.

* **Diabetes** occurring in non-diabetic women during pregnancy is called gestational diabetes (see also page 50). It occurs in approximately 4% of pregnancies, but women who are obese are much more likely to develop it. Usually if women monitor their diet and take regular exercise, gestational diabetes does not pose a problem. Sometimes, however, pre-eclampsia occurs, where the mother's blood pressure rises to unacceptable levels and protein appears in the urine. Babies of women who have badly controlled diabetes mellitus type 1 and 2 (meaning they have diabetes even when not pregnant) are at an increased risk of birth defects and prematurity.

* **Pre-eclampsia** (see also page 51) can also occur in women with no gestational diabetes. It is most common in women who have had it in previous pregnancies, older women, obese women and women carrying twins or more. If blood pressure gets unacceptably high, the baby will be delivered early either by induction or caesarean section, as failure to do so could cause serious brain damage.

* **HIV and AIDS:** AIDS is a life-threatening infection (usually sexually transmitted) caused by the human immunodeficiency virus (HIV). A mother can infect her baby with HIV in several different ways: during pregnancy across the placenta, during birth through contact with maternal blood or fluids, or through breastfeeding. However, transmission rates from mother to baby can be reduced to approximately 2% if anti-viral drugs are given during pregnancy, the baby is delivered by caesarean section and is not breastfed. If babies are born HIV positive, their average life expectancy is very low (three years) in countries where they are left untreated. Recent improvements in treatments available in the developed world mean that children born with HIV will live longer, but average life expectancy is still only 10 years old. Since the introduction of the antenatal HIV screening programme in Ireland in 1999, mother-to-child transmission of HIV has been dramatically reduced. Of the total of 106 babies born to HIV-infected mothers in 2008, only two were diagnosed with HIV infection, and one of these was born to a mother who was not known to be infected during pregnancy and who later tested positive.

* **Genital herpes:** Genital herpes simplex is an incurable sexually transmitted infection caused by the herpes simplex virus (HSV). There are two distinct types of HSV. Type 2 is most commonly associated with genital infection. Type 1 has also been found to cause genital infection but is more commonly associated with oral herpes (cold sores). Most infected individuals experience no symptoms or mild symptoms. If present, symptoms include one or more blisters at the site of infection and a burning sensation during urination. After the initial infection, HSV remains dormant in the body for life and may reactivate from time to time. If a baby passes through the birth canal of a woman with an active case of genital herpes, the risk to the baby is high – they may die or suffer brain damage. Therefore, a caesarean is normally performed in these cases.

* **Syphilis:** Syphilis is a sexually transmitted infection caused by the bacterium *Treponema pallidum*. If untreated, it can have serious effects on all the organs of the body. Unlike rubella, which damages organs during organogenesis, syphilis attacks organs after they have formed, causing blindness, learning delay, seizures and even death.

4 ENVIRONMENTAL HAZARDS

On 26 April 1986, there was a huge explosion at the nuclear power plant at Chernobyl in Ukraine. While it is reported that there were only 59 direct deaths, it is estimated that seven million people, many of them living in nearby Belarus, have been exposed to unacceptably high levels of radiation as a result of the accident. To this day, there is a 27-km exclusion zone around the plant. Birth defects and various childhood cancers, especially thyroid cancer, have increased

Chernobyl

dramatically in the years since the disaster in Ukraine and neighbouring countries. It is estimated that it will take over 200 years for radiation in the exclusion zone to reach safe levels. Today, there are a total of 433 nuclear reactors in 30 different countries worldwide. Twenty-four per cent of these are in the US, but France, Germany, Japan, Korea and Russia also have substantial numbers (World Nuclear Association 2020). The UK currently has a total of 15 nuclear reactors. In Ireland, there are concerns about the Sellafield plant in Cumbria, which is located only 170 km from the north-east coast of Ireland. Sellafield is no longer a nuclear reactor, but it is still a reprocessing plant for spent fuel from other nuclear power reactors and is a storage facility for nuclear waste. Concerns centre on its safety record and the dumping of liquid nuclear reactive waste from the plant into the Irish Sea.

Extend your learning

Read the article published in the *Irish Times* entitled 'Doctors raise concerns over health impact of nuclear plant discharges', which is available online. Consider the arguments put forward by two Irish doctors who were challenging the view that discharges from the Sellafield plant do not pose a serious health risk to people living on the north-east coast of Ireland.

X-ray radiation can also affect the developing embryo or foetus, especially in the first trimester. Potential effects include learning disability and leukaemia. Before having an X-ray, women should inform their doctor if they are pregnant or could be pregnant. The X-ray may be postponed or carried out in such a way that the abdominal area is not directly exposed.

Other environmental pollutants include carbon dioxide, e.g. exhaust fumes in traffic-clogged cities, lead, e.g. from water pipes or lead-based paints (now banned), mercury, e.g. from polluted fish or in dental fillings, and exposure to certain fertilisers and pesticides. All of these can affect cognitive development in the foetus.

5 OTHER FACTORS

Other factors that may affect prenatal development are maternal age, maternal diet and maternal stress, as well as paternal factors.

MATERNAL AGE

When considering maternal age and foetal development, two age groups are significant – adolescence and women aged over 35. According to figures from the Central Statistics Office (CSO), the number of teenage mothers who gave birth decreased by 60.2% between 2008 and 2018, with 956 teenage mothers giving birth in 2018 as opposed to 2,402 in 2008. Pregnant adolescents younger than 17 years have a higher incidence of medical complications involving mother and child than do adult women, although these risks are greatest for the youngest teenagers. The incidence of having a low birth weight infant (weighing less than 2,500 g) among adolescents is more than double the rate for adults, and the neonatal death rate (within 28 days of birth) is almost three times higher. The mortality rate for the mother, although low, is twice that for adult pregnant women. Why is this? Several factors are believed to be involved:

* Immature reproductive system
* Low pre-pregnancy weight and height
* Poor nutrition
* Low socioeconomic status, resulting in poverty
* Low education levels and lower rates of engagement with prenatal care
* Higher rates of sexually transmitted infections
* Substance misuse – cigarettes, alcohol and other drugs

Collaborate

In groups, discuss why the number of teenage mothers might have decreased so significantly over the past decade in Ireland. Share the thoughts of your group with the class.

Women who give birth over the age of 35 have a higher risk of giving birth prematurely, having a low birth weight baby, stillbirth, chromosomal defects in the baby, especially Down syndrome, labour complications, a higher incidence of caesarean section, and increased risk of gestational diabetes and high blood pressure, which can lead to pre-eclampsia and a pre-term birth for the baby.

The number of women in Ireland giving birth for the first time over the age of 35 has steadily increased in recent years. According to the CSO (2017), Ireland has the highest average age at maternity (32.8 years) of any country in the EU.

Collaborate

In groups, discuss why there has been a significant increase in the number of women in Ireland giving birth for the first time aged over 35 years. Share the thoughts of your group with the class.

MATERNAL DIET

A balanced diet is essential during pregnancy for the baby's general health. Obese women can pose a risk to their developing baby – there is an increased risk of prenatal death, gestational diabetes and pre-eclampsia (see page 51). Recent studies of children whose mothers gained excessive weight during pregnancy have shown that they are more prone to childhood and adolescent obesity themselves. Folic acid is also important for the prevention of neural tube defects and should be taken in tablet form to supplement dietary sources such as citrus fruits.

MATERNAL STRESS

When a pregnant woman experiences intense stress, there is an increase in the stress hormone cortisol, both in her blood and in the amniotic fluid surrounding her unborn baby. Cortisol has been found to pass from the amniotic fluid to babies of highly stressed women. The main cause of stress in pregnant women is relationship problems. While some studies (Glover *et al.* 2005) link stress during pregnancy with premature delivery, lower IQ and anxiety and attention problems in children, others believe that these effects merely reflect the environment the baby is born into or the effects of stressed mothers using alcohol or other drugs to cope with the stress.

PATERNAL FACTORS

There are several paternal factors that are thought to adversely affect foetal development.

* Exposure to radiation, lead, mercury, cocaine and certain pesticides can cause sperm abnormalities, leading to increased rates of miscarriage and childhood cancer.

* The babies of men whose diet is low in vitamin C also have increased rates of birth defects and cancer.

* Fathers who smoke during and after their partner's pregnancy may have children of low birth weight. Later, if the father continues to smoke, babies are at an increased risk of Sudden Infant Death Syndrome (SIDS) and childhood cancers.

* Fathers of advanced age (40+) are also more likely to have children with birth defects, although the link is much stronger between birth defects and maternal age.

SHOW YOU KNOW

1. Describe the genetic foundations of human development.

2. Outline what occurs during each of the following stages of pre-natal development: germinal; embryonic; and foetal.

3. Describe the three stages of childbirth.

4. Explain why and how pregnant mothers may require an assisted delivery.

5. Discuss the challenges that can be faced by babies born prematurely.

6. Describe the antenatal and post-natal care services available to pregnant women in Ireland.

7. Outline how a newborn baby is assessed after birth and during their six-week check-up.

8. Describe four factors that can adversely affect a baby's development during pregnancy and childbirth.

Section 2

Child Development and Learning Theories

Physical Growth and Development

4

What I will learn

* Typical patterns of growth in children aged 0–6 years
* How the nervous system develops in children aged 0–6 years
* Gesell's and Thelen's theories of motor development
* What primitive reflexes are; examples of primitive reflexes
* The development of gross and fine motor skills in children aged 0–6 years
* A range of toys and activities suitable for use in an ELC setting that promote physical development in children aged 0–6 years
* The ways in which Aistear promotes physical growth and development in children aged 0–6 years

4.1 PATTERNS OF GROWTH IN CHILDREN AGED 0–6 YEARS

GROWTH IN INFANCY (0–2 YEARS)

According to figures from the Central Statistics Office (CSO) (2017), the average Irish baby now weighs in at 3.5 kg (7 lb 11 oz), with boys weighing on average 140 g (5 oz) more at birth than girls. The average length at birth is 51 cm (20 inches). After an initial weight loss after birth, usually approximately 150 g (5 oz), babies gain up to 150 g per week for the first month once they begin feeding well. Babies will normally have doubled their birth weight by four months and tripled it by one year. In addition, their height will also increase rapidly, with the average baby reaching 71–74 cm (28–29 inches) in height by their first birthday. During the second year, growth slows considerably. By their second birthday, the average infant weighs 12.7 kg (2 stone) and is between 81 and 89 cm (32–35 inches) in height, reaching almost half their adult height. In fact, by doubling a child's height at age two, a rough estimate of their final adult height can be obtained.

The **cephalocaudal pattern** is the sequence of growth whereby the fastest growth always occurs at the top of the body, i.e. the head, and gradually moves downwards. As a proportion of total body length at birth, a baby's head makes up one-quarter. In contrast, the head makes up only one-eighth of an adult's total body length.

Cephalocaudal trend

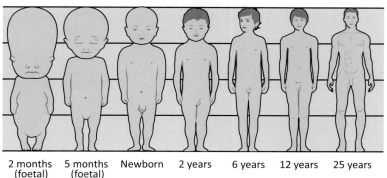

| 2 months (foetal) | 5 months (foetal) | Newborn | 2 years | 6 years | 12 years | 25 years |

GROWTH IN EARLY CHILDHOOD (2–6 YEARS)

During the pre-school and early school years, the rate of growth slows with each additional year. The head-to-body ratio evens out more as the child's trunk and limbs begin to lengthen. Children also being to lose fatty tissue and gain more lean muscle tissue (on average, boys gain more muscle tissue than girls). Up until about the age of two,  most children are roughly the same height. As children progress towards their fourth, fifth and sixth birthdays, however, some children will become noticeably taller or shorter than others. These differences are normally a result of heredity but may also reflect nutritional status, chronic illness or, in a small number of cases, congenital problems, e.g. pituitary dwarfism. Factors influencing children's growth and development are discussed in full in Section 3.

4.2 STRUCTURE AND DEVELOPMENT OF THE BRAIN

In the past, scientists believed that the brain's cells essentially stopped dividing early in childhood, and that therefore the child remained with whatever they were genetically born with. Since then, scientists have revised this idea, believing that the brain has plasticity, meaning that it can adapt to changes in the child's environment.

STRUCTURE OF THE BRAIN

The human brain consists of two halves or hemispheres (often called the right and left brain). The cerebral cortex is the name given to the outer layer of the brain (much as the flesh of a peach covers its inner stone). Each hemisphere within the cortex consists of four lobes, or areas, each of which carries out quite specific although sometimes shared functions (see diagram).

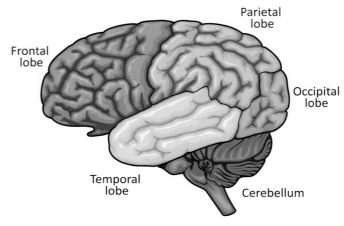

Structure of the brain

In addition, the inner core of the brain (much like the stone of a peach) contains the pituitary gland, amygdala (responsible for emotions) and the hippocampus (responsible for memory and emotions).

NEURONS

Neurons (nerve cells) are the basic working unit of the nervous system. Sensory neurons process information from the environment and motor neurons act on it. Within the brain, there are specialised clusters of neurons called neural circuits that process specific types of information. For example, there are extensive neural circuits for language and creative thinking in the left side of the brain, whereas neural circuits for logic and mathematical thinking are more extensive in the right side. In the past, this has been used to label certain people (particularly girls) as left brain dominant or others (particularly boys) as right brain dominant. Nowadays, however, this distinction is not believed to be as clear-cut. Studies using brain imaging techniques now believe most brain functions involve both hemispheres.

BRAIN DEVELOPMENT

The brain develops most during the prenatal stage and first two years of life (the human brain reaches 75% of its adult weight by the age of two years). Therefore, damage experienced at either of these stages can have serious consequences. In addition, studies have shown that children living in deprived environments show considerably less brain activity than children living in more enriching environments. These effects are not irreversible, however, and children's brains are believed to be highly adaptable and resilient. Thus, if the circumstances of babies born into deprived environments change for the better, e.g. through positive interventions at home or through foster care, they can make up for lost ground and develop towards their true potential. The rule of thumb is that the sooner this happens the better, because the brain becomes less adaptable as the child gets older.

Brain development basically means three things:

* **Myelination**, or development of the myelin sheath (an insulating layer) around neurons. This has the effect of speeding up the transmission of messages by neurons. Myelination of some neurons will occur before others, e.g. myelination of neurons connected with vision is almost complete by six months, hence infant vision is almost as clear as an adult's by six months, whereas myelination of neurons in parts of the brain connected with the development of hand–eye co-ordination is not complete until four years. Hence, children's hand–eye co-ordination is usually clumsy until then.

* **Increased connections between neurons**, which also results in the brain becoming more developed and sophisticated. The actual size of the brain does not increase dramatically after age two, but its internal structure, or 'wiring', does.

* **Increased specialisation** of areas of the brain.

4.3 MOTOR DEVELOPMENT

THEORIES OF MOTOR DEVELOPMENT

ARNOLD GESELL (1880–1961)

Arnold Gesell was a very influential developmental psychologist whose **biological maturation theory** of child development still forms the basis of much of the work done in this area today. Early in the twentieth century Gesell observed and documented patterns in the way children develop, showing that all children go through similar and predictable sequences, although each child moves through these sequences at their own rate or pace. This process comprises both intrinsic and extrinsic factors. The intrinsic factors include genetics, temperament, personality and learning styles, as well as physical and mental growth. Simultaneously, development is also influenced by extrinsic factors such as environment, family background, parenting styles, cultural influences, health conditions, and early experiences with peers and adults.

Arnold Gesell's photographic dome

Gesell was one of the first psychologists to adopt a scientific approach to the study of child development. He used one-way mirrors and the latest technology in his 'photographic dome' to observe some 12,000 children without their being consciously aware that they were being observed. Cameras rode on metal tracks at the top of the dome and were moved as needed to record the child's activities.

Gesell's research established normative trends for four areas of growth and development: motor; adaptive (cognitive); language; and personal-social behaviour. Originally published as the *Gesell Developmental Schedules* in 1925, these developmental schedules, most recently updated in 2010, continue to serve and guide paediatricians and psychologists throughout the world today.

ESTHER THELEN (1941–2004)

Esther Thelen was a New York-born psychologist who began studying infant motor development in the 1970s and 1980s. According to her **dynamic systems theory**, development is a reorganisation emerging from the interactions of the child with other people and their environment. Thelen challenged the then prevailing view of motor development as being determined by neural (brain) maturation. As seen above, psychologists such as Gesell believed that in the first two years an infant acquires a range of goal-directed behaviours such as reaching, grasping, sitting, crawling and walking. These so-called milestones are mainly attributed to the general process of the maturation of the central nervous system.

Thelen considered that motor development occurs as a result of babies acting on their environment and fine-tuning their movements according to the outcomes of their actions. For babies to act on their environment, it is important that they are motivated to do so. This is why a rich environment is important not only for cognitive skills (discussed in Chapter 5), but also for motor skills.

Babies who are strapped into chairs and buggies for long periods of time or are not given stimulating activities to do with their hands will not be motivated to develop their motor skills. Thelen would therefore advocate that babies be left without nappies as much as possible, given toys to reach for and soft surfaces to crawl and roll around on. Toddlers should be given push-pull toys, tricycles and other equipment to develop their gross motor skills. They should also be given plenty of opportunities to develop fine motor skills, e.g. colouring, cutting and pasting, threading and beading, cookery.

Extend your learning

There are numerous videos online showing Esther Thelen at work with young babies and speaking about her work. Thelen was not only interested in developmental theory itself but was particularly interested in how what is discovered in a laboratory setting can be applied to real-life situations. Thelen had mouth cancer in 1980 and after surgery had to undergo intense speech therapy. She was interested in how her very detailed observations of how children learn both gross and fine motor skills could be applied to individuals undertaking physical therapy for motor development injuries and problems. In her later years, Thelen became a practitioner of the Feldenkrais method of physical therapy. Research this method and discuss why you believe Thelen was particularly attracted to it.

REFLEXES

When babies are born, they have several inbuilt reflexes. Reflexes are automatic responses to stimuli in the environment. They do not involve the brain, only the spinal cord, and are therefore not under the infant's conscious control. Most (but not all) reflexes seem to have a survival function, which is why it is believed that they are genetically programmed. Reflexes allow the newborn baby to react to their environment before they have had an opportunity to learn anything about it.

Evolutionary psychologists see the existence of these primitive reflexes as evidence of our past, when humans were covered with long body hair and climbed trees in order to escape predators. For example, babies may have used the grasping reflex to cling to their mother's hair, the rooting reflex so that they could locate the mother's nipple, the startle reflex to break their fall should they be dropped by their mother and the tonic reflex to prevent the baby rolling off a surface.

Some others are not as easy to explain, e.g. the stepping or Babinski reflexes. Since reflexes do not involve the brain, they disappear as the brain becomes more sophisticated and takes over. If reflexes persist, this can be an indication that the brain is not developing normally.

REFLEX	DESCRIPTION	AGE WHEN DISAPPEARS
Blinking	Will close both eyes in response to a flash of light or puff of air	Permanent
Rooting	Turns head, opens mouth and begins sucking if cheek is stroked	3–4 months
Sucking	Sucks automatically if object is placed in the mouth	3–4 months
Grasping	Grasps finger if palm is stroked	3–4 months
Babinski	Fans out toes and turns foot in if sole is stroked	3–4 months
Stepping	Stepping action if feet are placed on a flat surface	3–4 months
Swimming	If an infant is put face down in water, will make co-ordinated 'swimming' actions	6–7 months
Tonic	Sometimes called the fencer's pose (see photo). If baby is placed on their back, they will make a fist with both hands, turning head to the right	2 months
Moro or startle	Responds to a sudden loud noise or movement – baby will arch its back, throw back its head and fling out its arms and legs, rapidly bringing them towards the body again	3–4 months

DEVELOPMENT OF GROSS AND FINE MOTOR SKILLS (0–6 YEARS)

The first gross motor skills to develop, such as crawling, walking, running and dancing, involve the large muscles of the body. Later gross motor skills to develop enable, in varying degrees, more specific and highly desirable skills such as playing football and other sports. Many educationists undervalue gross motor skills. This is strange considering the importance society puts on gross motor skills and how well many of our sports people are paid for their skills. Both gross and fine motor skills are often described in terms of when they are normally achieved. These are called developmental milestones or norms. While there are individual differences between children, most children achieve these milestones around the same time. The major milestones for physical development are outlined in Chapter 2.

4.4 PROMOTING GROSS AND FINE MOTOR SKILLS (0–6 YEARS)

0–1 month:

* Give plenty of physical contact – breastfeeding is best.

* Lots of facial expression – smiling, etc.

* Talk and sing to the baby.

* Baby massage.

* Mobiles with bright primary colours, e.g. Lamaze toys and mobiles use bright colours with pronounced patterns. Babies' eyesight is very poor at this stage and it is believed that these toys are more stimulating for them than more muted colours, e.g. pastels.

* Baby gyms.

Three months:

* Offer toys that can be held as well as looked at, e.g. a light colourful rattle that makes a noise.

* Sing songs with the baby on your knee.

* Baby gym of toys strung over cot will encourage the baby to reach out.

* Provide opportunities for exercise – allow the baby to lie on a mat in a warm room without clothes or nappy on so they can move their limbs freely, without restriction.

* Baths that provide support for the baby's head and body allow freedom of movement at bathtime. Never leave babies or young children unattended in the bath.

Six months:

* Provide bricks to hold and bang together.

* Offer nesting and stacking toys.

* Babies love placing toys such as blocks into containers and removing them again.

* Give babies paper to tear and rustle.

* Offer objects to grasp and that are safe to put in the mouth to explore.

* Offer finger foods – always under supervision.

* Allow babies to experiment with the texture of their food using their fingers.

* Give babies a plastic mirror to look at their own reflection.

* Play clap hands and peek-a-boo; encourage babies to wave bye-bye.

* Play finger rhymes such as 'this little piggy' and 'round and round the garden'.

* Allow babies to bang on upturned saucepans with wooden spoons.

Nine months:

* Roll a small ball towards the baby for them to catch as they sit.

* Bathtime can be fun, so provide bath toys to fill, pour and squeeze.

* Many of the toys suitable at six months are even more suitable now, e.g. stacking and nesting toys, blocks, Duplo, saucepans, cardboard boxes.

Twelve months:

* Push-pull toys are great for babies who are almost walking.

* Sit-on toys to propel with the feet.

* Small slides and climbing frames.

* Balls to throw, roll and follow.

* Bath toys to fill, pour and squeeze.

* Continue to play action games, e.g. clap hands and peek-a-boo.

* A treasure basket is enjoyable for this age group and older – fill a box or basket with interesting but safe objects, e.g. a brightly coloured block, a lemon, a piece of soft fabric, squeaky toy, etc. Allow the baby to explore.

* Shape sorters.

* Thick, non-toxic crayons to make marks on paper.

* Board books to point at and turn pages.

* Bricks and blocks to stack and build.

Fifteen months:

* Large beads and lace with knot on the end to thread.

* Crayons and paper to make marks on.

* Bricks and blocks to stack and play with.

* Child's spoon and fork at mealtimes to practise feeding.

* Bath toys to fill, pour and squeeze.

* Picture books with familiar objects to point at – books should be robust to allow the baby to turn pages easily.

Eighteen months:

* Closely supervised sand and water play – containers for pouring and filling, spoons, etc.
* Push-pull toys.
* Finger and foot painting.
* Crayons and paper for drawing.
* Children should be involved in daily cleaning routines, e.g. put dirty clothes in laundry basket.
* Threading beads.
* Large-piece jigsaws.
* Bricks and blocks.

Two years:

Note: All the activities suggested for 18 months are also suitable at two years.

* Simple ball games, e.g. gently kicking the ball to and fro.
* Provide a tricycle – will be able to push themselves along but cannot use pedals yet.
* Give children pencils and paper to draw on.

Three years:

* Ball games, e.g. football and donkey.
* Dolls and prams are also enjoyed and develop both gross and fine motor skills, e.g. pushing pram – avoiding obstacles; removing and putting on doll's clothes.
* Provide space for toddlers to ride their tricycles and other push-pull toys.

* Provide pencils, colouring pencils, paint, glue, bits and pieces for sticking, etc.
* Provide shape outlines and children's scissors (make sure to have left-handed pairs available).
* Provide construction toys such as Lego.

Four years:

* Provide jigsaw puzzles with thick pieces and allow time for completion.
* Painting and collage activities.
* Use of malleable materials – clay and playdough encourage development of the finger muscles.
* Give the child plenty of writing tools and paper, e.g. old diaries, to encourage 'writing'.

* Provide 'props' for imaginative play, e.g. kitchen sets, dress-up clothes, farm animals and equipment.
* Encourage sand and water play – provide equipment to make play as rich as possible.

Five years:

Note: All the activities listed above for four years are also suitable at five years.

* Encourage games such as skipping and hopscotch.
* Play ball games – some children are quite skilled, even at this stage.
* Provide plenty of art and writing materials.
* Gardening is a very useful activity.
* Provide space for cycling (most can cycle using stabilisers).

Six years:

* Some children learn to ride a two-wheeled bicycle at this stage without stabilisers. Provide plenty of flat space for them to do so.
* Encourage ball games.
* Encourage dance and rhythm movement to music.
* Provide more complex construction toys such as Meccano, Lego, K'NEX or Bionicles. Children may have to follow fairly complex instructions for correct assembly or may just create their own objects.
* Provide plenty of art and writing materials.

REFLECTIVE PRACTICE

The next time you are in your ELC work placement setting, conduct an audit of all the toys and resources that are available there for the promotion of children's gross and fine motor skills. How many of the toys and resources listed above are available? Are there any other resources available not mentioned above? Present your findings to the class.

4.5 OBSERVING AND RECORDING CHILDREN'S PHYSICAL GROWTH AND DEVELOPMENT

Parents and professionals who care for and work with young children have a responsibility for their wellbeing. As part of this responsibility, children's growth and development should be systematically observed and recorded so that our expectations of the child are realistic and within their capabilities, so that we provide activities and opportunities for them to stimulate the next stage of development and so that children who are not making progress are quickly identified and the appropriate interventions are put in place.

Careful observations and assessments are best carried out over a period of a time in an environment where the child feels at ease, e.g. home or playgroup. Unfortunately, while public health nurses carry out home visits during the first few weeks after birth, most developmental check-ups are carried out in clinics that are unfamiliar to the child.

Physical development is usually recorded by using either developmental checklists or centile charts.

Developmental checklists are generally used with children from zero to six years old. They list the norms for the various developmental areas for each age group. Children are observed and tasks are required of them at different ages. Their development is compared with the checklist. The purpose of the checklist is to give a general picture of the child's development, thus screening for potential areas of concern.

Developmental centile charts are charts that have been devised after studying the developmental patterns of thousands of children. They compare the growth and developmental progress of individual children against that of the 'average' child. Children's height, weight, etc. is expressed as a centile, e.g. a child in the 95th centile for height would be taller than 95% of children his or her age.

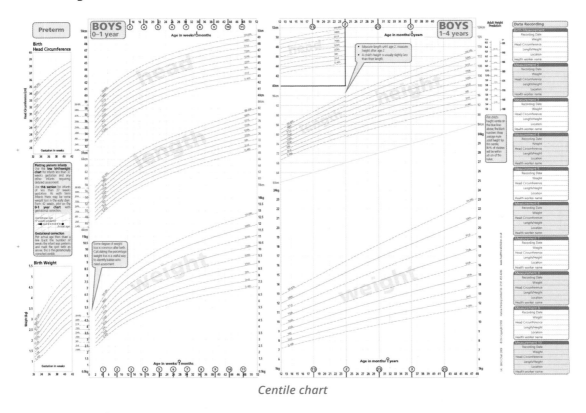

Centile chart

4.6 HOW AISTEAR PROMOTES PHYSICAL GROWTH AND DEVELOPMENT

While all of Aistear's four themes (see Chapter 2) promote physical development, Aim 2 of the theme Wellbeing does so very directly. The following table shows what Aistear sets out to do in this area of the early years curriculum. Early years workers provide unstructured and structured play opportunities designed to fulfil these aims and learning goals.

THEME: WELLBEING	
Aim	**Learning Goals**
Aim 2: Children will be as healthy and as fit as they can be.	In partnership with the adult, children will: 1. Gain increasing control and co-ordination of body movements. 2. Be aware of their bodies, their bodily functions and their changing abilities. 3. Discover, explore and refine gross and fine motor skills. 4. Use self-help skills in caring for their own bodies. 5. Show good judgement in taking risks. 6. Make healthy choices and demonstrate positive attitudes to nutrition, hygiene, exercise and routine.

Collaborate

In groups, discuss one activity or routine that each member of the group has engaged in recently that promotes one of the learning goals listed above. Feed back one example from our group to the rest of the class.

SHOW YOU KNOW

1. Describe typical patterns of growth in children aged either 0–2 years or 2–6 years.

2. Explain how the nervous system develops in children aged 0–6 years.

3. Discuss Gesell's and Thelen's theories of motor development.

4. Describe, with examples, three primitive reflexes.

5. Differentiate between gross and fine motor skills, with examples.

6. Describe a range of toys and activities suitable for use in an ELC setting that promote physical development in one of the following age groups: 0–1 year; 1–3 years; 3–6 years.

7. Write a note on the development of one of the following senses in children: vision; hearing; taste and smell; or touch and pain.

8. Explain why it is important that children's physical growth and development is observed and recorded.

9. Which of Aistear's learning goals specifically promotes physical growth and development in children aged 0–6 years?

5

Cognitive Development

What I will learn

* The concept of cognitive development and its various components
* Behaviourist theories of cognitive development
* Constructivist theories of cognitive development
* Social constructivist theories of cognitive development
* The concept of multiple intelligences
* The three most common learning styles
* What is meant by the term 'active learning'
* Ways in which cognitive development can best be promoted in an ELC setting

5.1 WHAT IS COGNITIVE DEVELOPMENT?

Cognitive development includes the development of each of the following:

* Imagination and creativity
* Memory skills
* Concentration skills
* Problem-solving and thinking skills
* Sensory development
* Concept formation

IMAGINATION AND CREATIVITY

Imagination is the ability to form mental images of objects or concepts that are not present or that do not even exist yet. Imagination forms the basis of many of the activities that humans find enjoyable, e.g. reading books, storytelling, dance, art, music and design. Closely linked to the concept of imagination are two others – problem-solving and original thought. Solving problems in new or original ways requires imagination and should be encouraged in children at every opportunity. Children should be encouraged to use their imagination in their everyday life to discover things for themselves and solve the small day-to-day problems they encounter.

Imaginative play, particularly **symbolic play**, helps children realise that one thing can represent another. For example, a cereal bowl full of water can be a swimming pool for small toy figures. This concept is important later for skills such as reading and writing, where letters have to represent words.

Role play that involves the child becoming somebody or something else also helps develop many other important skills. For example, a child pouring water into cups pretending to be serving coffee in a café is developing their hand–eye co-ordination, their knowledge of volume and their social skills.

Creativity is the expression of imaginative ideas in a unique and personal way. Creativity can be expressed in many ways, e.g. writing stories or poems, creating art or craftwork, making music, dance, cookery and gardening. Being creative is not imitating someone else's ideas. Children often come home from playschool with identical art and craft work; this is not being creative. Children should be given the resources to help them develop their creativity and allowed to go about it themselves. Sometimes adults provide a framework within which children work creatively, but the activity should not be too adult-led. Frameworks can be provided in different ways. For example, if a group is working on the theme of autumn, the adult could provide a range of materials in autumn colours.

MEMORY SKILLS

Memory is a vital part of learning and therefore cognitive development. Memory really involves three tasks: encoding (putting information into storage), storage (retaining information over time) and retrieval (taking information out of storage). The development of memory involves perfecting these three tasks. Whether something is memorised or learned depends on the following.

* **How much** there is to be learned – if too much information is presented at once, it will overload the working memory (also called the short-term memory) and information will not be encoded at all.

* Whether the new memory is **linked** to existing information – does the learner already know something about what is being learned? If they do, they are much more able to learn the new information.

* Does the learner **understand** what is being learned? Information that is not understood is difficult to memorise.

* **Repetition** – has the information been repeated often enough for it to stay in the long-term memory?

While infants begin to remember from about six months (Bauer 2007), most adults remember little, if anything, from their first three years of life. This phenomenon is known as infantile or childhood amnesia and is thought to be a result of the fact that during these first three years of life, the brain's prefrontal lobes (responsible for remembering events) are immature.

Collaborate

In groups, talk together about your earliest memories as children. Are there any common themes about the types of memories members of your group had?

Memory span is another aspect of memory that improves throughout childhood. This refers to the amount of information that can be held and processed in the working or short-term memory at any one time. Generally, memory span increases throughout childhood, from about two items of information at age two, to five items at age seven, to seven items at age 12 through to adulthood. It is important to know this so that too much information is not presented to a young child at one time.

Did you know?

The reason why phone numbers (minus the prefix) contain only 7 digits is because of the limitations of the human memory span.

REFLECTIVE PRACTICE

What does this information on memory mean for people working with young children? The example below illustrates how this theory translates into practice. Discuss in groups how this early years practitioner is showing that he understands the principals of memory described above.

CASE STUDY

Eoin has planned a series of activities to be presented over the next few weeks to enable the children to recognise the written numbers one to ten and begin to understand the concept of number value. The activities he has chosen are:

* Introduce number songs, e.g. 'Five Little Ducks Went Swimming One Day', 'Ten Green Bottles Hanging on a Wall'. As the songs are sung, he holds up the relevant numbers. Later, when children become familiar with the song, he gives each child a number to hold up at the relevant time.

* Art activities where children must decorate a large written number for display around the room.

* Children must make their favourite number out of playdough and talk about why they like the number.

* Number activities such as lotto, number jigsaws, etc.

* Sorting activities where children must sort groups of items into boxes numbered one to ten, depending on how many items are in the group.

* Movement games whereby children must get into line depending on the number they are holding.

CONCENTRATION SKILLS

Concentration is the skill of focusing your attention on a task. It is a necessary skill for learning to take place and children who do not develop this skill for whatever reason generally struggle in the educational environment, especially as they progress. Children will be encouraged to concentrate if:

* Activities are at the correct level for them – if activities are too difficult or too easy, children will quickly lose concentration.

* Activities are interesting and attractively presented.

* Adults encourage and praise the child's efforts.

Young children have quite short attention spans, so activities should not be too prolonged. Having said this, it is important to help develop children's attention span, so activities should be organised that stretch but do not surpass their ability. As a rule of thumb, a typical attention span is between three and five minutes per year of a child's age, so a two-year-old should be able to stay on task for at least six minutes, a three-year-old for at least nine minutes and so on. Attention span while engaged in passive activities such as watching TV or playing video games is not what is meant here, as children are not being challenged to process information while engaged in these activities.

Concentration skills can and should be encouraged by those who work with young children. Examples of how this may be done are as follows.

* Give children the freedom to choose activities that they are personally interested in (see Extend your learning on page 80).

* Encourage children to sit and listen to full stories.

* Encourage children to complete an activity, e.g. a jigsaw, before moving on to the next one.

* Play games, e.g. board games, that require children to persevere to the end.

* Limit time spent at activities that do not promote concentration skills, e.g. passively watching videos.

Extend your learning

Flow is a very interesting concept. It was originally coined by the Russian positive psychologist Mihály Csíkszentmihályi (pronounced 'Cheeks-sent-me-high'). Flow is a state of mind in which a person becomes fully immersed in an activity. While in this mental state, people are completely involved and focused on what they are doing, time flies by and people feel happy and content. When children are given the freedom to choose what they wish to do and are provided with interesting and stimulating resources to use and explore, they experience flow very frequently. The author of this book remembers very well her youngest son at three years of age or so playing on the landing with a set of cheap plastic soldiers. He would spend several hours engrossed in an imaginary war, totally immersed in what he was doing. Calling him or stepping across him would not break his concentration.

As an early years practitioner, how do you think the concept of flow should influence your work with young children?

Children with attention deficit hyperactivity disorder (ADHD) can have severe difficulty maintaining concentration. For more detail on this condition, please see Chapter 11, page 184.

PROBLEM–SOLVING AND THINKING SKILLS

The ability to think through and solve problems is another important aspect of cognitive development. When children begin to try to solve problems, they take a **trial and error** approach. A two-year-old child doing a jigsaw puzzle will try to fit each piece in one at a time until they eventually pick the one that fits. An older child may organise the pieces in some way before trying to fit them together, e.g. find the corner and edge pieces or pieces of the same colour first and work from there. This is the next stage in the development of thinking and problem-solving skills. Children will begin to identify the problem facing them and work out a possible solution before they try anything out. Children begin to be able to mentally predict what may happen. This is called the **hypothesis approach** to problem-solving. The children form a hypothesis or idea to be tested based on their knowledge of the world. The greater children's knowledge and experience, the more accurate their hypothesis is likely to be. Therefore, it is important to expose children to as wide a variety of learning experiences as possible. Children primarily solve problems using the trial and error approach until they are about two years of age. From this age on, they begin to hypothesise and think about the problems they face before deciding on a course of action. Naturally, the child's ability to hypothesise and consider possible solutions develops with age and depends on the child's experiences.

box called 'Skinner's Box' in which he trained lab rats through operant conditioning to press a lever a certain number of times for food (a reward). He was interested in observing the effects of punishment and different reward schedules on the animals' behaviour. What did Skinner find?

* Reward is a much stronger reinforcer than punishment. Punishments must be quite severe before they will effectively stop an undesired behaviour.

* When a desired behaviour is rewarded, it is repeated.

* The most difficult behaviour to stop is one that has been reinforced irregularly. This has been called the 'slot machine effect'.

For example, a mother tells her six-year-old son that he is not allowed to have crisps before his dinner. Nine times out of ten she sticks to her rule and does not allow crisps. On the odd occasion, however, if she is busy, she will give him a bag of crisps to keep him quiet until she has time to make the dinner. The boy frequently asks for crisps before dinnertime. Why?

REFLECTIVE PRACTICE

Does your ELC work placement setting set clear and consistent boundaries for the children? In groups, discuss the boundaries that are set for different age groups in your setting. Are all members of staff consistent with those boundaries?

APPLICATION OF BEHAVIOURIST THEORY TO ELC SETTINGS

Classical and, to a greater degree, operant conditioning form a basis for what ELC practitioners do every day – **behaviour modification**. They reinforce positive behaviours so that they will be repeated and modify undesirable behaviours by not reinforcing them (ignoring) or punishing them.

With behaviour modification there is no 'if' and no mention of a reward. The reinforcer (reward) comes only after the behaviour has appeared, usually in a way that is linked to the behaviour, e.g. 'Well done, Patrick, you tidied up all your blocks before going outside.' When using behaviour modification (sometimes called behaviour shaping), the only time that there is any mention of future outcomes is in terms of what is coming next, e.g. 'When everyone is sitting quietly on their bean bag, then we can start the story.'

Bribery must not be confused with behaviour modification. We might want a child to tidy up the Lego they have been playing with and have spread all over the floor. If we tell the child that they can have a sweet if they tidy up, this is bribery. In this situation the child might understandably feel that they are been given a choice and may decide to forgo the sweet and not tidy up and may be surprised when the adult gets annoyed with them. They might even see this as an opportunity to bargain – asking for two sweets if they tidy up. With bribery the child learns that the point of the positive behaviour is to please the adult and to get a reward, in this case a sweet. They do not learn that the point of the behaviour is to have the Lego safely tidied away for use at another time.

In terms of extinguishing undesired behaviours, behaviourists such as Skinner investigated the effect of lack of reinforcement and punishment. In the case of Skinner's rats, when they pressed the lever again and again and received no food, they eventually stopped pressing the lever. Skinner also experimented by giving the rats a shock for pressing the lever, which also stopped this behaviour. Skinner found that punishments had to be quite severe to stop the rats pressing the lever. They would endure milder shocks in order to receive food.

REFLECTIVE PRACTICE

In terms of applying this aspect of Skinner's theory to ELC settings, what effect does ignoring undesirable behaviour have? What forms of punishment are socially acceptable nowadays? Are they effective? In groups, discuss this aspect of behaviourist theory, drawing on your own experiences.

Critics of the behaviourist approach believe that human learning is much more complex than this. They believe that there are many factors other than whether something has been rewarded or punished to be considered.

Extend your learning

An interesting book by Lauren Slater, *Opening Skinner's Box* (2005), examines ten of the most important psychological experiments of the twentieth century. Slater writes about these experiments in a very accessible and interesting way. If time and interest allow, this is a very good read.

5.3 PIAGET'S CONSTRUCTIVIST THEORY OF COGNITIVE DEVELOPMENT

Jean Piaget (1896–1980) was a Swiss-born psychologist who, through careful observation of his own three children and many others, developed a theory of cognitive development that changed people's perceptions of how children's minds develop. Piaget became aware early on that the mistakes in learning made by young children were consistently different from those made by older children. He accounted for this by arguing that thinking or, more specifically, cognitive processing in younger children is essentially different from that in older children and adults. He proposed that children and adults demonstrate typical patterns of thinking and learning at different stages of their lives.

Jean Piaget

Piaget also believed that children actively construct their own cognitive worlds and are not just passive receivers of information – vessels into which information is poured. Piaget believed that as a result of exposure to the environment around them, children adjust and build their mental structures to suit what they are experiencing, something he called **adaptation**.

KEY CONCEPTS RELATED TO PIAGET'S THEORY

* **Schema:** Piaget believed that as the child begins to construct their understanding of the world, the developing brain creates schemas. A schema is a mental structure that represents some aspect of the world. For example, our schema for a pig is a pink, round, four-legged animal, perhaps with some mud on it. A schema can also be a mental structure for an action, e.g. how to form the letter 'B' on a page.

Collaborate

Close your eyes and think about the following schema – a cow, a kitchen chair, a goat and a tree. Now turn to page 146. Are these the images you had in mind? If so, why do you think you have these particular schemata for cow, chair, goat and tree in your mind, given that there are many types of these? It is likely because these were the images that you were first introduced to as a child. Discuss in groups.

* **Assimilation and accommodation:** Children adapt and change their schema over time. For example, at first a young child may call all vehicles that move on the road 'cars', e.g. cars, vans, trucks, motorbikes and buses. According to Piaget, they fine-tune things through two processes – assimilation and accommodation. Assimilation is when children incorporate new information into their existing schema. Accommodation is when children adjust their schema in light of this new information. Taking the example of 'cars', as the child experiences more of the world and assimilates more information about vehicles that travel on the road, they fine-tune their ideas about what a car is so that it excludes vans (no windows in the back), trucks (too big and no windows in the back), motorbikes (only two wheels and no windows) and buses (too big, too many windows) – this is accommodation.

* **Organisation:** This refers to the capacity of the human mind to organise and link or combine different schema together. For example, a three-year-old child has learned the following schema separately: walking downstairs safely; and that liquids spill if their container is not kept upright. They will combine both these schema in order to walk downstairs holding a beaker of juice.

* **Equilibrium and disequilibrium:** When a child (or indeed an adult) is exposed to something new about the world that conflicts with their existing ideas, they experience disequilibrium (lack of balance). For example, take a child who in the beginning calls any large four-legged creature a cow. After a while, and through experience, the child will notice that something is not quite right with some of their 'cows' (disequilibrium), and they will begin to change their thinking and come up with other categories, such as horses, zebras, etc. Once they have done this, equilibrium is restored. All human beings are motivated to seek equilibrium or understanding.

PIAGET'S STAGE THEORY OF COGNITIVE DEVELOPMENT

According to Piaget, individuals go through four stages of cognitive development. He believed that at each stage, a child's reasoning or way of processing information is qualitatively different from the stage that went before or comes after, and that it was not just that a younger child possesses less information than an older one. Piaget's four stages are as follows.

1. Sensorimotor stage (0–2 years)

2. Pre-operational stage (2–7 years)

3. Concrete operational stage (7–11 years)

4. Formal operational stage (11+ years)

SENSORIMOTOR STAGE (0–2 YEARS)

During the sensorimotor stage, the infant progresses from a newborn focusing almost exclusively on immediate sensory and motor experiences to the toddler who possesses a capacity for thinking. Piaget detailed development through the first two years of a child's life by observing his own three children, dividing the sensorimotor stage into six sub-stages.

SUB-STAGE	AGE (MONTHS)	CHARACTERISTICS OF SUB-STAGE
Reflex activity	0–1	Infants demonstrate innate reflexes, e.g. sucking and grasping.
Primary circular reactions	1–4	Infants repeat actions first encountered by chance, e.g. sucks its thumb by chance and will begin doing so intentionally. Actions all directed at self.
Secondary circular reactions	4–10	Infants begin to repeat actions that have not originated as reflexes, e.g. kicking toys hanging from a play gym. Interacts with objects in their environment – actions now no longer directed at self exclusively.
Co-ordination of secondary circular reactions	10–12	Infants begin to co-ordinate their schema and actions and may begin to use tools, e.g. a spoon.
Tertiary circular reactions	12–18	Infants actively use trial and error methods to learn about objects. Increased mobility allows them to explore and problem-solve.
Internal representation	18–24	Infants begin to be capable of mental action – being able to think about things that are not there in front of them. They begin to be able to use symbols to represent things and people, e.g. a block can become a car. A toddler who sees another toddler pull a playmate's hair may remember this action and do the same thing the following day.

The development of **object permanence** is one of the major feats of the sensorimotor stage. Object permanence is the understanding that objects or people continue to exist even when they cannot be seen, heard or touched. One way of testing for an infant's awareness of object permanence is by showing them an interesting toy, then removing the toy from view. If a child has no sense of object permanence, they will not look for the toy. At approximately seven months, an understanding of object permanence begins to emerge. Consequently, it is at this time that many babies begin to be upset when their primary carer leaves them to be cared for by someone else. This is because when the primary carer leaves, the baby remembers them and misses them in their absence. Prior to this, once the carer was out of sight, they were out of mind.

PRE-OPERATIONAL STAGE (2–7 YEARS)

During the pre-operational stage, the child does not yet perform **operations**. Operations are internalised actions that allow children to mentally carry out tasks. For example, an operation would be adding two numbers in your head without having to use physical props such as fingers. A child who is capable of operations is also able to mentally reverse actions. During the pre-operational stage, the child is preparing themselves to perform operations. The pre-operational stage is divided into two sub-stages:

* Symbolic function sub-stage (2–4 years)
* Intuitive thought sub-stage (4–7 years).

Symbolic function sub-stage (2–4 years)

During this stage, children become able to represent people and objects when they are not present, using scribble designs to represent people, houses, cars, animals, etc. Two limiting features of this stage are **egocentrism** and **animism.** Up to the age of four years, children are believed to be profoundly egocentric. This means that they are not capable of viewing things from another's perspective. For example, a young child speaking on the phone will often just nod or shake their head in reply to a question. They cannot consider that the person they are talking to cannot see them, because they can see themselves. Animism is another feature of this stage. Animism is the belief that objects have lifelike qualities and are capable of feelings and action. This is why if a child bumps their head off the edge of a table, for example, they are comforted somewhat if the table is punished for hurting them – 'Bold table for hurting Molly, bold table!' (adult slapping table).

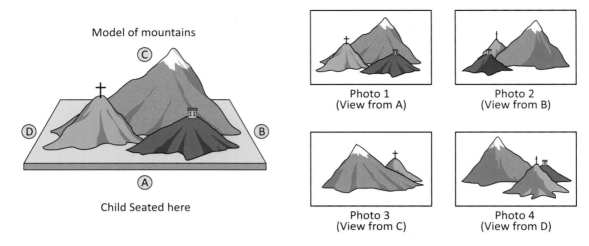

Model of mountains

Photo 1
(View from A)

Photo 2
(View from B)

Photo 3
(View from C)

Photo 4
(View from D)

Child Seated here

Piaget's **mountains experiment** demonstrates egocentrism in children under four years. Piaget and his colleague Bärbel Inhelder (1969) devised what is now called the 'three mountains task' to investigate young children's egocentrism. They found that children under four years of age had difficulty with the task and concluded from this that they were profoundly egocentric, meaning that they could not see something from another's perspective. During the task, the child walks around a model of three mountains (see above) and becomes familiar with what the mountains look like from different perspectives. The child is then seated on one side of the table (position A) and the experimenter then moves a doll around the table, seating it at positions B, C and D. Each time the doll is moved, the experimenter asks the child to pick out from a series of four photographs what the doll can see. Children under four consistently choose photo 1, believing that the doll can see what they can see. Piaget and Inhelder's findings have been since debated (see criticisms of Piaget on page 92).

Intuitive thought sub-stage (4–7 years)

At this stage, Piaget believed, children begin to use primitive reasoning and want to know the answers to all sorts of questions – When? Where? Why? Children are not yet able to understand the principle of cause and effect, e.g. a child is not able to mentally represent what would happen if a car hit them. Another characteristic of this stage is **centration**. Children tend to focus or centre on just one characteristic of an object or idea, thereby showing an inability to **decentre**.

Example: A group of children aged four to seven years old were shown a picture of a collection of dolls, some with hats on and others without, some male and some female. They would generally be able to answer the following question – How many dolls have hats on? Most, however, would have difficulty answering this question – How many boy dolls have hats on? This is because they have difficulty focusing on two things at once (hat wearing and gender).

Piaget demonstrated children's inability to decentre through his famous **conservation** experiments or tasks. He believed that because children under the age of seven could not decentre, they could not conserve. **Conservation** means understanding that just because the appearance of something changes, it does not automatically mean its basic properties have changed. Examine the following conservation experiments to further understand this idea.

TYPE OF CONSERVATION	STAGE 1 OF EXPERIMENT	STAGE 2 OF EXPERIMENT	PRE-OPERATIONAL CHILD'S LIKELY ANSWER
Volume	Child is shown two identical beakers full of coloured liquid. Child agrees that both contain the same amount.	Child sees the experimenter pour liquid from one beaker into a tall, thin one. Child is asked which one contains more or if they are both the same.	Child will choose the tall thin one – demonstrating that they cannot conserve volume.
Number	Child is shown two rows of buttons, one directly opposite the other. Child agrees that both rows contain the same number of buttons.	Child sees the experimenter spread out one row of buttons – child is asked which row contains the most buttons now or if they are both the same.	Child will pick the spread-out row – demonstrating that they cannot conserve number.
Mass	Child is shown two identical balls of playdough. Child agrees both balls contain the same amount of playdough.	Child sees the experimenter roll one ball into a long sausage shape – child is asked which contains the most playdough now or if they are both the same.	Child will pick the sausage shape – demonstrating that they cannot conserve mass.
Length	Child is shown two sticks, one directly opposite the other. Child agrees both sticks are the same length.	Child sees the experimenter push one stick forward – child is asked which stick is longer now or if they are both the same.	Child will pick the stick that has been pushed forward – demonstrating that they cannot conserve length.

CONCRETE OPERATIONAL STAGE (7–11 YEARS)

During this stage, children learn to conserve. For example, a child at the concrete operational stage will say when a round ball of clay is transformed into a sausage shape that 'It is longer, but it is thinner' or 'If you change it back into the ball it will be the same again.' In this way, children understand that actions can be reversed. Conservation of number usually occurs first (sometimes as young as five), with conservation of volume last (often not until ten or 11 years). Children can problem-solve at this stage if the problems are **concrete** in nature. For example, Anna is taller than Nina. Anna is smaller than Lily. Who is the smallest? This problem is difficult for a child at the concrete operational stage. However, if the child is given dolls representing Anna, Nina and Lily, they will have no problem answering the question because they have concrete 'props' to help them. Many children's maths books nowadays have counters or number lines at the top of the page to aid the concrete thinker.

FORMAL OPERATIONAL STAGE (11+ YEARS)

Piaget argued that it is not until this stage that children can reason hypothetically and understand abstract concepts. Ask a child of nine or ten to explain what the concept 'justice' means. If they have heard the word before, most are likely to explain with a concrete example: 'Justice is when your mother gives out to your brother for breaking your PlayStation controller.' Children at the formal operational stage also approach problems in a more logical, systematic way. Give a child at the concrete operational stage a big bunch of keys and ask them to find the one that opens a lock. They are is most likely to approach the problem in a disorganised way, trying different keys randomly. A child at the formal operational stage, on the other hand, is likely to take an organised, systematic approach. Critics of Piaget, e.g. Shayer and Wylam (1978), say that if children are coached, they can reach the formal operational stage early, concluding that Piaget's stages are not as clearly defined age-wise as he proposed.

CRITICISMS OF PIAGET'S THEORY

Criticisms of Piaget's theories centre on two main areas. The first is that children may have failed to complete many of his tasks not because they couldn't, but because the tasks were conducted in an environment very strange to the child (a laboratory setting). In addition, with many of his experiments, the child was confused about what they were being asked to do because the tasks did not make **human sense** (see Donaldson's policeman experiment below). The second criticism is that Piaget applied his theories quite rigidly and across the board; he took no account of the effects of education, training and culture.

MARGARET DONALDSON'S POLICEMAN EXPERIMENT

Margaret Donaldson described a series of experiments carried out by herself and her colleagues which showed that children as young as three and a half are capable of appreciating another's point of view. In this way, Donaldson sought to oppose Piaget's contention that children under seven years old are by and large egocentric, a finding supported by his three mountains task described earlier. The Donaldson experiment consists of two walls set up to form a cross; a toy policeman; and a boy.

The child is asked to help the boy hide from the policeman, so is required to place him where the policeman cannot see him (Donaldson and Hughes 1978). In some versions of the experiment, the boy must hide from two policemen, so the child has to appreciate two viewpoints other than their own.

Donaldson claimed that the policeman task made human sense and that it was realistic and interesting for the child: 'The task requires the child to act in ways which are in line with certain very basic human purposes (escape and pursuit). It makes human sense ... in this context, he shows none of the difficulty in "decentring" which Piaget ascribes to him ... the "mountains task" is abstract in a psychologically very important sense, in the sense that it is abstracted from all basic human purposes and feelings and endeavours' (Donaldson 1978: 24).

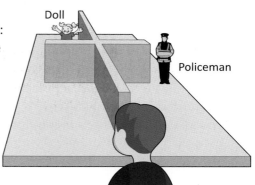

5.4 VYGOTSKY'S SOCIAL CONSTRUCTIVIST THEORY OF COGNITIVE DEVELOPMENT

Lev Vygotsky was born in 1896 in what is now Belarus and died of TB in 1934, aged only 38. Like Piaget, Vygotsky believed that children actively construct their knowledge and understanding and are not merely vessels to be filled with facts and information. Unlike Piaget, however, who saw the child as somewhat of a 'lone scientist', Vygotsky emphasised the importance of social relationships (other people) in a child's learning processes. Two concepts emerge from Vygotsky's work that are of particular importance to childcare staff: the zone of proximal development and scaffolding.

Lev Vygotsky

THE ZONE OF PROXIMAL DEVELOPMENT

The zone of proximal development (ZPD) is the area between what a child can do on their own and what they can do with adult or more able peer assistance. Tasks that children can just about master alone are at the very bottom of their ZPD and those they can master only with assistance are at the top. Tasks that are very easy or very difficult for the child are outside the zone altogether. Vygotsky believed that teaching is about finding each child's ZPD and guiding them along it. Tasks outside the zone – too easy (below) or too difficult (above) – should not be presented, as children will quickly become either bored and uninterested or frustrated and give up.

SCAFFOLDING

Closely linked to the zone of proximal development is Vygotsky's concept of scaffolding. He believed that the job of teacher (adult or more able peer) involves providing the correct level of support (scaffolding) to the learning child. When a child is first introduced to something new and challenging (at the top of their ZPD), the adult or more able peer provides a lot of support. The amount of support should lessen as the child becomes more competent. If children are given too much support (the adult half does the task for them), they usually hand over the task to the adult and stop trying themselves (see the case study on page 94).

CASE STUDY

St Brigid's crosses of rushes are traditionally made in Irish primary schools on the first day of February every year. When Sam was in first class, his teacher made crosses with the children. After a while (the children were working away happily on the crosses), the teacher realised that the crosses the children were making didn't look much like St Brigid's crosses, and she got the children to line up so that she could tidy them up for them. The children

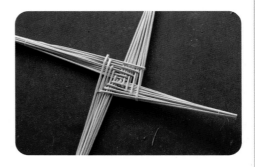

lined up and the teacher redid much of the work the children had done, eventually succeeding in making a whole classroom of very respectable crosses. After class, she wiped her brow and thought to herself that she wasn't going to try that one again, as the crosses were just too difficult for the children. Sam came out of school with his cross. When his mother complimented him on how good it looked, he said, 'Well, teacher sort of did it.' He left the cross in a pocket in the back seat of the car, where it withered and was only found the next time the car was cleaned out. The following year, Sam had a different teacher. He came out of school holding a misshapen cross tied unevenly with elastic bands. His mother asked him if he had done it all himself. He said, 'Well, teacher helped at bit, but mostly I did it.' That evening, Sam asked his mother where he could put the cross. They hung it over a photo in the living room for all to see.

REFLECTIVE PRACTICE

Read the case study above and explain how it relates to what you have learned in relation to Vygotsky's zone of proximal development and the concept of scaffolding.

5.5 THEORIES OF MULTIPLE INTELLIGENCES AND LEARNING STYLES

Robert Sternberg's (1949–) triarchic theory of intelligence proposes that intelligence comes in three forms – analytic, creative and practical. Most people tend to be stronger in one than the other two.

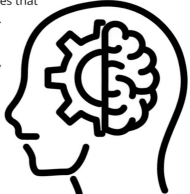

Someone with strong **analytic** intelligence finds it easy to analyse, evaluate, compare and contrast. As these are skills that are demanded by our education system, children with strong analytic intelligence tend to do very well in school.

Someone with strong **creative** intelligence has the ability to imagine, invent, design and create. Strong creative intelligence is useful for some subjects at school, such as art and technology, but is not as beneficial for others. In our education system, where many subjects are compulsory, children with strong creative intelligence must often take a lot of subjects that do not particularly play to their strengths. As a result, these children frequently do not achieve as well as those with analytic intelligence.

Someone with strong **practical** intelligence is good at doing things, assessing and solving practical problems. Children with strong practical intelligence are generally good at subjects that have a significant hands-on element, such as engineering or wood technology. As with creative intelligence, because children with strong practical intelligence must often do a number of subjects that require analytic skills, these children often do not achieve as well as those with analytic intelligence.

Howard Gardner (1943–) believes that there are nine frames of mind or types of intelligence. As with Sternberg's theory, he believes that people are stronger in some of them than others. He also believes that in the right environment all areas can be promoted in children.

Howard Gardner

FORM OF INTELLIGENCE	STRENGTHS
Verbal or linguistic	Good with words and language, can use the written word very effectively, e.g. journalists, actors, authors
Logical or mathematical	Good with numbers and at noticing patterns. Good at problem-solving, e.g. computer programmers
Bodily or kinaesthetic	Find it easy to develop and perfect new physical skills, e.g. sportspeople, dentists, surgeons, craftspeople
Visual or spatial	Good at thinking three-dimensionally, e.g. architects and artists
Musical or rhythmical	Sensitive to pitch and tone of music, enjoy music and can learn to play easily, good dance rhythm, e.g. musicians, dancers
Interpersonal	Find it easy to get along with others and work as part of a team, e.g. nurses
Intrapersonal	Have good self-knowledge and like to work independently, e.g. authors
Naturalist	Understand the natural world, e.g. farmers, landscape gardeners, botanists
Existential	Sensitivity and capacity to tackle deep questions about human existence, e.g. how we got here, what happens when we die

LEARNING STYLES

It is widely accepted that in addition to theories of multiple intelligences, people can have different learning styles. The three most common learning styles are visual, auditory and kinaesthetic.

Approximately 29% of people are predominantly **visual learners**; they learn best by looking. While studying, visual learners should make notes on Post-its or prompt cards, use diagrams, mind maps and flow charts and highlighting pens.

Approximately 34% of learners are predominantly **auditory learners**; they learn best by listening. While studying, auditory learners should read notes onto a recording device and listen back, read information that needs to be learned aloud and get friends or family to ask questions on what they have learned.

Approximately 37% of learners are **kinaesthetic learners**; they learn best by doing. While studying, kinaesthetic learners should walk around while reading work, write notes on Post-its and stick them around the room, walking from note to note while learning, run their finger under words.

Having said this, often the learning style that suits best depends on the subject matter being worked on, e.g. it would be very difficult to work on maths using auditory techniques.

5.6 ACTIVE LEARNING

There is a wide range of alternatives for the term 'active learning', such as: learning through play, technology-based learning, activity-based learning, group work and project method. It is vital that all learning in the ELC setting is active. Children will not benefit from passive learning, e.g. passively listening to the ELC practitioner, or doing activities that are too adult-led. They must be given opportunities to choose the activities they wish to engage in and complete them at their own pace. The following graphic should be used by ELC practitioners evaluating whether the environment they are providing for the children in their setting is active. If you find that an activity you are doing with the children in your setting is not involving the children in the ways described in the graphic, then it could be that you need to reflect on the types of opportunities being offered.

5.7 PROMOTING COGNITIVE DEVELOPMENT

There are many ways of promoting cognitive development.

* Talk and interact with a baby from birth. Try to provide the baby with good routines. Provide a stimulating environment when the baby is awake. Use child-directed speech ('motherese').

* Provide plenty of interesting active activities for the child – sand and water play, art materials, dress-up clothes, small world toys, jigsaws and other puzzles and construction toys such as Lego. Scaffold their learning but make sure not to help too much.

* Allow children to safely explore the wider environment with visits to the park, beach, zoo, etc.

* Provide plenty of reading and writing materials for children.

* Have children help with household tasks in a meaningful way – cooking, cleaning, gardening, gathering and sorting laundry, etc.

* Read with and for children and ask them their opinions on what they have read.

HOW AISTEAR PROMOTES COGNITIVE DEVELOPMENT

While all of Aistear's four themes promote cognitive development, the theme 'Exploring and Thinking' does so very directly. The following table shows what Aistear sets out to do in this area of the early years curriculum. Early years workers provide unstructured and structured play opportunities designed to fulfil these aims and learning goals.

THEME: EXPLORING AND THINKING	
Aims	**Learning Goals**
Aim 1 Children will learn about and make sense of the world around them.	In partnership with the adult, children will: **1.** Engage, explore and experiment in their environment and use new physical skills including skills to manipulate objects and materials. **2.** Demonstrate a growing understanding of themselves and others in their community. **3.** Develop an understanding of change as part of their lives. **4.** Learn about the natural environment and its features, materials, animals, and plants, and their own responsibility as carers. **5.** Develop a sense of time, shape, space, and place. **6.** Come to understand concepts such as matching, comparing, ordering, sorting, size, weight, height, length, capacity, and money in an enjoyable and meaningful way.
Aim 2 Children will develop and use skills and strategies for observing, questioning, investigating, understanding, negotiating, and problem-solving, and come to see themselves as explorers and thinkers.	In partnership with the adult, children will: **1.** Recognise patterns and make connections and associations between new learning and what they already know. **2.** Gather and use information from different sources using their increasing cognitive, physical and social skills. **3.** Use their experience and information to explore and develop working theories about how the world works, and think about how and why they learn things. **4.** Demonstrate their ability to reason, negotiate and think logically. **5.** Collaborate with others to share interests and to solve problems confidently. **6.** Use their creativity and imagination to think of new ways to solve problems.
Aim 3 Children will explore ways to represent ideas, feelings, thoughts, objects, and actions through symbols.	In partnership with the adult, children will: **1.** Make marks and use drawing, painting and model-making to record objects, events and ideas. **2.** Become familiar with and associate symbols (pictures, numbers, letters, and words) with the things they represent. **3.** Build awareness of the variety of symbols (pictures, print, numbers) used to communicate, and use these in an enjoyable and meaningful way leading to early reading and writing. **4.** Express feelings, thoughts and ideas through improvising, moving, playing, talking, writing, story-telling, music and art. **5.** Use letters, words, sentences, numbers, signs, pictures, colour and shapes to give and record information, to describe and to make sense of their own and others' experiences. **6.** Use books and ICT (software and the internet) for enjoyment and as a source of information.

Aim 4	In partnership with the adult, children will:
Children will have positive attitudes towards learning and develop dispositions like curiosity, playfulness, perseverance, confidence, resourcefulness, and risk-taking.	1. Demonstrate growing confidence in being able to do things for themselves. 2. Address challenges and cope with frustrations. 3. Make decisions and take increasing responsibility for their own learning. 4. Feel confident that their ideas, thoughts and questions will be listened to and taken seriously. 5. Develop higher-order thinking skills such as problem-solving, predicting, analysing, questioning, and justifying. 6. Act on their curiosity, take risks and be open to new ideas and uncertainty.

REFLECTIVE PRACTICE

Divide the class into four groups. Each group should take one of the aims listed above and write it out in the centre of a large piece of paper. Write the six associated learning goals around the central aim. Try as a group to think of as many activities and experiences that you could offer to children in your setting to work towards each learning goal. Some learning goals (e.g. aim 4, learning goal 2) will not be an activity or experience but instead a way of working with the child.

SHOW YOU KNOW

1. Write an informative note on two of the following elements of cognitive development: sensory development, concept formation, problem-solving and thinking, memory, concentration, or creativity and imagination.

2. Outline B.F. Skinner's behaviourist theory of cognitive development.

3. Describe Piaget's constructivist theory of cognitive development.

4. Explain Lev Vygotsky's social constructivist theory of cognitive development.

5. Explain Howard Gardner's concept of multiple intelligences.

6. Describe the three most common learning styles.

7. Explain what is meant by the term 'active learning'.

8. Describe one activity that you carried out in an ELC setting that actively promoted an aspect of cognitive development in the children you were working with.

9. Explain how your chosen activity ties in with Aistear's aims and learning goals under the theme of 'Exploring and Thinking'.

Language Development

6

What I will learn

* What is meant by 'language and communication'
* How spoken language is structured
* How children's oral language skills typically develop during the years 0–6
* The differences between the 'phonics' and 'whole-language' approaches to early literacy development
* Why second language learning is hugely beneficial to children and why it is beneficial for children to begin a second language in the early years
* The principles of the three broad theories of language development: nativist (or biological perspective); imitation (or behaviourist perspective); and interactionist
* How to compare, contrast and evaluate all three perspectives
* In line with Aistear, how language and literacy can be best promoted in the ELC setting

6.1 INTRODUCTION TO LANGUAGE AND COMMUNICATION

Language is any form of communication. It can be both expressive and receptive.

EXPRESSIVE LANGUAGE

Expressive language is the ability to communicate our thoughts and feelings using words, expressions, gestures, signs and symbols. It can be as simple as pointing to a desired object or as complex as writing a novel. Talking is the main form of communication that people think about when discussing expressive language but gestures (see non-verbal communication on page 101), sign language and writing are all forms of expressive language.

RECEPTIVE LANGUAGE

Receptive language is being able to understand the information or feelings that are being communicated. Information and feelings are communicated in a variety of ways, through sounds, words, sentences, through movement and gestures and through signs and symbols.

NON-VERBAL COMMUNICATION

Scientific research on non-verbal communication and behaviour began with the 1872 publication of Charles Darwin's *The Expression of the Emotions in Man and Animals*. Since then, a significant body of research has emerged regarding the types, effects and expressions of non-verbal communication and behaviour. As a child develops, they become more skilled at non-verbal communication, something that is no easy feat given that much non-verbal communication is very subtle and occurs at an almost subconscious level. There are eight broad categories of non-verbal communication.

1. **Facial expressions** are responsible for a huge portion of non-verbal communication. Consider how much can be communicated using a simple smile. The look on a person's face is normally the first thing we see, even before they say anything. While non-verbal communication practices can vary considerably between cultures, the facial expressions for anger, happiness, surprise, disgust, sadness and fear are very similar throughout the world.

2. **Gestures** are signals and deliberate movements that can communicate meanings without words. Common gestures include pointing and waving. There is cultural variation with some gestures, e.g. in northern Europe a quick firm handshake is the norm, whereas in some African countries this would be seen as aggressive and a limp handshake is standard. In Japan bowing to someone in greeting is used instead of a handshake. Some gestures can be very powerful, e.g. rolling the eyes to dismiss what someone is saying or jabbing with one's fingers in an aggressive manner.

3. **Para-linguistics** refers to the way the voice is used and is separate from the actual words spoken. Para-linguistics refers to the tone, volume, pitch and inflection of the voice. Inflection in speech means modifying the pitch within a spoken word. Take the word 'really'. If you want to make this sound like a question, upward inflection is used. To express disbelief or annoyance at what is being said, a downward inflection of the word will change its meaning. Consider a person asking his or her partner how they are feeling. The words 'I'm fine', depending on how they are said, can have different meanings.

4. **Body language and posture** can also be used to convey a lot of information in addition to the words that are being said. Body language and posture can be obvious, e.g. standing rigidly upright with hands on hips can portray annoyance. Body language and posture, however, can be a lot more subtle than this and it requires great skill to interpret it.

5. **Proxemics** is the amount of space that people feel it necessary to set between themselves and others. The amount of personal space required is influenced by several factors including cultural expectations, social norms, personality and level of familiarity. For example, in general people in Ireland and England prefer a greater distance than do people in Latin American countries.

6. **Eye gaze:** The eyes play an important role in non-verbal communication. Studies show that when we encounter people or things we like, blinking increases and our pupils dilate. The eyes can also be used to indicate hostility by staring or disbelief by rolling of the eyes. People also use eye gaze to try to determine if someone is being honest. Steady eye contact is normally taken to mean the person is being truthful, whereas looking away, or 'shifty eyes', can indicate the opposite.

7. **Touch** can be used to convey care and concern, but it can also be used to assert power, e.g. holding someone by the upper arm. Touch can also be used subtly in this way, e.g. a businessperson may put their hand on another businessperson's shoulder for this purpose.

8. **Appearance:** Our choice of hairstyle, clothing and other factors are also considered a form of non-verbal communication. **Gleaning details** are items such as particular types of clothing, tattoos or multiple piercings that can communicate strong non-verbal messages about the individual.

6.2 THE STRUCTURE OF SPOKEN AND WRITTEN LANGUAGE

All human languages have five rules that organise and order them: phonology, morphology, syntax, semantics and pragmatics.

Phonology is the sound system of a language. A phoneme is a basic unit of sound, e.g. 'ba'. Different languages have different phonemes. This is why, for example, many people from Pakistan have difficulty with the phoneme 'v' when speaking in English, as in the word 'very', since 'v' does not exist in Punjabi, the most commonly spoken language in Pakistan.

Morphology is the structure of words. **Morphemes** are the units that make up words. Sometimes words contain only one morpheme, e.g. 'rag', whereas sometimes they contain more than one, e.g. 'ragged' contains two. The grammar of a language depends on morphology. For example, 'he walks' and 'he walked' have two different meanings because of the morphemes added at the ends, 's' in one case and 'ed' in the other.

Syntax is the way words are combined in sentences to make understandable phrases. The same words combined differently can completely change the meaning of a phrase, e.g. 'John hit Peter' or 'Peter hit John'.

Semantics refers to the meaning of words and sentences. Every word has a set of semantic features related to its meaning. Some words are close semantically, e.g. man and boy are close, whereas others are semantically very different, e.g. chair and dog (the only common semantic feature would perhaps be that they both have four legs). For sentences to make sense, the semantics must be right. For example, while 'the horse spoke quietly to the boy' is grammatically correct, it is not semantically correct in that speaking is not a semantic feature associated with horses.

Pragmatics involves knowing how to use language appropriately in different contexts. Compare the way you would use language in an interview with how you would use it while talking to your friends over a cup of coffee. Pragmatics is closely linked to a child's social development (see Chapter 8) and learning what is appropriate in given situations. For example, a young child displays their lack of understanding of pragmatics when they declare loudly in church that they have to go wee wee.

6.3 OVERVIEW OF ORAL LANGUAGE DEVELOPMENT

(See also Chapter 2.)

The task of learning language is an extremely complex one, making it all the more remarkable that babies normally utter their first word by 13 months and by four years of age have mastered speech to an almost adult-like level. In order to learn even their first word, children must:

* Identify a word from a speech stream. (Think of how people speaking in a foreign language sound to you. Their speech seems to be just one long string of sounds with no gaps.)

* Remember what the word sounds like so they can recognise it again.

* Link the word with some consistent event, for example notice that every time the sound 'din dins' is said, food appears.

* Physically train the vocal cords, tongue and lips to produce the correct sound.

* Say the word in an appropriate context.

The process of learning language begins at birth and infants the world over follow a similar pattern of development regardless of what language they learn.

INFANCY

Long before babies speak recognisable words, they vocalise. There are several reasons for these early vocalisations, which include attracting attention, practising speech sounds and just for fun (babies love to experiment with their own voice). During the first year, babies' sounds go through a particular sequence.

* **Crying:** Babies cry from birth. Crying is initially used only to signal distress (hungry, wind, dirty nappy, tired). Later, though, crying is used for a variety of reasons, e.g. Pick me up; I am bored sitting here.

* **Cooing:** Babies first begin cooing between one and two months. Cooing is a gurgling sound made at the back of the throat and usually signals pleasure.

* **Babbling:** From about six months, babies begin stringing together speech-like sounds made up of a consonant and vowel – ba ba ba, da da da.

Infants begin to use gestures such as nodding or pointing between eight and 12 months. Children initially point without checking whether the adult is looking, but then they will point and look back to the adult to see if they are looking. No pointing is one of the early indicators of communication problems, e.g. autism.

Infants understand many words before they can speak them. This is called their passive or receptive vocabulary. Some infants, for example, recognise their own name as early as five months. By 16 months, girls understand on average over 200 words, with boys slightly fewer at approximately 180 (Fenson *et al.* 1994).

A child's first words usually include the names of familiar people, e.g. Nana, Dada, Mama; objects, e.g. ball; animals, e.g. doggy; body parts, e.g. eyes; foods, e.g. juice; and greeting terms, e.g. day-day. This is called their active or spoken vocabulary. While there are wide variations among children as to when they speak their first words (nine to 24 months), on average children utter their first words at around 13 months, speaking on average 20 to 50 words by 18 months.

Somewhere around 18 to 24 months (although, again, this can vary considerably), children begin to rapidly produce new words (sometimes as many as ten to 20 new words per week). This is called the vocabulary spurt. Another feature of language at this stage is the over- and under-extension of word meanings. For example, if a child has learned the word 'dada', they may apply this to all males (over-extension). In contrast, if a child learns the word 'doggy' in relation to their own dog (a black and white border collie), they may not recognise that a golden retriever is also a dog (under-extension).

Between 18 and 24 months, children usually begin to use two-word utterances such as 'Mammy go', 'Where daddy?', 'Juice gone'. While these utterances are not full, grammatically correct sentences, they are remarkably understandable. This type of speech, where the usual grammatical structures of language are not adhered to, is called telegraphic speech.

EARLY CHILDHOOD

From the age of two, toddlers move quickly from two-word utterances to creating three-, four- and five-word sentences. Sometimes children's understanding of the world around them is ahead of their speech.

Example

While playing with two toy figurines (soldiers), a three-year-old boy began removing their clothing. When the adult asked, 'Will they not be cold?', the boy replied, 'No they are fighting mans,' and began bashing them off each other. The three-year-old in this case had seen and understood the concept of being a soldier and understood that they are strong and tough but did not yet have the word for soldier. Note also the three-year-old's incorrect use of the word 'mans'. This feature of children's speech will be dealt with later (see the section on Noam Chomsky, page 108).

By the age of three, most children can pronounce all the phonemes (sounds) of their native language. Also, around this time, children begin to understand morphology rules, e.g. that if you want to make something plural you add an 's' and if you want to say something in the past tense you add 'ed'. In a classic experiment by Jean Berko (1958), the experimenter read out a series of cards (see example). Children were asked to pluralise a range of made-up words, e.g. wug.

Generally, the children were able to do so, demonstrating that children understand morphology rules from a young age. The fact that the words were made-up meant that the children could not have heard the plural of them before. This indicates that they were applying the rules of grammar themselves and not just learning through imitation.

This is a WUG

Now there is another one.
There are two of them.
There are two _____.

Another complex aspect of language is syntax, or word order, in a sentence. Consider these two sentences:

* Where is Daddy going?
* Daddy is going to work.

These seemingly simple sentences are actually very complex. To form them correctly, you must know the differences in word order between question-type sentences and non-question-type sentences.

* Question-type sentence order: (1) 'wh' word ('Where') (2) auxiliary verb ('is') (3) subject ('daddy') and (4) verb

* Non-question-type sentence order: (1) subject ('Daddy') (2) auxiliary verb ('is') (3) verb ('going') (4) catenative verb ('to work')

Yet by and large, children master syntax by age four. One of the last aspects of syntax to be mastered is called the auxiliary inversion rule; when you ask a question, 'is' comes before the subject of the sentence. This is why children may ask, 'Where Daddy is going?' In terms of semantics (word understanding), it is estimated that between the age of 18 months and six years, children learn on average one word for every hour they are awake, which totals approximately 14,000 words by age six (Clark 1993).

6.4 EARLY LITERACY DEVELOPMENT

EARLY LITERACY

A comprehensive report by the European Literacy Policy Network, *Literacy in Ireland* (2016), shows that 7.6% of girls in Ireland and 13% of boys are categorised as low-performing readers. This compares very favourably with other EU countries where on average 20% of children are considered low-performing readers at age 15. On the other end of the scale Ireland also performs well, with 11.4% of children in Ireland at the highest level of reading performance as compared with an EU average of 7% in this category. Having said this, in many areas designated as socially and economically disadvantaged the percentage of children with severe literacy difficulties can reach 30% and higher.

Low-performing readers at 15 years of age can read simple texts, retrieve explicit information or make straightforward inferences, but they are not able to deal with longer or more complex texts, and are unable to interpret beyond what is explicitly stated in the text. Given the difficulties that this poses for the individual throughout their education and indeed daily life, it is vital to understand how children's literacy skills develop or fail to develop.

Literacy skills start with the development of language skills; as such, it is necessary that parents talk to their children about what their child is interested in. For example, if a child is playing with its teddy, then parents' talk should be about the teddy – 'Oh, teddy is lovely and soft, isn't he?' A study by Harris, Jones and Grant (1983) found that the mothers of children with language delay tended to speak less often to them, and that when they did speak, they often did not relate what they said to what the child was doing at the time.

Before learning to read, children begin describing and drawing things that are not physically there. This is called symbolic representation and is vital in the process of learning to read. The child must understand the concept that symbols can have meaning. Generally, there are two approaches to teaching children to read:

* The phonics approach
* The whole-language approach

The **phonics** approach emphasises the breakdown of words into their component parts and learning to 'translate' letter symbols into sounds. It is only after the child has mastered this that they progress to reading stories and poems. In contrast, the **whole-language** approach is recommended by psychologists such as John Holt (1983) who believe that the phonics approach destroys the child's love of reading and takes away their natural ability to puzzle things out for themselves, just as they did while learning to speak. Holt recommends the use of real, interesting books for children even if they cannot read them from cover to cover.

Which approach is best is open to debate. Some studies show that the whole-language approach works best for children who are exposed to books at home, whereas children who have little exposure to books at home may get little practice outside school and may require the more direct phonics approach (Pressley 2007). Many children who come from homes where reading is a daily activity come to school already reading, or at least possessing many of the prerequisites for reading – knowing that reading progresses from left to right, identifying letters of the alphabet and perhaps knowing how to write their own name. Others come from homes where there is little reading done or little access to reading materials. These children start school at a distinct disadvantage and frequently fall behind in the first two years, with many remaining behind for the rest of their schooling.

Reading recovery is an early intervention programme developed for children aged 5–6 who have made very little progress in reading and writing during their first year at school. For more information on this programme, please see Chapter 11, page 179.

WRITING

Children's writing begins to emerge between the ages of two and three, when they start to draw and scribble. By age four, most children can write their own first name and by five most can print letters and copy short words. For the first few years of schooling, children with normal literacy abilities may reverse letters such as b and d, p and q. As with reading, writing takes practice and children who are given frequent opportunities to write generally progress much more quickly. Here is a notice that a child aged 6 created for the 'rules in the car'. This child has older siblings and is trying to influence what happens in the car so that he has some degree of control. From this

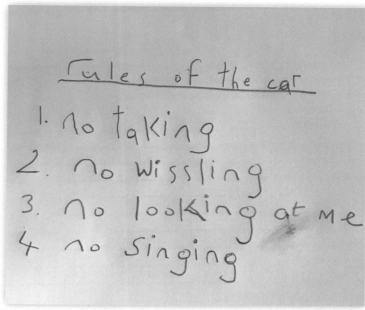

Rules for the car
1. *no talking*
2. *no whistling*
3. *no looking at me*
4. *no singing*

notice, you can see that the child understands the idea of a 'notice' and that rules are often listed and numbered. Some of his spellings are phonetic but are legible. This child is well on his way to learning how to read and write well.

BILINGUALISM AND SECOND LANGUAGE LEARNING

How difficult is it to learn a second language? Can adolescents and adults learn a second language to fluency? Generally speaking, if a second language is learned before the age of around ten to 12, the speaker will be more likely to achieve native-like pronunciation and accent, more accurate speech in terms of grammar and a more extensive vocabulary. This is not to say that adults or adolescents cannot learn a second language – it is just more difficult. This is why many people in Ireland would like to see the learning of a second European language during the primary school years (like many other countries) rather than beginning at secondary school, when the child has gone past the optimum age for language learning. There are many advantages to being bilingual, other than just having a second language. Studies show that being able to speak more than one language makes learning a third and subsequent languages easier and has a positive effect on other aspects of cognitive development, such as attention, concept formation and reasoning (Gibbons and Ng 2004).

6.5 THEORIES OF LANGUAGE DEVELOPMENT

So far, this chapter has described patterns of language development. Now we shall examine the theories about *how* this development occurs. As with every other aspect of child development, the debate about whether language development occurs as a result of nature or nurture is to the forefront. There are three broad perspectives about how language is acquired.

1. Nativist (or biological perspective)
2. Imitation (or behaviourist perspective)
3. Interactionist

NATIVIST (OR BIOLOGICAL PERSPECTIVE)

Language certainly has biological origins. You could try to teach a cat to speak until the cows come home, but you would not succeed. Studies of brain-damaged patients have identified two main areas of the brain concerned with language – Broca's area (speech production and grammar) and Wernicke's area (language comprehension). Patients with damage to Broca's area have difficulty pronouncing words correctly, while patients with damage to Wernicke's area produce streams of correctly pronounced words that do not make sense.

The linguist Noam Chomsky (1928–) has proposed that human beings are prewired to understand the complex grammatical structure of language. He believes that children are born with what he calls a language acquisition device (LAD) that enables them to detect rules and features of language such as morphology and syntax. According to Chomsky, children's LAD begins to weaken with age, particularly between the ages of ten and 12, and that native-like fluency after that age is virtually impossible, meaning that there is a critical period

Noam Chomsky

for language learning. His findings have been supported by rare cases such as Genie's (see Chapter 1), where children who grow up in virtual isolation are unable to achieve fluency despite intensive language exposure when discovered. One of Chomsky's key observations in support of his LAD theory is children's use of what he called virtuous errors. Very early on and all on their own, children seem to work out basic rules of grammar, such as adding 's' to pluralise a word and adding 'ed' to put a verb into the past tense. They then apply these rules even when they are not appropriate. Hence, children say things like 'My feets are dirty' or 'I runned home as fast as I could'. Chomsky contends that if English grammar (or indeed the grammar of other languages as well) followed its own rules, then these utterances would in fact be correct. Chomsky argues that environment could not be a factor here because children do not hear adults saying 'runned' and 'feets'.

IMITATION THEORY (BEHAVIOURIST PERSPECTIVE)

As discussed in Chapter 5, behaviourists such as Skinner believe that learning, including language learning, occurs as a result of reinforcement. For example, if a baby accidentally babbles 'da da da' and Dada rewards this with smiles, hugs and saying 'good girl', in time the baby will repeat this behaviour intentionally to receive the positive reinforcement, in this way learning the word 'Dada'. It is widely accepted nowadays, however, that behaviourism alone cannot explain children's language development. Children are not reinforced for every word they learn, and why do virtuous errors occur?

INTERACTIONIST THEORY

The interactionist view, while it does acknowledge the influence of biology, emphasises the importance of the child's social world in language learning. One of the most important aspects of a young child's linguistic environment is child-directed speech or 'motherese'. Motherese is the name given to the natural way we speak to babies and young children. It is high-pitched, uses simple words and short sentences. It usually relates to what the child is focusing their attention on at that moment. Other strategies automatically used by adults to help children's language development are recasting, expanding and labelling.

* **Recasting:** The adult tidies up what the child has said in a grammatically correct way. For example, if a child said, 'Mammy go home,' the adult may say, 'Yes, Mammy is going to go home now.'

* **Expanding:** The adult encourages the child to expand on what they have said. For example, the child says, 'Ice cream yum yum,' and the adult says, 'What colour ice cream is your favourite?'

* **Labelling:** Children constantly learn the names of things by pointing and asking. Adults patiently label items in their world for them.

The American psychologist Jerome Bruner (1915–2016) stressed the importance of the child's environment in language development. He believed that the adults and more able peers in a child's life provide what he called a language acquisition support system (LASS). Motherese, recasting, expanding and labelling all form part of this system.

Collaborate

In groups, consider the strengths and weaknesses of each of the three different perspectives described above in relation to language development. Try to come up with one strength and one weakness for each. Feed back your group's thoughts to the class.

6.6 KEY STAGES OF LANGUAGE DEVELOPMENT

Please go to Chapter 2 , pages 21–33 to revise the key stages a child goes through from 0 to six years in terms of language development.

6.7 PROMOTION OF LANGUAGE DEVELOPMENT

There are many ways language development may be promoted. For example:

* Use plenty of child-directed speech (motherese) with babies and toddlers. This type of speech is most easily understood by infants.

* Turn-take – allow infants time to 'answer' when you are talking to them.

* When talking to babies and young toddlers, talk to them about what their attention is focused on at that particular point in time.

* Use picture books, rhymes and action songs with younger children.

* Listen to young children and give them time to say what it is they are trying to say. Do not interrupt or finish their sentences for them.

* Enhance children's language by recasting, expanding and labelling (see above).

* Read stories to children, particularly books that rhyme or are funny, e.g. the Dr Seuss series.

* Build up a well-stocked, well-maintained library in the setting. It is ideal if the area is carpeted, away from noisy areas of the pre-school room and has comfortable seating.

* Children may like to listen to audio books while 'reading' them. This allows them to listen to interesting stories that they cannot read independently yet.

* Give children plenty of opportunity to practise writing. For instance, allow them to write out notices and signs for display around the ELC setting. Laminate and display their notices and signs so that their hard work is respected and used.

* There is some excellent interactive computer software available that encourages reading, such as The Computer Classroom, available in Ireland through Prim-Ed.

* Parents and afterschool service personnel should allow time every evening to talk to children. Discuss their day with them. Older children should be encouraged to discuss their opinions on things that are happening in the world.

* If possible, build a library visit into the ELC setting's weekly routine. This encourages children to read and assists language and cognitive development.

* Try to build up a good stock of interesting books in the ELC setting. For older children, books like *Guinness World Records* or *Ripley's Believe It or Not!* are very good for dipping in and out of.

* Supervise children's homework (at home or in afterschool services), challenging them to discover and use new words. Use the internet to assist with this.

* Some ELC settings have set up blogs where children can post their pictures and writings. Sensitively help older children in particular to spellcheck and proofread their work before it is posted.

7

Emotional Development

What I will learn

* What is meant by the term 'emotional development'
* The effect that an individual's innate temperament could have on their emotional development
* Bowlby's theory of attachment and internal working model
* Ainsworth's four patterns of infant attachment
* Harlow's theory of attachment
* Freud's psychoanalytic theories of personality and emotional development
* Erickson's psychosocial theory of personality development
* The differences between the terms 'self-esteem' and 'self-concept'
* Why it is important not to offer blanket, undeserved praise to children

7.1 WHAT IS EMOTIONAL DEVELOPMENT?

Emotional development involves learning what feelings and emotions are and understanding how and why they occur. The child must learn to recognise their own feelings and those of others and develop effective ways of managing those feelings.

An emotion can be described as a mental and physiological state associated with a wide variety of feelings, thoughts and behaviour. Because the same situation can affect people differently, emotions are subjective experiences, often associated with mood, temperament, personality and cultural differences. Examples of emotions include anger, joy, jealousy, fear, love, sadness, shyness, frustration, distress, pride, worry, contentment and disgust.

Emotional development involves developing the ability to recognise and deal with emotions in a positive, healthy and socially acceptable way. For example, a two-year-old toddler must learn that they cannot fly into a temper tantrum each time their request for something desirable is denied.

Emotions can be classified into **primary emotions**, e.g. joy, fear, disgust, anger, sadness and surprise; and **self-conscious emotions** (sometimes called **other-conscious emotions**), e.g.

jealousy, shame, pride, guilt, empathy and embarrassment. While primary emotions appear in the first six months, self-conscious emotions generally do not appear until after six months because in order to experience these emotions the child has to have a sense of 'self' in relation to others. Jealousy and pride are normally the first to appear, with others appearing towards the end of the second year.

In terms of emotional expression, crying is the primary way babies less than five or six weeks old express emotion. After six weeks, when the social smile first appears, babies begin to expand their repertoire and begin to be able to express joy, surprise and sadness. Fear as an emotion typically appears around six months with the emergence of **stranger anxiety**. Stranger anxiety usually gets more intense as the child gets older, peaking at between 15 and 18 months. Closely related to stranger anxiety is **separation distress** or **separation protest**. This is when the infant gets very upset when their main carer leaves. While patterns of separation distress vary between cultures (because of variations in childminding arrangements), it usually appears from six months, getting stronger and peaking at approximately 15 months.

Emotion regulation is an important part of emotional development. From early infancy, babies do exhibit some emotion regulatory actions, e.g. sucking their thumb, but most emotional regulation is external in nature, e.g. an adult rocks and sings to a crying baby. Adults should try to soothe infants before they get into a very agitated state, as this helps the infant regulate their emotions and reduces the levels of stress hormones released. Babies should not be left to cry, as responding quickly to the infant in the first year of life is important for secure emotional attachments (see 7.3). Studies of babies whose mothers responded promptly to them crying at three months cried less at a year than babies of mothers who did not respond promptly (Bell and Ainsworth 1972).

As children get older, they begin to experience a wider range of emotions during their day. They begin to be able to regulate their emotions more effectively, no longer relying as heavily on external regulators such as parents and carers to do so. They become better able to interpret other people's emotional states and how to deal effectively with them, e.g. how to show sympathy for another. As language emerges, children begin to be able to describe emotions and, in this way, can say how they feel about something rather than just act it out. From about four to five years, children begin to realise that emotional regulation is necessary to meet social standards. As discussed in Chapter 8, children who fail to regulate their emotions may experience rejection by their peers and have difficulty forming friendships.

7.2 INFLUENCE OF TEMPERAMENT ON EMOTIONAL DEVELOPMENT

Over the years, several studies have been carried out categorising infants' temperaments and investigating the extent to which temperament is either inherited or emerges as a result of environmental influences. These studies are important in understanding emotional development because a baby's temperament, whether it is easy or difficult, may have a bearing on how that baby is treated and as a result influence their emotional development.

In a longitudinal study of infant temperament, psychiatrists Stella Thomas and Alexander Chess (1977) found three basic temperament types:

1. **Easy babies** (40%) are generally very positive, cry very little and quickly get into sleep and feeding routines. They adapt well to change.

2. **Difficult babies** (10%) cry frequently, are slow to get into sleep and feeding routines and do not like change.

3. **Slow to warm up babies** (15%) are not very active and are often negative in terms of mood.

Thomas and Chess were unable to clearly classify 35% of the babies they studied.

Goodness of fit is an important concept related to studies of children's temperament. If a baby has a difficult temperament, this will only negatively affect their emotional development if the people caring for them react negatively to it. If, on the other hand, there is a goodness of fit, i.e. their carers are patient and positive towards them despite their difficult temperament, then being a 'difficult baby' should not adversely affect emotional development.

REFLECTIVE PRACTICE

Go to Chapter 8, page 138 and read about Bronfenbrenner's bioecological systems theory of development. In pairs, apply his description of the mesosystem level to support the concept of 'goodness of fit'.

7.3 ATTACHMENT THEORY

Attachment is a close emotional bond between a child and their carer. Strong or secure attachments are considered vital to healthy emotional development and are generally fostered in the first two years of life. John Bowlby (1969) argues that infants are born predisposed to form attachments. They cry, coo, smile and later crawl and walk after their carer. All of these behaviours are designed to keep their carer nearby and them safe from harm. Schaffer (1996) believes that attachment behaviours emerge gradually over four phases during the course of the first two years of life:

* **0–2 months:** The baby cries and from five or six weeks and will smile (but at anyone who smiles and chats to them).

* **2–7 months:** The baby focuses its attachment behaviours on one or two people, known as their primary attachment figure(s). The baby becomes able to distinguish familiar from unfamiliar people. They show a preference for familiars, smiling more and calming down more easily for familiars if upset.

* **7–24 months:** Specific attachments develop. The baby will actively seek contact with their primary attachment figures, crawling or walking after them. Separation anxiety emerges in that the baby will become upset if they are left to be cared for by someone other than their primary attachment figures.

* **From 24 months:** Children begin to become aware of others' feelings, goals and plans and start to take these into account, e.g. 'Mammy has to go to work now, I'll be back to pick you up later.'

INTERNAL WORKING MODEL

A central premise of Bowlby's attachment theory is that infants learn ways of relating to others based on early relationships with their attachment objects (primary carers). On the basis of these early experiences, they build what Bowlby termed an internal working model or IWM. This IWM influences how they approach new situations that could be perceived as threatening.

For example, one infant might have a carer who is devoted and is with the infant most of the time they are awake. This carer is also very responsive if the infant becomes in any way distressed, e.g. if they are tired, hungry or need a nappy change. This infant will be likely to construct an IWM in which they see themselves as capable of calling for comfort when needed and as worthy of receiving comfort. The infant will have an expectation that comfort will be given when needed and that their carer will show concern for the infant's state.

Another infant, in contrast, may have a carer who is depressed, spending a lot of time in a low mood or a self-absorbed state. This infant may spend long periods of time alone or with an emotionally unavailable carer, where distress is not responded to. When infant distress is responded to, it is sometimes done responsively but sometimes it is done to relieve the carer's stress from having to listen to a crying infant. Sometimes the carer handles the infant roughly. In this situation, the infant's IWM will be confused – sometimes worthy of attention and comfort but not always. This infant will have an IWM that is less able to generate accurate predictions of what will happen if they are distressed and as a result will feel less emotionally secure.

DIFFERENCES IN ATTACHMENT BEHAVIOURS

Mary Ainsworth (1979) studied differences in the quality of babies' attachments to their mothers. This was done by evaluating infant behaviour in what she called the **strange situation**. In the strange situation, the infant and mother play together in a room; the infant is free to explore and play with toys in the room. A stranger then enters the room and tries to interact with the infant. Sometime later, the mother leaves the room, returning after a period of time. The infant's reactions to all of this are observed and recorded. Ainsworth categorised infants in one of four ways:

* **Securely attached:** These infants used the mother as a secure base from which to freely explore the room and examine the toys available. They were not unduly worried by the stranger entering the room. When the mother left the room, they protested mildly, seeking to follow. When she returned, they sought to re-establish contact, smiling and sometimes climbing up on her lap.

* **Insecure avoidant:** These infants show insecurity by avoiding the mother. They interact little with her, are not distressed when she leaves the room and do not seek comfort from her on her return. If the mother tries to make contact, the baby may lean or look away.

* **Insecure resistant:** These infants cling to the mother but at the same time fight the closeness by kicking or pushing her away. These infants in the strange situation clung to their mother and explored the playroom very little. They cried loudly and persistently when the mother left the room and pushed her away when she tried to comfort them on her return.

* **Insecure disorganised:** These infants are disorganised and disoriented. In the strange situation, they appeared fearful and confused. To be classified as insecure disorganised, babies had to show strong avoidance of their mother or extreme fearfulness.

EFFECTS OF EARLY ATTACHMENTS ON LATER EMOTIONAL DEVELOPMENT

HARLOW'S STUDIES OF MATERNAL DEPRIVATION

In what would nowadays be considered an ethically unacceptable series of experiments, Harry Harlow (1958) studied the effects of maternal deprivation on rhesus monkeys by separating large numbers of baby monkeys from their natural mothers at birth and isolating them, giving them no contact with other monkeys. Because rhesus monkeys share some 98% of their genetic material with humans, he believed that his experiments would shed light on human attachment behaviours and the effects of maternal deprivation. Some monkeys were reared by milk-producing wire surrogate mothers while others had two mothers – a milk-producing wire one and a cloth one that produced no milk. Harlow found that babies clung to the cloth mother for up to 15 hours per day and only went to the wire mother to feed.

When these monkeys were returned to the group, they were anxious, fearful and had difficulty forming relationships. They did not wish to breed and when they were forced to do so they frequently mistreated their young, sometimes killing them.

Harlow later developed a cloth mother that he called the iron maiden. She shot spikes and cold water at her babies, often injuring them. The babies continued to return to her even though she abused them. These monkeys were very disturbed, rocking back and forth; one even chewed off its own hand. None of these monkeys made even adequate parents, with most killing their offspring.

While most people object strongly to Harlow's methods, his findings are considered significant to human child development, particularly in relation to the effects of inadequate or abusive parenting on children's social relationships and future parenting skills.

EVALUATION OF ATTACHMENT THEORIES

While attachment theory is widely accepted as having great significance for healthy social and emotional development, aspects of attachment theory have also been criticised.

* **The mother as sole attachment figure:** Much of the work on infant attachment focuses exclusively on babies and their mothers. In modern society, babies are often cared for by others, e.g. there are currently 9,200 stay-at-home fathers in Ireland, according to 2017 figures from the CSO.

* **The strange situation:** The strange situation used by Ainsworth to categorise infants is considered by some as being 'too strange'. These experiments were carried out in laboratory settings with which the child was unfamiliar, which could cause infants to behave in ways unnatural to them.

* **Culturally specific:** Much of the work carried out on attachment theory has been conducted in the USA and the UK, not taking into account differences in childrearing practices. For example, in many agriculture-based societies, babies are cared for shortly after birth by older siblings and grandparents. In north German society, babies are encouraged to be independent from a young age, possibly explaining why a larger than usual proportion of German children are classified as insecure avoidant. In Japanese society, mothers are not encouraged to allow anybody else to care for their baby, which possibly explains why a larger than usual proportion of Japanese babies are classified as insecure resistant.

* **Finality of attachment:** Some psychologists, e.g. Kagan (1987), believe that attachment theorists place too much emphasis on early attachments. Kagan argues that children are adaptive and just because they do not have strong emotional attachments in infancy does not mean that they will not develop them later in life.

Despite these criticisms, secure attachments are seen as important for overall child development. It is important that children are cared for by a small number of consistent, caring adults, particularly during the first two years of life.

7.4 PSYCHOANALYTIC THEORIES OF PERSONALITY AND EMOTIONAL DEVELOPMENT

SIGMUND FREUD (1856–1939)

Sigmund Freud is widely regarded as the father of psychoanalysis (see also Chapter 8, page 136). In relation to emotional development, Freud's theories about the unconscious mind are very interesting. He proposed that the mind is divided into three areas – the conscious mind, the preconscious and the unconscious mind. The conscious mind contains thoughts and sensations that we are fully aware of; the preconscious mind contains thoughts and sensations that we can bring to consciousness with effort, for example you meet someone in town and cannot bring their name to mind, yet you know you know it. Later that day you remember their name. For the period you could not bring the name to mind this fact was in the preconscious.

Sigmund Freud

Freud believed the unconscious mind to be the most influential in the formation of personality and in emotional development. He likened the unconscious mind to an enormous storehouse holding all the thoughts, feelings, experiences and emotions from an individual's past. Many of these thoughts and feelings could not or would not ever be brought to consciousness.

His theory in this regard was that much of our behaviour and personality is determined by the contents of our unconscious mind and that humans suppress feelings or thoughts that cause them anxiety using a variety of defence mechanisms. These defence mechanisms include denial, displacement, repression, regression, sublimation and projection. The preconscious mind can sometimes be involved in these defence mechanisms.

Freud felt that personality change is difficult because so much of our personality is driven by the unconscious.

Some of Freud's defence mechanisms:

* **Denial:** Denying or avoiding an unpleasant thought or feeling, e.g. a child who has difficulty reading may go to the toilet during reading time.
* **Displacement:** Redirecting negative feelings onto a safe target, e.g. a child is being bullied at school by another child; they come home and bully a younger sibling.
* **Repression:** The mind pushes unpleasant thoughts or experiences down into the unconscious mind, e.g. some adults who were abused as children cannot remember the abuse because they have repressed it.
* **Regression:** Going back to a time when the problem did not exist, e.g. a child who is toilet-trained may go back to wetting or soiling themselves upon the arrival of a new sibling.
* **Rationalisation:** Trying to justify what is going on through rational argument or making excuses, e.g. someone who is drinking too much may justify what they are doing by saying they need to relax because of their very heavy workload.
* **Reaction formation:** A person behaves in the opposite way to how they feel, e.g. a child who is being bullied may begin to speak and act very aggressively.
* **Projection:** Unacceptable thoughts or feelings are projected onto others, e.g. a woman has an affair and beings to gossip about other women, calling them 'tarts'.
* **Sublimation:** This is one of the few healthy defence mechanisms. It occurs when an individual displaces their negative thoughts and feelings in a positive or healthy way, e.g. going for a run, drawing or painting.

ANNA FREUD (1895–1982)

Anna Freud (1895–1982) was the sixth and last child of Sigmund and Martha Freud. Like her father, Anna was very interested in the area of psychoanalysis. With the outbreak of World War I, Anna travelled with her father and the rest of her family to London. Here she founded the Hampstead War Nursery (renamed the Anna Freud Centre after her death). She also worked after the war in the Bulldog's Bank Home, an orphanage for child concentration camp survivors. Through this work Anna observed first-hand children who had experienced very distressing childhoods.

Anna Freud

Anna built on her father's work, particularly with regard to the importance of the ego in warding off displeasure and anxiety, in identifying additional defence mechanisms. In 1936 she published a paper entitled 'The ego and the mechanisms of defence'. Unlike her father, who believed that most defence mechanisms are unconscious (the individual is not aware they are using them), she believed that some of them are conscious and can be controlled by the individual, e.g. thought suppression – deciding not to think about something because it is unpleasant.

Anna, much more than her father, was interested in children from latency period onwards. While her father believed that our personalities are pretty much a reflection of our unconscious minds, Anna placed much greater importance on the value of the intellect. She believed that we can think about how we feel and make conscious efforts to change.

She believed that daydreaming is a necessary part of childhood and that sometimes it is used as a substitute for unacceptable impulses. As part of her work Anna was very interested in the effects of parental deprivation. Many of the children she worked with had witnessed their parents being killed or tortured in concentration camps. She found that many of these children survived remarkably well emotionally and that the comfort and support the children gave to each other was the main reason for this. She believed that play is a very important aspect of childhood, particularly when used to alleviate anxiety or tension. Anna also believed that children should talk and think through what is causing them anxiety. She was therefore in favour of adults taking time to observe and talk to children if they seem anxious or worried.

MELANIE KLEIN (1880–1960)

Melanie Klein came to London in 1926. While she supported much of their work in relation to psychoanalytic theory she disagreed in other ways, for example she disagreed with Sigmund Freud regarding the importance of sexual desire and with Anna's methods of using psychoanalysis with children. Klein is probably best known for her use of **play therapy** with children to help them overcome emotional and behavioural problems. Her methods

are still being used today. Play therapy provides a way for children to express their experiences and feelings through a natural, self-guided, self-healing process. Klein used all sorts of play equipment including small world toys, clay, sand, puppets, art and craft materials, toys soldiers and guns.

D.W. WINNICOTT (1896–1971)

Donald Woods Winnicott was a very influential and important English paediatrician and psychoanalyst. He was born into a well-known and prosperous family; his father, Sir John Frederick Winnicott, was knighted in 1924. Winnicott, however, did not have an easy childhood; his mother, Elizabeth Martha Woods Winnicott, suffered severely with depression and he felt very protective and responsible for her. He remembered as a child 'trying to make my living by keeping my mother alive' (Winnicott in Minsky 1996: 134).

Winnicott trained as a doctor and after qualifying began working at Paddington Green Children's Hospital as a paediatrician and child psychoanalyst, a position he held for the next forty years. Winnicott was a contemporary of both Anna Freud and Melanie Klein; in fact, he studied psychoanalysis under Klein for several years. Later, though, he began developing his own independent ideas, for which he is now well known.

Like Anna Freud and Melanie Klein, Winnicott worked with young people displaced by war and also with children from dysfunctional families. It is through this work that he came up with the concept of the 'good-enough mother' (Winnicott referred mainly to the child's mother, probably reflecting the fact that most women did not work outside the home when he was forming his theories). He realised very early on that there is no such thing as a perfect mother but that a 'good-enough mother' will have characteristics that are important to healthy psychological development. Likewise, by talking to and studying the lives of children experiencing psychological problems he was able to identify aspects of their lives that he believed lay behind their difficulties.

THE CONCEPT OF HOLDING

Winnicott believed that babies and children need to be frequently and attentively held by their mother. The mother is a baby's security blanket, providing frequent and affectionate handling. Later this broadens to other people in the child's world, but initially he believed the mother to be the important figure. The concept of holding means not only physically holding the child but also anything the mother, and later family and wider society, do to make the child feel secure and 'held'. Winnicott observed that this 'concept of holding' was absent from the lives of many children he worked with, causing what he termed an 'antisocial tendency'. He believed that if children do not feel secure at home they will seek security elsewhere, e.g. in gangs. He says in his work *The Child, the Family and the Outside World* that 'a child whose home fails to give a feeling of security looks outside his home for the four walls … looking to society instead of his own family or school to provide the stability he needs (Winnicott 1973).

FALSE AND REAL SELF

Winnicott believed that none of us is born with a clear sense of self and that it develops as we grow. In this way Winnicott is very much an advocate of the nurture side of the nature vs. nurture debate. He did not believe that we are born with a certain type of personality, rather that our personality grows over time, and is very much influenced by our environment.

Winnicott was very interested in the concept of the 'premature development of the ego function'. He believed that when children have to grow up too fast (their ego is forced to develop too quickly), their psychological development suffers and a 'false self' is created. This could happen, for example, if the eldest child of dysfunctional parents has to care for younger siblings on a daily basis. As his own mother had depression during his childhood Winnicott was interested in the effects that this and other family problems have on children. He believed that problems such as this cause a phenomenon he called 'compliance'. The child tries to solve the problem by being 'good'. In adulthood their actions will always be motivated by a desire to please others. This leaves the person open to abuse and being used by others.

On the other hand, children who experience 'good-enough' parenting grow up trusting their world and are therefore free to be their 'true self' most of the time. Winnicott believed that in reality we are all a mix of both our 'true' and 'false' selves, but that as long as the 'false' self does not take over we will be psychologically healthy. He realised that as part of life sometimes we have to 'people please'.

TRANSITIONAL OBJECTS

Winnicott is well known for his belief in what he called **transitional objects**, or comfort objects, such as a teddy bear or blanket. He believed that these objects are very useful and beneficial in helping a child cope with transitions, for instance separation from their mother when she returns to work after maternity leave.

IMPORTANCE OF PLAY

Unlike many other psychoanalysts, Winnicott saw play as being vital and central to healthy development. He believed that being a 'good-enough mother' involved being a playful mother and that playing games, such as peek-a-boo, is essential. Winnicott believed that play is vital throughout life, even in adulthood, as it is an essential way of relieving stress and anxiety. Children whose lives involve too much work and not enough play significantly lose out in this regard; he believed this to be very serious for their psychological health.

7.5 PSYCHOSOCIAL THEORIES OF EMOTIONAL AND PERSONALITY DEVELOPMENT

ERIKSON'S THEORY OF PERSONALITY DEVELOPMENT

Erik Erikson (1968) believed that throughout the lifespan, people are faced at different stages with various 'crises' that require resolving. If the 'crisis' is successfully resolved, then a life-stage virtue is achieved; if it is not, the person suffers emotional distress. Erikson believed there are eight psychosocial stages (later, after his death, his wife added a ninth stage), as follows:

1. **Hope:** Basic trust vs. mistrust (0–2 years). During this stage, the infant basically learns to see the world generally as either a safe and predictable or unsafe and unpredictable place. This stage is closely linked with attachment theory, as described above – does the child believe its caregivers are reliable?

2. **Will:** Autonomy vs. shame and doubt (2–4 years). The child needs to learn to explore the world. If parents are too smothering or completely neglectful, the child will develop self-doubt and be unsure of or ashamed of their abilities.

3. **Purpose:** Initiative vs. guilt (4–6 years). Can the child plan or do things on their own, such as dress themselves? If 'guilty' about making their own choices, the child will not function well. Erikson has a positive outlook on this stage, saying that most guilt is quickly compensated for by a sense of accomplishment.

4. **Competence:** Industry vs. inferiority (around age six to puberty). The child compares their self-worth to others (such as a classmate) and can recognise major disparities in personal abilities relative to other children. Erikson places some emphasis on the teacher, who should ensure that children do not feel inferior.

5. **Fidelity:** Identity vs. role confusion (11 to 19 years). Questioning of self. Who am I, how do I fit in? Where am I going in life? Erikson believes that if parents allow the child to explore, they will conclude their own identity. However, if the parents continually push them to conform to their views, e.g. a doctor insisting her son also does medicine, the adolescent will face identity confusion.

6. **Love:** Intimacy vs. isolation (19 to 40 years). Who do I want to be with or date? What am I going to do with my life? Will I settle down? This stage has begun to last longer as young adults choose to stay in school and not settle as early as in years gone by.

7. **Caring:** Generativity vs. stagnation (40 to 64 years). Individual measures accomplishments/ failures. Am I satisfied or not? The need to assist the younger generation. Stagnation is the feeling of not having done anything positive with one's life, especially to help the next generation.

8. **Wisdom:** Ego integrity vs. despair (65+ years). Some handle death well. Some can be bitter, unhappy and dissatisfied with what they have accomplished or failed to accomplish within their lifetime. They reflect on the past and either feel satisfaction or despair.

REFLECTIVE PRACTICE

Before moving on to the next section, reread the first three of Erickson's psychosocial stages. In groups, discuss each stage and give examples of good practice in ELC settings that would promote trust, autonomy and initiative in children aged 0–6 years.

IMPLICATIONS OF ERIKSON'S THEORY FOR THOSE CARING FOR CHILDREN

Erikson's first three stages are most relevant to people working and caring for young children. The following points are important.

* Children in childcare settings should have a key worker, someone they can form a close bond with and can rely on.

* It is important for children's emotional wellbeing that crèches and preschools do not have a high staff turnover or high rates of staff absenteeism. Owners need to ensure that childcare staff are well treated and adequately paid to encourage loyalty. This can make quality childcare expensive. Parents need to realise this.

* Children should be encouraged to do things for themselves, e.g. spoonfeed. Sometimes crèches, in the interests of speed and keeping children's clothing clean, do too much for children. This is not desirable for development. Likewise, parents should not expect children to come back from day-care as clean as they went into it.

✳ Childcare staff should set tasks and activities at the correct level for children so that the child has a reasonable chance of succeeding at the activity with only a small amount of adult guidance. Avoid over-helping children.

7.6 SELF-ESTEEM AND SELF-CONCEPT

Both self-esteem and self-concept have wide-reaching implications for children's development. **Self-esteem** is defined as a person's general evaluation of themselves, e.g. I am a good person. **Self-concept** is how a person sees themselves in specific areas, e.g. am I attractive looking? Am I good at sports? Am I good academically? The two concepts are closely linked. People's self-esteem and self-concept may not be accurate. For example, a child with low self-esteem may see themselves as unattractive, academically weak and bad at sports (negative self-concepts), even though they are not any of these things.

MEASURING SELF-ESTEEM

One of the best-known tools for measuring self-esteem is a ten-item questionnaire developed by Morris Rosenberg in 1965. It is still being used today.

1 = strongly agree, 2 = agree, 3 = disagree, 4 = strongly disagree				
ITEM	**1**	**2**	**3**	**4**
1. On the whole, I am satisfied with myself				
2. At times, I think I am no good at all				
3. I feel I have a number of good qualities				
4. I am able to do things as well as most other people				
5. I feel I do not have much to be proud of				
6. I certainly feel useless at times				
7. I feel that I am a person of worth, at least on an equal plane with others				
8. I wish I could have more respect for myself				
9. All in all, I am inclined to feel that I am a failure				
10. I take a positive attitude towards myself				
Scoring the questionnaire:				
For questions 1, 3, 4, 7 and 10: 1 = 1 point, 2 = 2 points, 3 = 3 points and 4 = 4 points				
For questions 2, 5, 6, 8 and 9: 1 = 4 points, 2 = 3 points, 3 = 2 points and 4 = 1 point				
Scores below 15 suggest low self-esteem				

For younger children, measures such as Susan Harter's Self-Perception Profile for Children (1985) have been used. This tool is designed to be used with children between approximately six to ten years and looks at five areas: perceived physical appearance; scholastic (academic) competence;

social acceptance; behavioural conduct; and athletic competence. Of these, a child's perception of their physical appearance is most closely linked with self-esteem.

INCREASING CHILDREN'S SELF-ESTEEM

Today, two main problems or issues arise in relation to children's self-esteem: the old one, whereby children are not given sufficient recognition and praise for their efforts and are instead frequently run down and criticised; and the new one, whereby children are praised anyway, even if what they do is an effortless, mediocre or even a poor attempt.

Both situations can cause self-esteem issues for children. Children in the first situation may grow up with low self-esteem and be extremely self-critical, while children in the second situation may grow up with no clear ideas about their own self-worth and may be unable to cope effectively with competition or even constructive criticism.

In order to promote self-esteem, it is important not to offer blanket, undeserved praise. Children have good levels of self-esteem when they perform well in areas important to them. They should therefore be encouraged to identify their areas of strength and work on them. For example, a child who is not very good at sports but is good musically should be encouraged and praised for joining the local brass band. They should be helped and encouraged to practise to achieve a good level of competence so that they are appreciated by other band members, thus raising self-esteem.

7.7 HOW AISTEAR PROMOTES EMOTIONAL DEVELOPMENT

Promoting children's emotional development is at the very heart of the Aistear curriculum framework and runs through all its themes.

Aistear advocates:

* Celebrating each child's uniqueness

* Treating each child equally and with respect

* Appreciating and valuing diversity, e.g. culture, region, language

* Respecting children as citizens

* Helping children feel secure in the setting by forming close relationships with the home environment

* Allowing children to learn through active hands-on experiences, thus giving children a sense of achievement and confidence in their own abilities

* Listening to children carefully, respecting what they have to say

* Using positive discipline techniques to help children monitor and guide their own behaviour

* Allowing children to express their emotions through creative and physical activities

* Observing children's development (including emotional) in the setting and putting developmentally appropriate interventions in place as required

* Praising and encouraging children's efforts

REFLECTIVE PRACTICE

Choose four of the ways Aistear advocates to promote children's emotional wellbeing (listed above). Think of two activities or experiences that you could offer to children in your setting that would promote each of the four items you have chosen.

SHOW YOU KNOW

1. Define the term 'emotional development'.

2. Describe the possible effect that an individual's innate temperament could have on their emotional development.

3. Outline Bowlby's theory of attachment and internal working model.

4. Describe Mary Ainsworth's four patterns of infant attachment.

5. Critically evaluate the theories of attachment proposed by Bowlby, Ainsworth and Harlow.

6. Discuss Freud's psychoanalytic theories of personality and emotional development.

7. Outline Erickson's psychosocial theory of personality development.

8. Differentiate between the terms 'self-esteem' and 'self-concept'.

9. Explain why it is important not to offer blanket, undeserved praise to children.

Social Development

What I will learn

* The skills required for positive social development in children aged 0–6 years
* How infants and young children acquire the skills necessary to interact effectively and form good relationships with others
* How young children gain an understanding of social norms
* Piaget's and Kohlberg's theories on the development of moral thought
* Bandura's social modelling theory, and how it applies to everyday practice in an ELC setting
* Freud's theory on moral development and the making of morally demanding decisions
* How parenting style can influence moral development
* Bronfenbrenner's bioecological systems theory of development
* How adults can help young children manage their own behaviour
* How Aistear promotes social development in young children

8.1 WHAT IS SOCIAL DEVELOPMENT?

Social development involves developing the following social skills:

* The ability to interact effectively and form relationships with others
* An understanding of the norms (ways) of the society in which you live
* A sense of right and wrong (moral development)

8.2 INTERACTING EFFECTIVELY AND FORMING RELATIONSHIPS WITH OTHERS

INFANCY

Babies are predisposed to be social from birth. There is nothing like a new baby's cry to attract attention and the power of an infant's smile is like no other. As John Bowlby (1958) said, 'It is fortunate for their survival that babies are so designed by nature that they beguile and enslave mothers.' Two types of smile can be distinguished in infants: the reflexive smile and the social smile. The reflexive smile occurs during the first month after birth, usually during sleep, and is caused by

some internal stimuli, e.g. wind, not by the child's external environment. The social smile occurs as early as four to six weeks, becoming more frequent as the baby gets older, and is in response to a carer's voice and smiles. After six months, smiles are accompanied by the Duchenne marker (constricting or crinkling of the eyes).

EARLY CHILDHOOD

While infants as young as six months take notice and sometimes show an interest in other babies, it is not until approximately 18 months to two years that toddlers begin interacting with peers, and even then, **parallel play** still predominates, whereby the toddler will play happily alongside peers but not with them. By two and a half, toddlers engage in sustained role play, and after watching other children at play with interest may join in for a few minutes. By three years, **social**

play beings to emerge, the toddler understands what it is to share and joins in make-believe play with other children. By four years, the child will understand turn-taking as well as sharing and will co-operate with peers. By this age, the child seeks out the companionship of others and will alternate between playing and fighting with peers. Also by four, the child understands that arguments, e.g. over a toy, need to be sorted out verbally and not by physically fighting. By five years, children understand the need for rules and fair play, and they begin to choose their own friends.

FORMING RELATIONSHIPS

SIBLING RELATIONSHIPS

Over 80% of children born in Ireland have one or more siblings. Sibling relationships can be very important in developing social skills such as helping, sharing, teaching and conflict resolution. Judy Dunn (2007) found that sibling relationships showed three main characteristics: the expression of intense positive and negative emotions; siblings tended to alternate between being highly supportive of each other to teasing and undermining each other; and siblings tended to describe each other in either warm and affectionate ways or as being irritating and mean.

When siblings fight, parents tend to deal with it in one of three ways: intervene and help siblings sort out differences; give out and threaten; or do nothing and let them sort it out themselves. In terms of learning social skills, the first strategy is considered best, as it allows children to practise the skills needed to effectively resolve conflict situations in a calm and respectful manner (Kramer and Radley 1997).

What about only children? Contrary to popular belief, only children do not turn out to be self-centred and spoiled; research shows that they tend instead to be achievement-oriented and display many positive personality traits. When only children first attend pre-school or school, they frequently have a lot of ground to make up in terms of social development, but most manage to do so and there is no research to show that only children are less socially able than children with siblings.

PEER RELATIONSHIPS

From about four years, children begin to observe their peers with interest and compare themselves to them. They begin to try to work out how to integrate themselves smoothly into peer activities and begin friendships with selected peers. Longitudinal research has shown that success at forming peer relationships is very important for later development. Some children need a great deal of support to play well and get on with other children, whereas others, because of their social experiences, have very good access strategies.

* First the child will tend to circle around the edge of the activity the other children are engaged in, trying to work out what is happening, or they will watch what is happening from another area.

* Then they will approach and imitate what the other children are doing, e.g. if children are engaged in sand play, the child will join in this activity. This is called using a side-by-side strategy. This helps the child join in with the group.

If a child has difficulty joining groups, they may think the way to join is to ask the group if they can join. At this age, members of the group will very often say 'no'. If an adult is helping a child join the group, they should say to the child, 'Do you want to join in? Let's look at what they are doing, shall we? Don't ask them if you can do the same, just do the same.'

Three social skills are particularly important in forming successful peer relations: perspective taking, social information processing and emotional regulation.

* **Perspective taking** involves the child being able to consider a situation from another's point of view. This skill is very important for successful peer relations. According to Piaget (see Chapter 5), children have difficulty with this until about the age of four and tend to see things only from their own perspective. Adults should encourage the development of this skill in children by asking children things like, 'How do you think Josh felt when you pushed him over like that?'

* **Social information processing** involves the child accurately interpreting what is going on in a given situation and acting appropriately. For example, two children, Peter and Keith, are playing in the playground. Peter, who is big for his age, accidentally bumps into Keith and knocks him over. If Keith is good at processing social information, he will interpret the situation as being accidental and tell Peter it's okay. On the other hand, if Keith is poor at processing social information, he could react aggressively or go and tell the supervising adult. Children who repeatedly misinterpret social information like this often have difficulty with peer relations and may become unpopular with their peers.

* **Emotional regulation** involves the child being able to control their emotions, particularly anger and aggression. Adults can help children with these strong emotions by helping them put their feelings into words – 'I feel angry because Josh won't let me share the Duplo bricks with him.'

These three factors are seen to be important in determining a child's peer status. Wentzel and Asher (1995) interviewed large groups of schoolchildren, asking them who in their class group they liked most and least. They found that children can be divided into five different peer status groups.

* **Popular children** have mastered the three social skills above, are frequently nominated as a best friend and are rarely disliked by peers. Popular children usually listen to others, have a positive, happy disposition, control their negative emotions, show concern for others and are self-confident.

* **Average children** receive an average number of both positive and negative nominations from their peers.

* **Neglected children** do not receive many nominations, either positive or negative, from their peers. These children are usually very quiet and shy.

* **Rejected children** are not often nominated as someone's best friend but are frequently nominated as someone who is disliked. Generally, they have not mastered any of the three social skills mentioned above and can behave aggressively towards their peers.

* **Controversial children** are frequently nominated as a best friend, but also as someone who is disliked.

REFLECTIVE PRACTICE

In groups, discuss the ways in which ELC practitioners can help children develop the skills necessary to form strong peer relationships in the ELC setting. Share your group's ideas with the class.

8.3 UNDERSTANDING THE NORMS OF SOCIETY

Social norms are descriptions of or 'rules' about people's behaviour, beliefs, attitudes and values in a society or social group. Blowing your nose into a tissue and being quiet while in a library are both examples of social norms. Social norms can vary subtly between social groups within society and in different social situations. For example, using bad language in everyday speech is socially acceptable in some groups in society; in others it is frowned on as being crude and uneducated. Social norms are not legal rules, but the penalty for not obeying them may be social exclusion, depending on how important the social norm is. Children generally learn social norms through experience, and there are two broad theories about how they do this: the behaviourist view and the social modelling or social learning theory.

BEHAVIOURIST VIEW

The behaviourist view, influenced predominately by the work of B.F. Skinner, is that children learn as a result of reinforcement (see also Chapter 5). Reinforcement can be either negative (punishments) or positive (rewards). Behaviourists believe that positive reinforcements are much stronger and more effective learning tools than negative ones. From very early on, parents and other people around children begin the process of teaching them social norms. For example, if a two-year-old child begins picking their nose, they will be told, 'No, no, no – we must use a tissue,' and is then given a tissue to use. If the child begins using the tissue, even very ineffectually, they will be praised: 'Yes, good boy, using his tissue.'

SOCIAL MODELLING OR SOCIAL LEARNING THEORY

Social modelling or social learning theory is predominantly the work of the psychologist Albert Bandura (1925–). Basically, social learning theory proposes that people learn through observing others' behaviour and attitudes and the outcomes of those behaviours and attitudes. This is why it is vital that children are exposed to good role models from early on and why behaviours and attitudes learned in childhood through social modelling are so difficult to change. Take this example: children from a local ELC setting are out for a walk in a nearby park and are having a small picnic. When everyone has finished, the children are told to keep their litter in their hands until they find a bin and dispose of it there. While one of the children is being driven home later by a parent, they witness the parent throwing litter from their car window. Is this child likely to litter or not?

Extend your learning

The bobo doll experiment is the collective name for a series of experiments Albert Bandura carried out to test out his social learning theory. Between 1961 and 1963 he studied the behaviour of 72 children aged between three and five years after they each individually watched an adult acting aggressively towards a bobo doll. The adults hit, punched and kicked the doll while shouting words like 'kick him', 'hit him down' or 'pow'. Bandura found that the children tended to imitate what they had witnessed, even though there were lots of other toys available to them. Bandura obtained similar results when children were shown a movie version of an adult and a cartoon cat being aggressive towards a bobo doll.

What implications do you think Bandura's findings have for how adults should behave in the company of children?

8.4 MORAL DEVELOPMENT

Moral development involves how we think, feel and behave regarding standards of right and wrong. There are four different aspects of moral development, which we shall deal with in detail below.

1. **Moral thought:** How the individual thinks about morally demanding questions

2. **Moral behaviour:** How the individual acts in morally demanding situations

3. **Moral feeling:** How the individual feels in morally demanding situations

4. **Moral personality:** The role of personality in moral development

1 MORAL THOUGHT

Two psychologists who studied how moral thought develops in children were Jean Piaget (1932) and Lawrence Kohlberg (1958). They were similar in that they both believed that moral thought occurs in a series of stages.

PIAGET

Piaget developed his theory of children's moral development by interviewing and observing children at play. He asked them questions about ethical issues such as telling lies, stealing, punishment and justice. Piaget found that children go through two distinct stages in their moral development with a period of transition in between.

* **Heteronomous morality (up to age seven):** During this stage, children see morality in a very black and white manner. They see rules and regulations as being fixed and unchangeable, handed down from on high, e.g. the ELC practitioner. Whether they will or will not be punished for some wrongdoing will be the main focus. At this age, children do not take into account the intentions of another person when an act of wrongdoing has been committed.

For example, Ellie accidentally knocks Josh over in the back yard. If Josh is at this stage of moral development, he will not consider whether Ellie meant to knock him over. He will feel that Ellie should be punished for knocking him over because his key worker says you should be careful not to knock people over in the yard. This is called **immanent justice**, a belief that misdeeds are automatically connected to punishments. Immanent justice also leads to the belief that if something unfortunate happens to an individual, this is punishment for some earlier misdeed, e.g. if Ellie subsequently falls in the yard, Josh will think of this as punishment for having knocked him over. It is because of this link between misdeed and consequence that children are so preoccupied with punishment, frequently telling on each other even for small incidents, e.g. 'Teacher, Sarah is after spilling some sand on the floor.' Children at this age generally cannot tell lies about whether they carried out a misdeed. This is because they have not yet developed the understanding that if a misdeed is not witnessed, only they know what they did. Because of egocentric thinking (see Chapter 5), they think everybody else knows what they know.

* **Transition phase (7–10 years):** During this stage, children show some features of both stages.

* **Autonomous morality (7 years upwards):** Children during this stage become aware that rules and regulations are created by people and that they are there to be negotiated. When children are judging and acting at this stage, they can take the intentions of the 'wrongdoer' into account. Using the example above, Josh would get up and dust himself off, saying, 'It's okay, Ellie, I know it was an accident.' After the age of seven, as outlined in Chapter 5, children can decentre, i.e. see things from more than one point of view or perspective, which also enables them to lie. They begin to realise that they can possess information that other people do not have. In the beginning, some children lie even when all the evidence is against them, e.g. a child lying about eating chocolate cake even though it is all over their face. Later, children can weigh up the evidence to determine if a lie is believable or not. Some children, however, even if they are cognitively able to lie, choose not to. These children tend to come from households and schools where parents and teachers discuss wrongdoing with the children and involve the children in dealing with it.

KOHLBERG

Kohlberg (1927–1987), like Piaget, believed that children pass through a series of stages during moral development. Piaget, as we saw above, believed that there were two main stages with a transition period in between. Kohlberg believed there were three distinctive stages, each with two sub-stages. Kohlberg gathered the data for his stage theory by presenting children of different ages with moral dilemmas, followed by a series of questions. Kohlberg then categorised the children's answers. Here is an example of one of Kohlberg's dilemmas.

CASE STUDY

Dilemma

Judy was a 12-year-old girl. Her mother promised her that she could go to a special rock concert coming to their town if she saved up from baby-sitting and lunch money to buy a ticket to the concert. She managed to save up the 15 dollars the ticket cost plus another five dollars. But then her mother changed her mind and told Judy that she had to spend the money on new clothes for school. Judy was disappointed and decided to go to the concert anyway. She bought a ticket and told her mother that she had only been able to save five dollars. That Saturday she went to the performance and told her mother that she was spending the day with a friend. A week passed without her mother finding out. Judy then told her older sister, Louise, that she had gone to the performance and had lied to her mother about it. Louise wonders whether to tell their mother what Judy did.

1. Should Louise, the older sister, tell their mother that Judy lied about the money or should she keep quiet? Why?

2. In wondering whether to tell, Louise thinks of the fact that Judy is her sister. Should that make a difference in Louise's decision? Why or why not?

3. Does telling have anything to do with being a good daughter? Why or why not?

4. Is the fact that Judy earned the money herself important in this situation? Why or why not?

5. The mother promised Judy she could go to the concert if she earned the money. Is the fact that the mother promised the most important thing in the situation? Why or why not?

6. Why, in general, should a promise be kept?

7. Is it important to keep a promise to someone you don't know well and probably won't see again? Why or why not?

8. What do you think is the most important thing a mother should be concerned about in her relationship with her daughter? Why is that the most important thing?

9. In general, what should be the authority of a mother over her daughter? Why?

10. What do you think is the most important thing a daughter should be concerned about in her relationship with her mother? Why is that the most important thing?

11. In thinking back over the dilemma, what would you say is the most responsible thing for Louise to do in this situation? Why?

Kohlberg's three levels and six stages of moral development

Level 1 *Pre-conventional level*	Level 2 *Conventional level*	Level 3 *Post-conventional level*
No internalisation – up to about age 10	Some internalisation – adolescence and early adulthood	Full internalisation – many people never reach this stage
Stage 1 *Heteronomous morality*	**Stage 3** *Mutual interpersonal expectations, relationships and interpersonal conformity*	**Stage 5** *Social contract or utility and individual rights*
Children obey because adults tell them to. Actions are determined by chance of external rewards or avoidance of punishments	Children and adolescents value and trust loyalty. They adopt the moral standards of the significant adults around them, wishing to be seen as a good person by them	People at this stage reason that certain values, rights and principles are sometimes more important that the laws of society
Stage 2 *Individualism, purpose and exchange*	**Stage 4** *Social systems morality*	**Stage 6** *Universal ethical principles*
The principle of equal exchange becomes important, e.g. it is all right to hit him as he hit me	Adolescents at this stage begin to base their moral judgements on the need for social order, the law, justice and duty	A person at this stage has developed a moral standard based on universal human rights. When faced with a decision between law and conscience, this person will follow conscience even if it brings personal risk

2 MORAL BEHAVIOUR

Moral behaviour is how an individual acts in morally challenging situations. As with the learning of social norms (see above), children learn their moral behaviour in two main ways: by **conditioning** and **social modelling**.

At its simplest, when individuals are rewarded for moral behaviour, they are encouraged to repeat it, whereas when they are punished for behaviour that is morally wrong, they are encouraged not to repeat it. In reality, though, things are not as simple as this; if they were, people would only ever spend one term in prison. Punishment is not a very effective tool. Skinner found that for punishment to be effective, it had to be severe enough to stop the undesirable behaviour and had to follow the undesirable behaviour straight afterwards. Severe immediate punishments are usually not possible or, indeed, desirable, so encouragement of moral behaviour is much more effective.

Bandura's social modelling theory (1977) also applies to moral development. Children who witness moral behaviour at home, in their community, in the ELC setting and later at school are much more likely to develop high moral standards themselves.

3 MORAL FEELING

Moral feeling is how you react emotionally to moral decisions. Do you feel guilt when you do something morally suspect? Happy when you do something morally good? Does whether or not you are going to get found out have any bearing on your feelings?

PSYCHOANALYTIC THEORY OF MORAL DEVELOPMENT

Sigmund Freud spent many years exploring this aspect of personality. He believed that the personality is composed of three parts: the id, the superego and the ego.

1. **Id:** This is the selfish, pleasure-seeking part of the personality. The id encourages the individual to satisfy its needs and does not consider consequences. During the first two years of life, a child's actions are almost exclusively governed by the id.

2. **Superego:** This part of the personality is sometimes called the high priest. Moral teaching by parents, ELC settings, schools, the Church, the media and the community in which the child lives help form the superego. Because children are brought up in different environments, their superego can vary. For example, a child brought up in an environment where adults swear regularly may form the opinion that swearing is morally fine.

3. **Ego:** The ego is the part of the personality in touch with reality. The ego weighs up the pros and cons of carrying out a particular action and then makes a decision. It tries to balance the needs and wants of the id with the demands of the superego.

Collaborate

Lily and Tara are twin sisters. A neighbour has just given Lily a small packet of sweets to share with her sister. Tara does not know that Lily has been given the sweets. Explain how Lily's id, ego and superego will all be involved in Lily's decision-making about the sweets.

EMPATHY

Empathy is another aspect of moral feeling. Empathy is not just sympathising with another person; it is feeling what someone else is feeling, putting yourself emotionally in their place. Damon (1988) proposes three stages in the development of empathy.

* Global empathy is characteristic of babies and toddlers (0–2 years). For example, if they see another child fall and hurt themselves, they may react in sympathy, crying themselves, perhaps sucking their thumb and seeking comfort. It is as if they have been hurt themselves. This does not always happen, however; the toddler may just stand staring at the injured child, curious about what has happened to them.

* By early childhood, children can differentiate between their own hurt and that of others. By this stage they will also be able to empathise with another and respond appropriately, e.g. on the first day of pre-school a little boy is very upset, so one of his classmates comes over, puts his arm around him and asks him if he wants to play with his toy blocks.

* From approximately ten to 12 years, children become capable of empathising with others even if they are not present with them, e.g. people living in poverty.

4 MORAL PERSONALITY

Some people have strong morals and also have the strength to act on those moral convictions. A high standard of morality is part of their identity or how they view themselves. There is debate around how much of our moral personality is innate and how much is due to environment. Freud (see above) would contend that both are involved, with the id being present from birth and the ego and superego strongly influenced by environmental factors. There are individuals, however, who are reared in morally corrupt environments yet emerge from these environments morally strong.

INFLUENCES ON MORAL DEVELOPMENT

Parents

While both Kohlberg and Piaget believed that peers have a much bigger influence on a child's moral development than adults, they did not deny that parents and other adults in the child's life have some influence. How much influence they have largely depends on three factors:

1. The quality of the adult–child relationship – this is very important. Children who are securely attached (see Chapter 7) and confident in their relationship with their parent or carer are much more likely to engage with them and respond to their moral guidance.

2. The form of discipline used by adults – this is also very important. Hoffman (1970) identified three different discipline techniques used by parents.

    * **Love withdrawal:** The parent/carer withholds attention or love from the child, perhaps refusing to talk to the child or saying to the child, 'I don't like you when you do that.'

    * **Power assertion:** The parent/carer tries to gain control over the child and the child's resources. An example is removing privileges.

✳ **Induction:** The parent/carer uses reasoning and explains the consequences of the child's actions to the child. An example would be saying, 'Don't hit him. He didn't mean to bump into you. Hitting hurts.'

Of the three techniques, induction is seen to be the most effective. With love withdrawal and power assertion, the child is likely to be highly anxious and aroused, thinking more about the punishment than the lesson behind it. With induction, the child is calm and more likely to take on board the reasoning behind what is being said.

3. Whether or not the parent is proactive – being proactive means preventing misbehaviour before it takes place. With younger children, this may mean removing them from the situation or distracting them. With older children and adolescents, this may mean discussing the potential misbehaviour before it even happens, e.g. discussing smoking before children are offered a cigarette.

Early learning and care settings

In any ELC setting, there is both an explicit and a hidden curriculum. The explicit curriculum is usually written down and intended to be taught. The hidden curriculum comprises the messages that the organisation sends out to the child that are not part of the explicit curriculum. In some ways, the hidden curriculum is even more important for moral development than the explicit curriculum. For example, if an ELC practitioner talks to the children about the importance of using quiet kind words and then shouts at the children, the children are getting a very mixed message. In addition, it is important that ELC settings advocate a care perspective for the promotion of moral development. Such a perspective concentrates on educating children about the importance of engaging in pro-social behaviours, such as considering the feelings of others, being sensitive to the needs of others, and helping each other. This perspective ties in closely with the use of induction as a discipline technique (see above).

8.5 BRONFENBRENNER'S BIOECOLOGICAL SYSTEMS THEORY OF DEVELOPMENT

Urie Bronfenbrenner (1994) suggested that the environment of the child is a nested arrangement of structures, consisting of five systems, each contained within the next. He named these structures:

✳ Microsystem   ✳ Exosystem   ✳ Chronosystem
✳ Mesosystem   ✳ Macrosystem

He organised them in order of the degree of impact each system has on a child. Because the five systems are interrelated, the influence of one system on a child's development depends on its relationship with the others. This idea formed the basis of his bioecological systems theory of development (including social development).

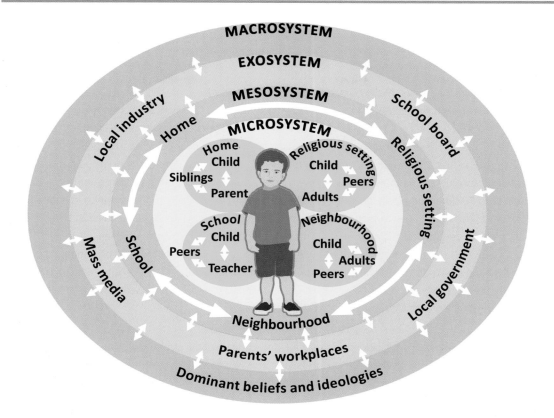

The **microsystem** is the first level of Bronfenbrenner's theory and consists of the people who have regular direct contact with the child in their immediate environment, e.g. parents, siblings, early years practitioners, teachers and peers. Relationships in the microsystem are bi-directional, meaning that the child can be influenced by the people in their system and vice versa. Strong nurturing relationships are essential for healthy positive development of the child.

The **mesosystem** consists of the interactions between members of the child's microsystem, e.g. interactions between parents and early childhood practitioners. If interaction is positive and supportive, this in turn has a positive effect on the child's development.

The **exosystem** incorporates other formal and informal social structures, which do not directly contain the child. They do, however, have an indirect impact on the child as these structures affect one of the child's microsystems. Examples include neighbourhoods, parent's workplaces, parent's friends and the media.

The **macrosystem** focuses on cultural and societal factors that can influence the child's development. Examples include socioeconomic status and ethnicity. The macrosystem does not refer to the specific environment of one developing child but rather the established society and culture that the child is developing in.

The **chronosystem** refers to all the environmental changes that occur over the lifetime of the individual. This includes major life transitions and historical events. Examples include parental separation or indeed the recent Covid-19 pandemic.

CASE STUDY

Alex was born a healthy 8 lb and had no complications at birth. From the outset, his parents would describe him as a difficult baby compared with their other two children. He didn't sleep very much and as a result was frequently tired and cranky. He had colic and cried a lot. As he grew into a toddler, he could be described as hyper, constantly running around, climbing and exploring, and he never seemed to rest. He was quite accident-prone and didn't appear to think before acting. He caught his fingers in doors, ran into things, constantly bumped his head and fell off furniture. He wouldn't stay at one thing for any length of time and bringing him out anywhere could be quite difficult. One Sunday, the family decided to go out for lunch in a nice restaurant. They put Alex in a high chair to keep him quiet, even though he was almost three years old and very big for his age. He squirmed and protested, but eventually they got him to sit. About halfway through the meal, somehow Alex released himself and stood up on the high chair, belly flopping down on top of the table. Luckily Maureen, his mother, was there to half catch him, avoiding scattering everything off the table. The family had to finish the meal quickly and leave, as they were afraid that Alex was disturbing other diners.

Alex started playschool when he was three and a half years old. The staff there did their best, but when Alex arrived at nine o'clock, it was as if a whirlwind swept through the place. He would pull down toys and abandon them a few seconds later. He would throw water and sand, shout and sometimes kick and punch other children. Other parents began to complain about Alex, so the playschool had to arrange with Maureen that Alex came to the playschool only in the afternoons, when it was quieter, and they had the staff to supervise him more closely. Maureen and her partner, Paul, split up just after Alex turned three. She felt that perhaps the difficulties herself and Paul had been having since shortly after Alex was born, and now the split, could be a factor in Alex's behaviour.

Maureen had to move into social housing after breaking up with Paul as the family was under considerable financial strain having to keep two houses. The area has considerable levels of poverty, unemployment and antisocial behaviour at night. This worries Maureen, who fears it may negatively impact on her children as they grow up.

Collaborate

Apply what you have learned about Bronfenbrenner's bioecological systems theory of development to the case study above.

8.6 SPECIAL NEEDS THAT AFFECT SOCIAL SKILLS

AUTISTIC SPECTRUM DISORDER (ASD)

Autistic spectrum disorder is the term used to describe a collection of developmental disorders primarily affecting a child's ability to communicate and form social relationships. For more detail on ASD, please see Chapter 10, pages 162–4.

8.7 PRO-SOCIAL AND ANTISOCIAL BEHAVIOUR IN CHILDREN

PRO-SOCIAL BEHAVIOUR

Pro-social behaviour means being concerned for the rights and welfare of others, being able to empathise and acting in ways that benefit others. Learning to share with others is one of the earliest forms of pro-social behaviour that children demonstrate. William Damon (1988) suggests that up until about the age of three, children share because it is something they have been taught they must do, and it is not generally for empathic reasons. From approximately four years, however, children begin to share because they feel empathy for the other child, but generally they will share only if they have more than enough for themselves and if what they are sharing is not too coveted. The important thing about sharing in terms of social development is that the child understands that sharing is an important part of forming and maintaining social relationships and that it is morally right to share.

Developing a sense of fairness is another important part of developing pro-social behaviour. Fairness is usually defined in terms of equality (that everyone is treated equally), merit (extra rewards come to those who work hard for them) and benevolence (special consideration should be given to those who need something most). Until children are about eight years of age, they think of fairness in terms of equality only. From about eight years on, they can begin to think of it in terms of merit and benevolence as well. Studies that seek to understand how children understand the concept of fairness suggest that children learn considerably more from their peers in this regard than from the adults in their lives. Pro-social behaviour generally develops earlier in girls than in boys.

ANTISOCIAL BEHAVIOUR

Most children act out from time to time and on occasion act in a destructive and troublesome way. If children do so regularly, however, and their behaviour is interfering with their peer relationships, relationships with adults around them and their educational progress, they may be showing signs of one of several emotional and/or behavioural disorders.

OPPOSITIONAL DEFIANT DISORDER (ODD)

With ODD, the child shows a recurrent and unusual pattern of negative, defiant, disobedient and hostile behaviour towards adult authority figures in particular. For ODD to be diagnosed, the behaviour must have continued for at least six months with four or more of the following symptoms present:

* Often loses temper

* Often argues with adults

* Often actively defies/refuses to comply with adults' requests or rules

* Often deliberately annoys people

* Often puts the blame for their own mistakes or behaviour on others

* Is often easily upset or annoyed by others

* Is often angry and resentful

* Is often spiteful and vindictive

While it would be very rare for a child in an ELC setting to have a diagnosis of ODD, it is important that if young children are beginning to show these behaviours appropriate interventions are put in place. Children with ODD are often shunned by peers because of their behaviour and frequently fall behind in their progress due to the fact that much of their energy is spent opposing playgroup leaders and teachers rather than carrying out the tasks set for them. Children with ODD also tend to spend periods of time excluded from their groups. Children with ODD usually possess a 'counter-will', meaning the more one tries to have the child behave appropriately, the more opposition is experienced.

8.8 EFFECTIVE MANAGEMENT OF CHILDREN'S BEHAVIOUR

* Adults should intervene and help peers and siblings sort out differences in a calm and fair manner.

* If one child hurts another, always encourage the offending child to think about how the other one feels.

* Encourage children to manage their anger, e.g. take a deep breath and count to ten, go outside with the child for a little walk and a quiet chat.

* Reinforce social norms with praise and encouragement, e.g. saying, 'Yes, good girl, we always wash our hands after going to the toilet.'

✳ Set clear yet fair and consistent boundaries for children to follow. Use the positive expectation model – explain to children what you want them to do rather than telling them what you do not want them to do, e.g. 'Say please and thank you', 'Use your quiet voice', etc.

✳ Always seek to encourage good behaviour rather than punish bad behaviour.

✳ Practise what you preach, e.g. if an ELC practitioner asks the children not to shout, they should not shout themselves.

✳ Use induction as a discipline technique – reason with the child and discuss the consequences of their actions with them.

✳ Advocate a care perspective. Teach the importance of considering others' feelings, being sensitive to the needs of others and helping others.

✳ When children misbehave, use positive discipline techniques. Wrongdoing should be discussed with the child, and a plan put in place to prevent it happening again. In this way behaviour management is always forward-looking.

✳ The Maltese physician and author Edward de Bono (1933–2021) makes a very interesting point in relation to dealing with differences of opinion. When a child, particularly an older child, has a disagreement with an adult, e.g. a teacher, very often the child is not really listening to the adult's point of view and vice versa. De Bono suggests that a discussion should happen in which the adult asks the child, 'What do you think I am thinking? And I will tell you what I think you are thinking.' In this way the two parties can actively try to see things from the other's point of view in a more democratic way.

✳ One very interesting and important aspect of William Glasser's (1925–2013) choice theory is the issue of power. He believed that one reason some children misbehave in pre-school and school environments is that the environment makes them feel powerless. Giving children choices at school or pre-school helps alleviate power inequalities. For example, children are given a choice of three activities and they can choose whichever one they like best.

8.9 HOW AISTEAR PROMOTES SOCIAL DEVELOPMENT

Promotion of social development is at the very heart of the Aistear curriculum and its approach to working with young children. One of its main pedagogical principles is that **children learn through positive interactions with others**. Aistear's *Guidelines for Good Practice* states:

Aistear recognises that relationships are at the very centre of early learning and development. The good practice guidelines identify a range of interaction strategies and methods the adult can use to enhance children's learning and development. Effective interactions between adults and children need to be respectful, playful, enjoyable, enabling, and rewarding.

(NCCA 2009: 27)

All of Aistear's four themes have elements of social development within them. The following table shows what Aistear sets out to do in relation to the promotion of social development in the early years. Early years practitioners take these aims and learning goals and provide unstructured and structured play opportunities designed to fulfil these aims and goals.

143

THEME: WELLBEING	
Aims	**Learning Goals**
Aim 1 Children will be strong psychologically and socially.	In partnership with the adult, children will: **1.** Make strong attachments and develop warm and supportive relationships with family, peers and adults in out-of-home settings and in their community. **2.** Be aware of and name their own feelings, and understand that others may have different feelings. **3.** Handle transitions and changes well. **4.** Be confident and self-reliant. **5.** Respect themselves, others and the environment. **6.** Make decisions and choices about their own learning and development.

REFLECTIVE PRACTICE

Divide the class into six groups. Each group should take one of the learning goals listed above and discuss how this learning goal can be promoted in the ELC setting.

THEME: IDENTITY AND BELONGING	
Aims	**Learning Goals**
Aim 1 Children will have strong self-identities and will feel respected and affirmed as unique individuals with their own life stories.	In partnership with the adult, children will: **1.** Build respectful relationships with others. **2.** Appreciate the features that make a person special and unique (name, size, hair, hand and footprint, gender, birthday). **3.** Understand that as individuals they are separate from others with their own needs, interests and abilities. **4.** Have a sense of 'who they are' and be able to describe their backgrounds, strengths and abilities. **5.** Feel valued and see themselves and their interests reflected in the environment. **6.** Express their own ideas, preferences and needs, and have these responded to with respect and consistency.
Aim 2 Children will have a sense of group identity where links with their family and community are acknowledged and extended.	In partnership with the adult, children will: **1.** Feel that they have a place and a right to belong to the group. **2.** Know that members of their family and community are positively acknowledged and welcomed. **3.** Be able to share personal experiences about their own families and cultures, and come to know that there is a diversity of family structures, cultures and backgrounds. **4.** Understand and take part in routines, customs, festivals and celebrations. **5.** See themselves as part of a wider community and know about their local area, including some of its places, features and people. **6.** Understand the different roles of people in the community. »

Aim 3	In partnership with the adult, children will:
Children will be able to express their rights and show an understanding and regard for the identity, rights and views of others.	1. Express their views and help make decisions in matters that affect them.
	2. Understand the rules and the boundaries of acceptable behaviour.
	3. Interact, work co-operatively, and help others.
	4. Be aware of and respect others' needs, rights, feelings, culture, language, background and religious beliefs.
	5. Have a sense of social justice and recognise and deal with unfair behaviour.
	6. Demonstrate the skills of co-operation, responsibility, negotiation and conflict resolution.

REFLECTIVE PRACTICE

Divide the class into groups. Each group should take one of the aims listed above and write it out in the centre of a large piece of paper. Write the six associated learning goals around the central aim. Try as a group to think of as many activities and experiences that you could offer to children in your setting to work towards each learning goal. Some learning goals will not be an activity or experience but instead a way of working with the child.

THEME: COMMUNICATING	
Aims	**Learning Goals**
Aim 1	In partnership with the adult, children will:
Children will use non-verbal communication skills.	1. Use a range of body movements, facial expressions, and early vocalisations to show feelings and share information.
	2. Understand and use non-verbal communication rules, such as turn-taking and making eye contact.
	3. Interpret and respond to non-verbal communication by others.
	4. Understand and respect that some people will rely on non-verbal communication as their main way of interacting with others.
	5. Combine non-verbal and verbal communication to get their point across.
	6. Express themselves creatively and imaginatively using non-verbal communication.
Aim 2	In partnership with the adult, children will:
Children will use language.	1. Interact with other children and adults by listening, discussing and taking turns in conversation.
	2. Explore sound, pattern, rhythm and repetition in language.
	3. Use an expanding vocabulary of words and phrases, and show a growing understanding of syntax and meaning.
	4. Use language with confidence and competence for giving and receiving information, asking questions, requesting, refusing, negotiating, problem-solving, imagining and recreating roles and situations, and clarifying thinking, ideas and feelings.
	5. Become proficient users of at least one language and have an awareness and appreciation of other languages.
	6. Be positive about their home language, and know that they can use different languages to communicate with different people and in different situations.

SHOW YOU KNOW

1. Outline the three skills that are required for positive social development in children aged 0–6 years.

2. Describe how infants and young children acquire the skills necessary to interact effectively and form good relationships with others.

3. Explain from a theoretical perspective how young children gain an understanding of social norms.

4. Discuss Piaget's and Kohlberg's theories on the development of moral thought.

5. Describe Bandura's social modelling theory and illustrate how it applies to everyday practice in an ELC setting.

6. Discuss Freud's theory on moral development and making morally demanding decisions.

7. Explain how parenting style can influence moral development.

8. Describe Bronfenbrenner's bioecological systems theory of development.

9. Suggest six ways adults can help young children effectively manage their own behaviour.

The below images refer to the Collaborate exercise on page 87.

Section 3

Factors Influencing or Impacting on Child Development

Genetics and Single-Gene Inheritance Disorders

What I will learn

* The basic concepts associated with genetics and heredity:
  * Genotype and phenotype
  * Dominant-recessive gene principle
  * Sex-linked gene principle
  * Genetic imprinting principle
* Various single-gene inheritance disorders

9.1 INTRODUCTION

Child development is a gradual unfolding of biologically determined characteristics and traits that arise as a child grows and learns from their experiences in the environment in which they develop. There are many factors, both positive and negative, that can influence this development. This chapter focuses on genetic factors that can influence or impact on a child's development. In order to understand how and why certain genetic factors influence how a child may develop we need to have some understanding of human genetics.

We all know that offspring resemble their parents more than they do unrelated individuals. If you examine the mother and daughter shown in the photograph you can pick out some similarities between them.

The transmission of traits from one generation to the next is called inheritance or **heredity**. However, sons and daughters are not exact copies of their parents or indeed their siblings. Along with inherited similarity there is also **variation**.

Genetics is the scientific study of heredity and hereditary variation. **Genes** are the basic units of genetics. Human beings have approximately 20,000–25,000 genes. Genes are made up of strands of DNA (short for deoxyribonucleic acid). Genes (made up of DNA) are packed into **chromosomes** in each cell of the body. All body cells, except for the ova (eggs) and sperm cells, contain 23 pairs of chromosomes – one set of 23 from the mother and one set of 23 from the father.

How genes function is best described by using our understanding of written language. Just as your brain translates the word 'banana' into the mental image of a long yellow fruit, cells translate genes into characteristics such as blue eyes, curly hair or freckles.

In addition, certain conditions and syndromes that are transmitted genetically can pose mild to severe challenges for children's development. The remainder of this chapter looks at a range of these conditions and asks you as an early childhood practitioner to consider how children with these conditions and syndromes can be best supported in a quality ELC setting.

In general, when we speak about genetic inheritance causing developmental disorders and syndromes there are three main categories:

1. Single-gene inheritance disorders

2. Complex multifactorial inheritance disorders, also called polygenic inheritance disorders

3. Chromosomal disorders

Before we begin to investigate these three categories, there are some other important genetic concepts and terms that we need to understand.

9.2 GENOTYPE AND PHENOTYPE

All of us obtain genetic material from both our parents. This is called our **genotype**. However, not all genetic material 'comes out' in the individual. For example, a child may have a blue-eyed mother and a brown-eyed father, so both blue eyes and brown eyes will form part of their genotype. If they actually have brown eyes, then while blue eyes are part of their genotype, it is not part of their **phenotype** (the characteristics that actually come through). Phenotypes include physical characteristics, such as hair and eye colour, height and foot size, as well as psychological characteristics, such as personality and intelligence. In addition, how the phenotype emerges can sometimes depend on environmental factors, e.g. a child born into a family in the developing world who is genetically predisposed to having great mathematical ability may not develop that trait due to lack of opportunity.

9.3 GENETIC PRINCIPLES

There are several genetic principles (apart from environmental factors) that determine how a genotype is expressed to create a specific phenotype. While many of these are still unclear, some have been more widely researched and are therefore more fully understood.

DOMINANT-RECESSIVE GENE PRINCIPLE

In some gene pairs, one gene is 'stronger' than the other. The 'stronger' gene is called the **dominant gene** and the 'weaker' one is called **recessive**. When a recessive gene and a dominant gene form the genotype, the dominant gene always comes out in the phenotype (person). This is called the dominant-recessive gene principle. Recessive genes come out in the phenotype (person) only if they are inherited from both parents.

Did you know?

The discovery of the dominant-recessive gene principle is credited to the Augustinian friar Gregor Johann Mendel (1822–1884). While Mendel conducted his research on pea plants, the genetic principles he discovered (sometimes called Mendelian principles) and developed enable us to understand a lot more about human genetics.

	DOMINANT TRAITS	RECESSIVE TRAITS
Eye colour	Brown	Grey, green, hazel, blue
Vision	Long-sightedness	Normal vision
	Normal vision	Short-sightedness
	Normal vision	Colour blindness
Hair	Dark hair	Blonde, red hair
	Curly hair	Straight hair
	Full head of hair	Baldness
	Widow's peak	Normal hairline
Facial features	Dimples	No dimples
	Unattached earlobes	Attached earlobes
	Freckles	No freckles
	Broad lips	Thin lips
Other	Double-jointed	Not double-jointed
	Immune to poison ivy	Susceptible to poison ivy
	Normally pigmented skin	Albinism
	Normal blood clotting	Haemophilia
	Normal hearing	Congenital deafness
	No phenylketonuria (PKU)	PKU

Extend your learning

Sandra Byrne has blue eyes (bb) and her partner Jack has brown (Bb) eyes. They have three children, two of whom (Sam and Jason) have brown eyes and one (Anne) who has blue eyes. Look at the table above and write out Sandra, Jack, Sam, Jason and Anne's genotype for eye colour.

Ellen Holdcroft is double-jointed (JJ); her husband, Patrick, is not (jj). They have two children, Brian and Sean, both of whom are double-jointed. Look at the table above and write out Ellen's, Patrick's, Brian's and Sean's genotype for joint rotation.

Thomas is congenitally deaf, as is his wife, Irene. Will their children also be congenitally deaf? Explain your answer.

SEX-LINKED GENE PRINCIPLE

Most mutated genes, e.g. the genes for cystic fibrosis, Duchenne muscular dystrophy and sickle cell anaemia, are recessive. This means that an individual must have inherited the gene from both parents to have symptoms of the condition. However, if a mutated gene is carried on the X chromosome, this will have more serious consequences for boys than for girls, since boys have only one X chromosome. If a disease-causing gene is carried on the X chromosome, boys do not have another healthy X chromosome to balance things out and may therefore experience the condition more severely, even if it is recessive. Girls, on the other hand, have a second X chromosome, which is unlikely to also carry the condition. Thus, while girls may act as carriers of the condition, they are unlikely to have the condition. Haemophilia and fragile X syndrome are examples of X chromosome-linked inherited conditions.

GENETIC IMPRINTING PRINCIPLE

As you know, half of an individual's genes are inherited from their mother and half from their father. Genetic imprinting occurs when a chemical process in the body 'silences' one half of a gene pair. Sometimes the maternal gene is silenced; sometimes the paternal gene is silenced. Genetic imprinting only occurs with a small number of gene pairs. Most gene pairs do not follow this principle, but rather the dominant-recessive gene principle as described above. If genetic imprinting does not occur when it should, development is disturbed. Wilms' tumour (a cancer affecting the kidneys) and Beckwith-Wiedemann syndrome (a condition whereby children overgrow and are prone to childhood cancers) are examples of conditions resulting from a failure of genetic imprinting.

Extend your learning

Carry out some research on Wilms' tumour and/or Beckwith-Wiedemann syndrome. Present your findings to the class.

9.4 SINGLE-GENE INHERITANCE DISORDERS

Single-gene inheritance disorders occur when abnormalities occur in the DNA sequence of a single gene. There are thousands of known single-gene disorders and syndromes causing varying degrees of challenge for the individual. The following conditions impact most significantly on children aged 0–6 years:

* Cystic fibrosis (CF)
* Hearing impairment
* Marfan syndrome
* Duchenne muscular dystrophy
* Sickle cell anaemia
* Phenylketonuria (PKU)

CYSTIC FIBROSIS

Cystic fibrosis (CF) is Ireland's most common life-threatening genetically inherited disease. Currently there are approximately 1,400 people living with CF in Ireland, the highest proportion per head of population in the world (Cystic Fibrosis Registry of Ireland 2019).

CF is a multi-organ disease that primarily affects the lungs and digestive system. A defective gene and its protein cause the body to produce unusually thick, sticky mucus that clogs the lungs, leading to life-threatening lung infections, obstructing the pancreas and preventing natural enzymes help the body break down and absorb the food the individual consumes. As a result, people with CF are prone to constant lung infections and malnutrition.

The impact of CF varies from person to person. There are some people with CF who have severe symptoms and do not live beyond their teens; others live into their 50s and later. Ireland has among some of the most severe strains of CF and has three times the incidence as the USA and the rest of the EU. Over 35 new cases of CF are diagnosed in Ireland each year.

Approximately one in 19 Irish people is a carrier of the CF gene, and where two carriers parent a child together, there is a one in four chance of the baby being born with CF. Individuals with CF inherit one copy of a defective cystic fibrosis transmembrane conductance regulator (CFTR) from each of their parents. To date, approximately 2,000 CFTR gene mutations have been identified, each of which may cause varying levels and severities of CF disease. In Ireland F508del is the most common CFTR gene, causing 91.7% of cases.

At birth, some babies with CF will present with a bowel obstruction and will not pass their first dark stool (meconium). Therefore, hospitals ask mothers to keep their baby's first dirty nappy for inspection. Routine newborn screening for CF, the National New-born Bloodspot Screening Programme, was first introduced in Ireland in July 2011. Babies who are suspected of having CF are then given further tests to confirm a diagnosis.

The symptoms of CF are chronic or recurrent respiratory symptoms such as a cough or wheeze and pneumonia. Children will fail to thrive despite a normal appetite. They may have malformed, bulky, offensive stools with an oily appearance, and chronic diarrhoea. A rectal prolapse may also occur. Skin will taste salty and there may be prolonged jaundice in infants. Treatment for CF includes the use of nebulisers and antibiotics to help breathing and control lung infections, daily physiotherapy to loosen mucus, nutritional supplements and pancreatic enzyme replacement therapy. Even with these interventions, symptoms tend to become more severe with age, for example without a lung transplant lung function on average reduces from 94% (age six) to 58% (age 45) (CFRI Annual Report 2019).

Many people with CF are awaiting lung transplant operations, which significantly prolong life. Lung transplants are in the main undertaken in the Mater Hospital in Dublin, with on average 75 carried out each year.

Extend your learning

Examine the graphic below. Compare this daily routine with the routine of a child with no such additional need.

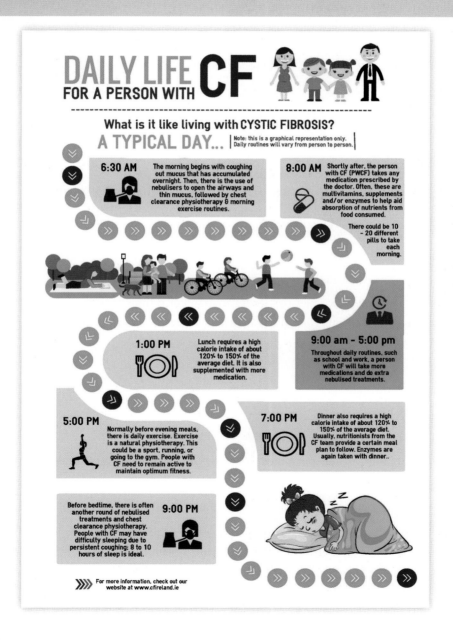

DUCHENNE MUSCULAR DYSTROPHY

Muscular dystrophy (MD) refers to a group of genetically inherited muscular diseases that weaken the muscles of the body. MDs are characterised by progressive weakening and wasting of the external and internal muscles. There are at least nine different forms of muscular dystrophy; Duchenne MD is the most common and most severe.

Duchenne MD is caused by a mutation of a gene located on the X chromosome. This gene is needed for the production of the protein dystrophin, an important structural component of muscle tissue. Because the mutated gene is located on the X chromosome, Duchenne MD affects only males, except in exceptional cases. Because females have two X chromosomes (only one is usually affected), they are generally carriers. Since Duchenne MD is genetically transmitted, it tends to run in families, although it can occur spontaneously.

Babies do not show any symptoms initially, though the child may be late walking. Symptoms will usually begin to appear in male children before the age of six, although some may be visible in early infancy. The disease typically progresses through five stages: pre-symptomatic, early ambulatory, late ambulatory, early non-ambulatory and late non-ambulatory. Symptoms include the following:

* Progressive muscular wasting, causing muscular weakness

* Poor balance and frequent falls

* Enlargement and pains in the calves of the legs

* Low endurance and difficulties in standing unaided or climbing stairs

* Difficulty walking, with a waddling gait (usually by age ten, the child will need braces and/or a frame to walk and eventually the child will be unable to walk)

* Limited range of movement

* Respiratory difficulties

* Drooping eyelids (ptosis)

* Gonadal atrophy (decrease in size of penis and testes)

* Scoliosis (curvature of the spine; most children will need to use a wheelchair by age 12)

* Paralysis

* Intellectual disabilities (in a third of boys), although the severity of disability does not increase with age

* Heart issues in some types of muscular dystrophy, causing cardiomyopathy or arrhythmias (irregular heartbeats)

As Duchenne MD is inherited, families will often be aware of relatives with the condition. However, for a significant percentage of boys there is no family history and the genetic abnormality occurs spontaneously. Diagnosis normally takes the form of a blood test – a child with the condition will have raised levels of serum creatine kinase (CK). In addition, a sample of muscle tissue (muscle biopsy) will be taken to confirm diagnosis.

There is no known cure for muscular dystrophy, but effective management can ensure a good quality of life for the child and limit the disease's associated problems. Inactivity (such as bed rest or prolonged sitting) can worsen the condition. It is also important that the child does not become overweight, as this puts extra strain on the muscles. Thus, a well-balanced, varied diet is essential. A smoke-free, healthy environment is very important, as the child's chest muscles weaken. Physiotherapy can help the condition considerably. The child may have to carry out as much as four hours of physical therapy a day. Sometimes physiotherapy involves passively moving the child's limbs to prevent contracture of the muscles, i.e. the muscles shortening and tightening up. Hydrotherapy can be extremely beneficial, as limb movement is much easier in water. Occupational therapy teaches and practises skills such as self-care and self-feeding, which are important for the child to maintain as much independence as possible. An occupational therapist may advise the home or school regarding changes to the child's environment that would increase the child's level of independent functioning. Speech therapy and mobility aids such as crutches, leg braces or callipers, wheelchairs and frames are also very important.

It is vital that the adults in the child's world help him maintain social relationships and friendships. The child should be encouraged and facilitated to be out and about as much as possible and to take part in activities with his peers. Hobbies that he will be able to take part in as his condition worsens should be encouraged, e.g. reading, computers and listening to music.

REFLECTIVE PRACTICE

Eric is a six-year-old boy who was diagnosed with Duchenne MD when he was four years old. Eric's parents took their son to the doctor after noticing signs of muscular weakness that had not been there previously. Eric began to fall frequently, had difficulty getting up from a sitting position or from an all-fours position on the floor and was finding it difficult to climb the stairs in their home with any speed.

Imagine Eric has just begun senior infants in his local primary school and each evening after school he attends the ELC setting in which you work, along with four other boys from his class.

When the children arrive in the ELC setting after their day in school they usually like to go outside to play tag or football to let off steam. Staff have observed that Eric has started to hold back from these activities as they seem to tire him, and he trips and falls frequently. He also sometimes says that he gets pains in his legs after running around.

Staff are concerned that Eric may become socially isolated in the setting because of this. As a group, come up with some ideas for activities that you feel all five boys might be interested in and that would suit Eric's specific needs.

HEARING IMPAIRMENT

Some forms of deafness can be inherited from parents. The most common inherited form of deafness is called DFNB1, also known as connexin 26 deafness or GJB2-related deafness. This form of deafness is caused by an abnormality of a gene on chromosome 13. Approximately 10% of the 3,300 deaf and hard of hearing children in Ireland have deaf parents.

Other causes of deafness (not related to genetics) include infections such as meningitis, measles or mumps in infants and children, rubella, herpes, syphilis and HIV/AIDS passed to the foetus during pregnancy or birth. Almost 60% of children with foetal alcohol syndrome (FAS) have some degree of deafness due to their mother drinking during pregnancy. Birth trauma, head injuries after birth and brain tumours can also cause deafness in children.

To hear sound, sound waves are picked up from the atmosphere around us by the pinna (the part of the ear attached to the outside of your head). These sound waves travel along the external auditory canal (ear canal) to the tympanic membrane (eardrum), causing it to vibrate. Three small bones are then activated by the eardrum – the malleus (commonly called the hammer), incus (anvil) and stapes (stirrup). The malleus is the bone touching the eardrum – it vibrates, amplifying the sound and passing the vibrations on to the incus and finally the stapes. The stapes is attached to the cochlea, which is a snail shell-shaped structure filled with fluid. The vibrations cause this fluid to move, stimulating millions of tiny hair cells on the inside of the cochlea. This causes an electrical message to be passed to the cochlear nerve, which travels to the brain to be interpreted as sound.

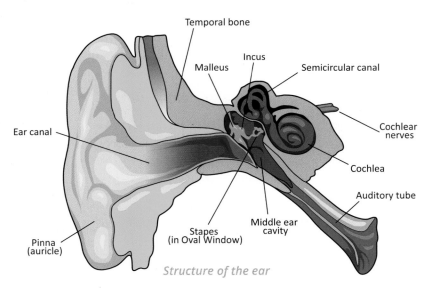

Structure of the ear

In babies, a symptom of hearing loss will normally be that they do not reach the expected milestones for language and social development. A profoundly deaf baby will not reach any of these milestones. Babies with mild or moderate hearing loss may reach many of these milestones, but will generally have less distinctive speech, which is why their hearing loss sometimes goes undetected.

TREATMENTS AND SUPPORTS FOR DEAF AND HARD OF HEARING CHILDREN

* **Hearing aids** are fitted for children who are not profoundly deaf but hard of hearing. Hearing aids magnify sounds entering the ear, thus amplifying the sound. Radio hearing aids have two parts and are often worn in ELC and school settings because there is a lot of background noise. The ELC practitioner wears a transmitter that is connected to the child's hearing aid. The teacher's voice is then transmitted to the child's hearing aid without all the background noise.

* **A cochlear implant** is a small, complex electronic device that allows someone who is severely or profoundly deaf to hear sound. The principle behind the implant is that if someone's cochlear is so damaged that it cannot be stimulated and in turn stimulate the auditory nerve naturally by sound, the auditory nerve must be stimulated directly so that the brain can in turn be stimulated to interpret the signal as sound.

* **Irish Sign Language (ISL)** is the first and preferred language of deaf people in Ireland. As with the spoken word, there are up to 300 different forms of sign language used around the world today. As with all language, sign language is best learned at as young an age as possible. In fact, many parents are teaching their hearing children simple sign language so that they can communicate their needs before they are able to speak. Sign language is used extensively in the deaf community in Ireland, but very few hearing people can sign, which has the effect of isolating the deaf community. Sign language classes are widely available throughout the country, with most Education and Training Boards (ETBs) offering it as a night class. Finger spelling (where words are spelled out – the Irish sign alphabet uses only one hand) and Lámh (a more limited signing system) are also sometimes used.

Did you know?

Irish sign language is a gender-specific sign language, i.e. males and females in Ireland have different sign languages due to traditionally being educated in separate schools – St Mary's School for deaf girls and St Joseph's School for deaf boys – both in Cabra, Dublin.

* **Lip reading** is the technique of understanding speech by visually interpreting the movements of the lips, face and tongue along with information provided by the context and any residual hearing. Because some words use similar lip movements, sometimes lip reading is accompanied by cued speech, where words that are similar to others are accompanied by a hand sign to show which word is being said. When speaking, it is not advised to exaggerate lip movements – since the lip reader has been trained to read normal movements this distorts what is being said. Lip reading is extremely tiring, so most deaf people supplement it with gesture, mime and writing.

Extend your learning

In Ireland there are currently 32 visiting teachers for deaf and hard of hearing children located around the country. These teachers visit the child from when they are first diagnosed at home or in educational settings such as ELC and schools. They engage with the child and educate those working and caring for them, such as parents, ELC practitioners and teachers. Go to the National Council for Special Education website to find out more about this service.

SICKLE CELL ANAEMIA

Sickle cell anaemia is a genetically inherited life-threatening condition that affects red blood cells. Sickle cell anaemia is a recessive gene, so both parents must have the gene for the child to have significant symptoms. Signs and symptoms usually appear at around five months of age.

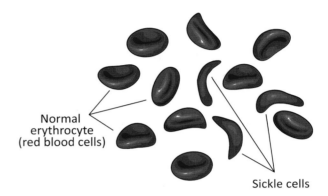

Normal erythrocyte (red blood cells)

Sickle cells

Sickle cell anaemia mainly affects black people living in or originating from sub-Saharan Africa, but it is also less commonly found among Greeks, Indians, Italians, Saudi Arabians, South Americans and Turks. The reason for this distribution is thought to be because sickle cell carriers are resistant to malaria, so is an adaptive trait in countries where malaria is present. Prevalence of the disease varies from country to country. In Nigeria, for example, 24% of the population are carriers of the mutant gene and the prevalence of sickle cell anaemia is about one in 50 births. This means that in Nigeria alone, more than 100,000 children are born annually with sickle cell anaemia (WHO 2005).

Someone with sickle cell anaemia produces abnormal sickle-shaped red blood cells, which are inefficient oxygen carriers and tend to clump together in the blood vessels, causing very painful episodes called 'crises' and an increased risk of stroke. Normal red blood cells function for approximately 120 days before having to be replaced, whereas sickle cells last only 10–20 days; this can result in anaemia and severe fatigue.

Sickle cell anaemia may also cause organ damage, particularly to the spleen and kidneys, which can cause increased susceptibility to infection. The tiny blood vessels that supply the eyes can become blocked with sickle cells, causing vision problems. In developing countries where there is limited access to medical care, some children with sickle cell anaemia do not make it through childhood. In more developed countries there is an increasing number of treatments available that help treat the symptoms of the disease. Such treatments include a special diet, folic acid supplements, blood transfusions, pain relief medication and ongoing antibiotic therapies. In some cases, bone marrow transplants are carried out. As a result, more and more people with the disease, particularly in developed countries such as the USA, are living long and healthy lives.

MARFAN SYNDROME

Marfan syndrome is a genetic disorder that affects the body's connective tissue. Connective tissue is needed to bind or hold the body's cells, organs and other tissues together and is essential for normal growth and physical development. Marfan syndrome affects approximately one in 5,000 children of both genders and in all ethnic groups.

Connective tissue is made up of proteins. The protein that plays a role in Marfan syndrome is called fibrillin-1. Marfan syndrome is caused by a deficit in the gene that 'tells' the body how to make fibrillin-1. This then causes the body to increase production of another protein called transforming growth factor beta. It is this that causes problems with connective tissue throughout the body.

Some children with Marfan syndrome experience the effects and symptoms in early childhood; others may not experience them until late childhood and adolescence. The severity of symptoms can vary significantly between individuals, even within the same family. Some features of Marfan syndrome are more visible than others. For example, many children with Marfan syndrome will have:

* Long arms, legs and fingers
* A very tall, thin body type
* A curved spine
* Loose, painful and very flexible joints
* A chest that sinks inwards or protrudes outwards
* Flat feet
* Crowded teeth
* Stretch marks on the skin that are not related to weight loss or gain

Other signs can only be detected with a diagnostic assessment. Marfan syndrome, if not identified and treated, can cause serious issues with the heart (especially the aorta), the spine (scoliosis), the eyes (dislocation of the lens and/or detached retina) and reduced lung function. Children's intellectual ability is not affected by Marfan syndrome.

Various symptoms of Marfan syndrome are treated in different ways and by a range of different health professionals. Physiotherapy, pain relief and anti-inflammatory medication assist with joint issues and pain. Children who have developed scoliosis may require a back brace or surgery. Individuals will be under the care of a cardiologist, who will closely monitor and treat heart-related complications with medication and, if necessary, surgery. Likewise, eye health will be closely monitored and treated when necessary.

In terms of living with Marfan syndrome, a healthy balanced diet is essential, combined with moderate exercise. Strenuous activities and contact supports are normally advised to be avoided.

Did you know?

Most often single-gene inheritance disorders are inherited from a parent. In some cases, however this is not what has happened, and the individual is the first in their family with the condition. This is called **spontaneous mutation**.

PHENYLKETONURIA

Phenylketonuria (PKU) is a genetic disorder caused by a defect in the gene that helps create the enzyme necessary to metabolise or break down the amino acid phenylalanine (found in protein foods, including breastmilk). If undetected, phenylalanine builds up in the system, causing brain damage. PKU results from a recessive gene and occurs in approximately one in 15,000 births worldwide. Ireland has a much higher incidence of the condition, at one in 4,500 births. PKU is detected in newborns using the 'heel prick' test. If PKU is diagnosed, the infant will be put on a phenylalanine-free diet. The child will continue to follow this diet throughout their life – foods such as meat, chicken, fish, cheese, milk, nuts, legumes and some cereals must all be eliminated.

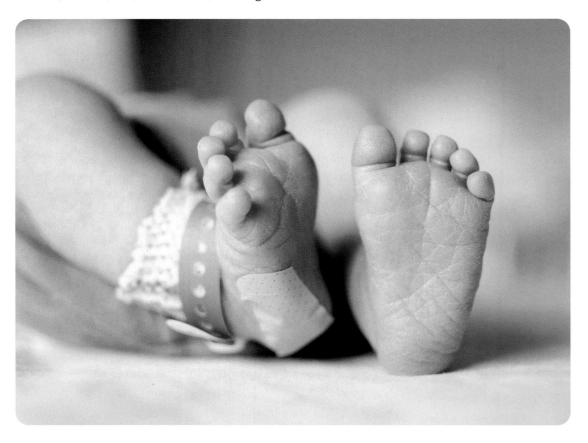

Please note that end of chapter questions have been incorporated into the Show You Know questions on page 192.

Complex Multifactorial Inheritance Disorders

What I will learn

* Various complex multifactorial disorders or polygenic inheritance disorders
* The causes, symptoms and treatments required for children with complex multifactorial disorders.

10.1 INTRODUCTION

Complex multifactorial inheritance disorders are sometimes called polygenic inheritance disorders. These occur when more than one factor causes a trait or health problem. The main factor is genetic, but the cause can include many other factors, such as:

* Nutrition
* Lifestyle
* Alcohol or tobacco consumption
* Some medicines
* Illness
* Pollution

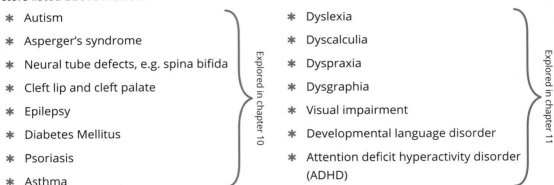

Due to the genetic component of many of these conditions and the shared environment over many generations, these conditions tend to run in families. This of course is not always the case; these conditions are complex and multifactorial and therefore identifying an exact 'cause' is frequently not possible. Conditions that have a genetic element and may also be in part caused by the other factors listed above include:

* Autism
* Asperger's syndrome
* Neural tube defects, e.g. spina bifida
* Cleft lip and cleft palate
* Epilepsy
* Diabetes Mellitus
* Psoriasis
* Asthma

Explored in chapter 10

* Dyslexia
* Dyscalculia
* Dyspraxia
* Dysgraphia
* Visual impairment
* Developmental language disorder
* Attention deficit hyperactivity disorder (ADHD)

Explored in chapter 11

10.2 AUTISTIC SPECTRUM DISORDER

Autistic spectrum disorder (ASD) is an umbrella term used to describe a range of disorders that primarily affect the child's social and emotional development. Boys are four times more likely to have ASD than girls. Scientists believe that both genetics and environment likely play a role in ASD. There is great concern that rates of ASD have been increasing in recent decades without a full explanation as to why. Researchers have identified several genes associated with ASD. Twin (especially identical twin) and family studies suggest that some people have a genetic predisposition to ASD. Many of the genes found to be associated with ASD are involved in the function of chemical connections between brain neurons (synapses).

AUTISM

Most children are predisposed to become sociable and begin to develop communication skills from birth. Babies quickly realise that other people are important for comfort, to share pleasure, to ask for help and to learn from. Many parents of children diagnosed with autism report that up until between 18 months and two years their baby did socially interact, did engage in eye contact and even began to speak. Parents often report that over a short period of time these skills seemed to disappear, and their child seemed to retreat into a 'world of their own'.

If a child has autism, they will experience difficulties in three areas:

1. Social interactions
2. Communication (verbal and non-verbal, e.g. eye contact)
3. Narrow range of interests and a need for repetitive routines

SOCIAL INTERACTIONS

Difficulty with social interaction may manifest itself in several different ways, e.g. the child may not use eye contact, may find it difficult to consider something from another person's perspective, be more interested in objects than people, be unaware of social rules or react with fear to unfamiliar people or situations. To assist the child in this area, it is important that staffing is consistent in the setting so that the child learns to trust the adults working with them. Social stories can be used to help children to become more aware of new social situations and how to respond in these situations. Social stories are presented as a sequence of pictures telling a 'story'. For example, if a new child is joining the class, a social story could be created about opening the door for that child and saying hello to them.

COMMUNICATION DIFFICULTIES

There is a wide variation among children with autism with regards to their language development. Some children use little or no language; others learn to speak easily. However, all children will have communication difficulties. Children may repeat words and phrases, they may speak out of context or find it difficult to 'join' a conversation by staying on the same topic as everyone

PECS board

else. Their understanding of language can often be very literal – for example if someone said after a large meal 'I'm about to explode' a child with autism might understand this in its literal sense. For children who have yet to acquire language, the Picture Exchange Communications System (PECS) was developed in 1985 by Dr Andy Bondy and Lori Frost. Using this system, the child indicates their wants and needs using a series of pictures. The word is always spoken by the adult so that an association between words and their meanings is established.

NARROW RANGE OF INTERESTS AND A NEED FOR REPETITIVE ROUTINES

Children with autism find reassurance in routines and the familiar. A child with autism may become very upset if a familiar routine changes and will often avoid new experiences. Many children with autism develop repetitive body movements called stimming, e.g. rocking or hand flapping, which provide comfort for the child. Children with autism usually have a narrow range of interests and will think or talk about these interests very frequently. To help the child it would be helpful to say, 'Let's say two more things about Spiderman and then we'll talk about something else.'

Additionally, some children with ASD experience sensory processing disorder (SPD). Signs of SPD include:

* Over- or under-sensitivity to touch, movement, sight, sound or smell

* Overly high or low activity levels

* Poor organisational behaviour

* Sensory-seeking behaviours, e.g. hand flapping or head banging

* Reduced general awareness of what is happening around them, as they are focused on a narrower range of stimuli from the environment

Extend your learning

Research PECS boards online and create one for use in your workplace. PECS can be used with all pre-verbal children and will help them associate words with meaning.

ASPERGER'S SYNDROME

Asperger's syndrome (AS) is an autism spectrum disorder that was first described by the Austrian paediatrician Hans Asperger in 1944. People with Asperger's syndrome, like those with other conditions on the autistic spectrum, show significant difficulties in social interaction, along with restricted and repetitive patterns of behaviour and interests. AS differs from autism in that language and cognitive development are not usually severely impacted. Also, although not required for diagnosis, physical clumsiness and atypical use of language are frequently reported. People with AS are often described by their peers as eccentric. In Ireland, it is estimated that several thousand people have the syndrome, with about nine times as many males affected as females (Asperger's Syndrome Association of Ireland, 2009).

Children with AS often experience difficulties with the basic skills of social interaction and often find it difficult to make friends. They frequently use little eye contact and can adopt unusual postures or gestures, e.g. some children may have unusual tics or habits such as facial grimaces. Unlike children with autism, children with AS do approach others and do want to make friends but sometimes lack the social skills to do so. For example, a child with AS may engage in a one-sided, long monologue about a topic of interest to them. They may not pick up on the clues that the other child has lost interest and wants to talk about something else.

The pursuit of specific and narrow areas of interest is one of the most striking features of AS. Individuals with AS may collect volumes of detailed information on a relatively narrow topic such as train timetables without necessarily having a genuine understanding of or interest in the broader topic. For example, a child might memorise camera model numbers while caring little about photography. This behaviour is usually apparent by age five or six.

Although individuals with AS acquire language skills without significant general delay, their speech typically displays some unusual characteristics that will affect their ability to communicate effectively with others and thus their social development. One of the most important characteristics is verbosity, also called prolixity. What this means is that the individual uses an excess of words. They will often speak in long, wordy monologues, not realising that their listeners are not keeping up or are not interested in what they are saying. People with AS also use quite literal speech and may find it difficult to understand metaphor, irony or jokes.

Some children with AS may also have what is called auditory processing deficits. This means that sometimes the child will have difficulty 'hearing' what is being said to them despite normal physical hearing. For example, a child may hear little of what their teacher is saying to the class in general, only hearing what she is saying when she is speaking directly to him or her. Children with AS may use unusually formal speech and may also use unusual intonation (flatter than normal), pitch and loudness.

Collaborate

Read the case study below and imagine that Sam is a child in your ELC setting. Suggest ways in which Sam's social skills could be supported in the setting.

CASE STUDY

Sam didn't talk very much until he was about two and a half years old, but when he did, he spoke in a posh accent and quickly developed a sophisticated vocabulary. He is now four and attending pre-school. He has developed an intense interest in a small number of topics and activities. Currently he is very interested in dinosaurs, space and building structures out of Lego. When staff try to engage him in other activities, he shows little interest and puts no effort into them. Academically, he seems very bright; he is already reading and recognising numbers. While the other boys in the class play together all the time, Sam is often left on the periphery. In the beginning this did not seem to bother him, in that he seemed to prefer his own company. Lately, however, he has been trying to join his peers while at play but does not seem to have the social skills to do so.

10.3 SPINA BIFIDA

Spina bifida is a relatively common neural tube defect (NTD), affecting about one in every 1,000 babies born per year in Ireland. Ireland has one of the highest incidences of spina bifida births in the world, with the exception of Malta. This is believed in part to be because of Irish legislation on termination of pregnancy.

Spina bifida is caused by the incomplete development of the spinal cord. Translated, it literally means 'split spine'. The spine is made up of separate bones called vertebrae, which normally cover and protect the spinal cord. With spina bifida, some of these vertebrae are not completely formed. Instead, they are split, and the spinal cord and its coverings usually protrude through a sac-like bulge, covered with a thin membrane, on the back.

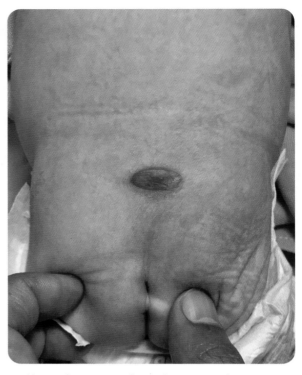

The degree of disability experienced depends on how much of the spinal cord is protruding, where it is protruding and how much damage has been done to the nerves. There are at least five different forms of spina bifida, the most common of which is myelomeningocele (pronounced my-uh-lo-men-IN-jo-seal). The split normally occurs in the lumbar region (lower back), and as a result, there is usually some degree of paralysis and loss of sensation from this region down.

The cause in most cases is multifactorial, which means that both genetic and environmental factors interact to cause spina bifida. Some cases may be due to the inheritance of specific gene mutations, chromosome abnormalities, or foetal exposure to teratogens. The vast majority of NTDs arise as a result of the interaction between susceptible genes and some environmental trigger. Which particular genes make a couple susceptible to having a child with an NTD is not yet fully understood. At least one environmental trigger is now well known: folic acid (vitamin B complex) has proved to be an extremely important factor. It is now known that women who take daily folic acid supplements or multivitamins containing at least 400 mcg of folic acid daily both before conception and for the first 12 weeks after conception reduce their chances of having a baby with spina bifida by approximately 75%.

Did you know?

A recent UCD study of a large number of women attending the Coombe maternity hospital in Dublin indicated that three out of every four women booking antenatal care had inadequate folic acid supplementation at the start of pregnancy (Sweeney *et al*, 2021).

Extend your learning

Countries where there is mandatory food fortification with folic acid e.g. USA, Canada, South Africa and Chile, have found that incidences of NTDs such as spina bifida have decreased. Folic acid food supplementation is voluntary in all EU countries except Sweden. A recent study headed by Dr Mary Rose Sweeney of DCU found that folic acid fortification of foodstuffs in Ireland has decreased since 2004. This decision taken by food manufacturers in an ever more price-sensitive foodstuffs market is believed to offer a partial explanation for the recent increase in the incidence of NTDs nationally (Sweeney et al, 2021).

As a class, examine a range of common foodstuffs in a variety of supermarket outlets for evidence of folic acid fortification. Is there evidence of differences between different supermarket chains?

10.4 CLEFT LIP AND CLEFT PALATE

Cleft lip and cleft palate are openings or splits in the upper lip, the roof of the mouth (palate) or both. Cleft lip and cleft palate result when the developing facial structures in the unborn baby do not close completely. A cleft lip may affect just one side of the lip or there may be two clefts. In Europe the combined prevalence of cleft palate and/or cleft lip is approximately one in 700 live births (Leslie *et al.* 2016). Cleft lip and palate are immediately identifiable at birth and a treatment plan is begun within the first 3–6 months.

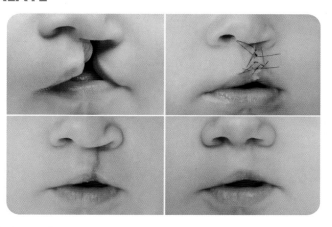

Nowadays in developed countries cleft lip and palate are corrected with surgery, restoring normal functioning of the mouth and a more normal appearance with minimal scarring. This process does, however, take time. Children with a cleft lip and/or cleft palate will need several treatments as they grow up. The cleft itself is treated by a plastic surgeon specialising in this area. A typical care plan for a child with a cleft lip and palate is:

AGE	CARE PLAN
Birth–12 months	Babies with a cleft lip and palate can have difficulty breast and/or bottle feeding; they may use a flexible specially designed bottle or occasionally may have to be tube fed
3–6 months	Surgery to carry out repair to cleft lip

AGE	CARE PLAN
6–12 months	Surgery to carry out repair to cleft palate. In some cases, an additional surgery called pharyngoplasty is completed at this time. This involves repositioning some of the tissue from the palate to the back of the throat to prevent air escaping though the nose which would result in a nasal speech sound
18 months	Speech and language assessment and therapy where required
3 years	Speech and language assessment and therapy where required
5 years	Speech and language assessment and therapy where required
8–11 years	When adult teeth are just about to erupt, a bone graft is performed to repair the cleft in the gum area
12–15 years	Orthodontic treatment to align teeth and monitor jaw growth. Children with cleft lips and palates are more prone to tooth and gum decay, so careful monitoring and oral hygiene is essential
16–18 years	When necessary, plastic surgery may be carried out to improve the appearance of the nose (rhinoplasty). This is not carried out until the face is fully grown. Cartilage from the ear is used in this process

Less commonly, a cleft occurs only in the muscles of the soft palate, which are at the back of the mouth, covered by the mouth's lining. This type of cleft is called a submucous cleft palate. This type of cleft sometimes goes unnoticed at birth and may not be diagnosed until associated issues develop. Such difficulties include:

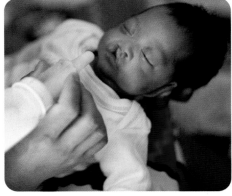

* Difficulty feeding

* Difficulty swallowing

* Nasal voice

* Frequent ear infections

In developing countries, however, many children must live without this surgery, causing significant problems for them. Children have difficulty eating, drinking and speaking, and due to their appearance may suffer social isolation and bullying.

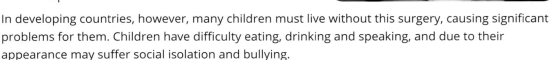

Extend your learning

Dr William Magee, an American plastic surgeon, and his wife Kathleen, a nurse, founded Operation Smile in 1982. An international charity, Operation Smile has undertaken hundreds of thousands of successful surgeries on children born with cleft conditions. In groups, visit the Irish Operation Smile website (www.operationsmile.ie) to find about more about this charity and the work it does.

CASE STUDY

Mary is nine months old and was born with both a cleft lip and a cleft palate. When she was five months old, she had surgery to repair her cleft lip. She is due to have another operation when she is 12 months old to repair her cleft palate. Mary is a very active, happy child. She is crawling and can sit without support. She enjoys playing with the blocks, stacking cups, shape sorters and the wooden bead maze. She has not made any word sounds yet and when she babbles, she does make a nasal-type sound. Mary's mum has told staff in the ELC setting that she has had a number of ear infections since birth and to watch out for this.

Feeding is the only real challenge that staff in the setting are working to overcome. None of the staff in the setting has ever cared for a child with a cleft palate before and they are a little anxious. While Mary has a specialist bottle for feeding, she frequently has wind afterwards in her tummy and can get quite distressed due to the discomfort caused. Sometimes milk enters her nose during feeds, which can leave her snuffling and uncomfortable. Mary has been weaned but is still taking puréed foods only. She finds it difficult to swallow foods with greater texture. Sometimes her solid food also enters her nasal passage, causing her to sneeze and rub her nose.

10.5 EPILEPSY

Epilepsy is a neurological disorder that affects the brain. A person with epilepsy has seizures. There are different types of seizures depending on what part of the brain the seizure begins in, whether the person is aware that they are having a seizure and if there is movement while having the seizure. Epilepsy is very common; approximately 100,000 children in Ireland have epilepsy (Epilepsy Ireland 2021).

While the cause of epilepsy is not known in 50% or more of cases, some types of epilepsy run in families and have a genetic component. A seizure occurs as a result of too much electrical activity in the brain. The main treatment for epilepsy is anti-epileptic-drugs (AEDs). Which AED is prescribed will depend on the type of seizure, and sometimes more than one type of AED is needed. All AEDs are designed to stop too much electrical activity in the brain.

If epilepsy is well controlled, there will be little impact on a child's development. However, some children may have seizures very regularly and as a result miss a lot of time in pre-school or school, which may have an impact on their progress.

If a child in an ELC setting has a seizure, it is very important that staff know what to do, particularly if the child has lost consciousness.

* Protect the child from injury (remove any harmful objects nearby).

* Cushion their head.

* Gently place the child in the recovery position.

* Time the length of the seizure.

* Stay with the child until recovery is complete.

* Calmly reassure the child.

An ambulance should be called:

* If it's the child's first seizure

* If the seizure continues for more than five minutes

* If one seizure follows another without the child gaining awareness

* If the child is injured or you believe the child needs medical attention

Sometimes rescue drugs such as buccal midazolam are prescribed to stop the seizure while the child is having it. With buccal midazolam the contents of a pre-filled oral syringe are emptied into the space between the inside of the cheek and the lower gum.

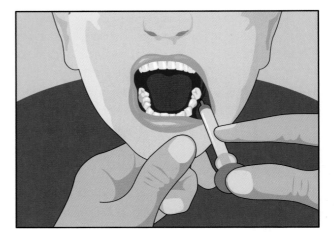

Staff caring for a child with epilepsy will be asked to keep a seizure diary recording information such as the date and time of seizure, type and duration of seizure and any possible triggers.

Extend your learning

Find out where you can receive training in administering buccal midazolam.

10.6 DIABETES MELLITUS

There are two main categories of diabetes mellitus: type 1 and type 2. Type 1 diabetes tends to occur in childhood or early adulthood and always requires treatment with insulin injections. Type 2 diabetes usually develops slowly in adulthood. It is progressive and can sometimes be treated with diet and exercise, but more often, type 2 diabetes may require anti-diabetic medicine and/or insulin injections.

It is estimated that approximately one in every 500 children in Ireland has diabetes. Most of these children have type 1, but an increasing number of obese older children and young adults are developing type 2.

Diabetes mellitus is a lifelong condition caused by the body's own immune system destroying the insulin-making cells (beta cells) of the pancreas. Insulin is a vitally important hormone that acts like a key to open the doors into body cells, letting sugar (glucose) in. With diabetes, the pancreas makes too little insulin to enable all the sugar in the blood to get into the muscle cells and other cells of the body to produce energy. If sugar can't get into the cells to be used, it builds up in the bloodstream.

Diabetes is therefore characterised by high blood sugar levels. Excess sugar is also excreted in the urine, hence the practice, in days gone by, of tasting urine to diagnose the condition. Type 1 diabetes can be caused by both genetic factors and environmental triggers. Type 1 diabetes is classified as a polygenic disease, meaning that it is caused by several different genes.

The four main symptoms of type 1 diabetes are easy to remember:

1. **Thirst:** Excess drinking, unable to quench thirst
2. **Toilet:** Frequent urination, particularly at night
3. **Tiredness:** Lack of energy, sleeping more than usual
4. **Weight loss:** Rapid weight loss over a short period of time

Less common symptoms include vomiting and abdominal pain, constipation, bed wetting, mood swings, frequent infections and itchy skin infections (Diabetes Ireland 2021).

Diagnosis will be made via blood and urine tests. Patients will be asked to fast (blood sugar levels would normally drop as a result) and if blood sugar levels remain high even with fasting, this will normally indicate diabetes. In addition, because blood sugar has not been used for energy production, protein and fat stores in the body will have been used. A by-product of protein metabolism for energy production is ketones in the urine. This will be picked up by a urine test.

Currently, diabetes cannot be cured, but it can be treated. Diet and insulin therapy are the two main methods of controlling diabetes. Generally, the person (or their carer) monitors their blood sugar levels at intervals throughout the day (the skin is pricked, a small amount of blood taken and tested with a blood glucose monitor). The person (or their carer) then administers insulin by way of a subcutaneous injection. Children are usually taught to do this from a relatively early age. Some children may be fitted with a continuous glucose monitor and an insulin pump. Continuous

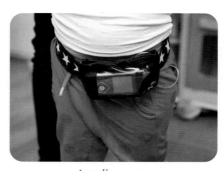

Insulin pump

glucose monitors measure glucose levels through tiny sensors inserted under the skin, and information about glucose levels is displayed on a small monitor or on a mobile phone app. Insulin pumps are small computerised devices that are programmed to deliver a certain amount of insulin throughout the day (a basal rate). At certain times they also deliver a 'bolus' quantity of insulin for meals.

In terms of diet, people with type 1 diabetes generally avoid foods high in refined sugars, e.g. cakes, sweets, in favour of foods that release energy more slowly. Individuals with type 1 diabetes must eat regular meals and snacks.

Did you know?

The term 'diabetes' means excessive urination and the word 'mellitus' means honey. Why do you think the condition was given this name?

Extend your learning

The Diabetes Federation of Ireland has produced a very good booklet on diabetes for children called 'Pete the Pancreas'. This booklet can be downloaded at www.diabetes.ie.

In the short term, if an individual's blood sugar becomes too low, they may have what is called a hypoglycaemic attack. This may occur because: (a) too much insulin has been injected; or (b) blood sugar has been used up too quickly, e.g. the person has expended a lot of energy; or (c) not enough food has been consumed, e.g. the person has skipped meals. Symptoms of hypoglycaemia include blurred vision; a fast or pounding heartbeat; feeling cranky, nervous or aggressive; headache; shaking, trembling or sweating; weakness, and confused thinking. The person may faint or, in severe cases, go into a diabetic coma. If this occurs, medical attention should be sought immediately.

If blood sugar levels are too high, this is called hyperglycaemia. This is not as immediately dangerous as hypoglycaemia, but if it occurs frequently over periods of time it can cause organ damage and failure.

REFLECTIVE PRACTICE

Bella is a six-year-old girl attending the ELC setting in which you work. She was diagnosed with type 1 diabetes a year ago when she was five. Her family have been very good and with the help of the health service professionals involved in her care, she has a very clear understanding of diabetes and is able to explain this to the other children in the setting. Bella has been fitted with a blood glucose monitor, which is read from an app on her mobile phone, and also an insulin pump. Several staff in the setting have been trained in how these devices work. A trip to Dublin Zoo has been planned as an end-of-year treat for the children.

In groups, come up with a list of items that staff in the setting will have to remember to ensure that Bella can go on the trip safely.

10.7 PSORIASIS

Psoriasis is an autoimmune condition affecting the skin and scalp that tends to run in families. Approximately 2–3% of people have psoriasis and it is equally common in males and females. Several different genes have been identified as being linked to psoriasis, but the exact way psoriasis moves from generation to generation has not yet been fully established. Although the potential to develop psoriasis is genetically inherited, environmental factors can also play a role. In some cases, emotional stress, infection or certain medications can trigger it, while certain lifestyle factors may worsen it.

> **Did you know?**
>
> Psoriasis affects approximately 73,000 people in Ireland (Irish Skin Foundation 2021).

Psoriasis is a chronic (it cannot be totally cured) inflammatory skin condition in which there is an increase in the rate at which skin cells are produced and shed. Normally skin cells reproduce, mature and shed within a 28-day timeframe; with psoriasis the process takes only about four days. The new skin cells reproduce too quickly and move towards the skin's surface in an immature form causing a build-up of white/silvery scale, which is made up of dead skin cells. There is also increased blood flow to the skin causing a thickening of the epidermis (outer surface of the skin). This leads to patches of raised 'plaque' on the surface of the skin. The most common type of psoriasis is plaque psoriasis, which appears as small round patches of

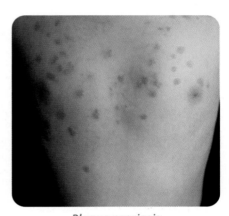

Plaque psoriasis

different sizes that can occur anywhere on the body. Psoriasis can impact on children's emotional and social wellbeing, particularly as they get older. Sometimes hurtful comments from peers can affect self-esteem and self-image. Children may become self-conscious about wearing certain types of clothing, e.g. shorts, and may avoid certain activities, e.g. swimming. It is very important that children are educated about the condition and understand that it is not contagious.

Although there is no cure for psoriasis there are a range of treatments options available.

1. **Topical treatments:** These are special creams or ointments applied to the skin to slow down the rate at which skin cells are produced and to reduce inflammation. Some contain steroids; others, e.g. Dovonex, are topical forms of vitamin D that mimic the effect of a steroid but without the potential side effects. Some tar-based creams are also used. Most people with psoriasis have it on their scalp, particularly behind the ears. To treat this, a topical tar-based preparation, e.g. Cocois, is applied and left for several hours, scales are gently removed with a comb, hair is washed with a tar-based shampoo and then sometimes a topical steroid is applied.

2. **Phototherapy:** The patient is exposed to artificial ultraviolet light in a hospital dermatology department.

3. **Systemic treatments:** Medications that work throughout the body, e.g. Acitretin, are used when other treatments such as topical treatments or phototherapy are not working. Systemic treatments work on the underlying causes of psoriasis. These treatments come in liquid, tablet or injection form.

4. **Biological treatment:** Medications are administered to suppress the parts of the immune system causing skill inflammation, e.g. Adalimumab, an injection licensed for children aged four years and over.

CARING FOR A CHILD WITH PSORIASIS

Where necessary, skin should be regularly moisturised during the day using an emollient cream, e.g. Silcock's Base. Apply cream gently in a smooth downward motion in the direction of hair growth. Never use fingers to remove cream from the jar; use a spoon or spatula.

If children are going outside, it is important that a broad-spectrum sun protection cream is applied, factor 30+, which offers protection against both UVA and UVB. Children should wear loose-fitting cotton clothing. If the child wishes to wear synthetic clothing, e.g. a football jersey, it should be worn over a cotton vest.

It is important that the other children in the setting understand what psoriasis is and that it is not contagious.

Extend your learning

The Irish Skin Foundation has a very informative booklet called 'What you Need to Know about your Child's Psoriasis'. Read the case study 'Aoife's story' on page 26 of the booklet. This booklet features an older child, but the issues raised could also be relevant to younger children in ELC settings.

If a child in your ELC setting had severe psoriasis, how could you work with the child and other children in the setting to ensure they all had a full understanding of the condition?

10.8 ASTHMA

Asthma is a common condition that affects the airways carrying air in and out of the lungs. When an individual has asthma, their airways become over-sensitive and react to things that would not normally cause a problem, e.g. cold or dust. When someone has an asthma attack the walls of the airways tighten up, causing them to narrow and making it difficult for air to flow in and out of the lungs. This tightening of the muscles around the airways can happen quickly and is the most common effect of mild asthma. This can normally be successfully treated with the correct inhaler (usually blue). However, sometimes the lining of the airways can become swollen and sticky mucus is produced, further clogging the airways. This happens more slowly. Normally a preventer inhaler (usually brown) is taken daily to stop this happening.

Did you know?

Ireland currently has the fourth highest incidence of asthma in the world (behind Australia, New Zealand and the UK), with approximately one in eight people having the condition (HSE 2021). The prevalence of asthma is steadily increasing in Ireland. Why do you think this might be?

The causes of asthma are not fully understood. An individual can develop asthma at any time in life, although it most commonly begins in childhood. Genetics are thought to play a role in that asthma often runs in families, but it can occur without any family history. Individuals with other conditions such as hay fever, eczema or other allergy-type conditions are more prone to asthma. Environmental factors are also thought to be important. Most Irish children, for example, now live in centrally heated, very well-insulated homes, which may be contributing to our increasing asthma levels. Another factor thought to be contributing to increasing levels of asthma in children is the increase in processed foods in their diet. Adult onset asthma usually develops after a serious respiratory tract infection.

The most common symptoms of asthma are:

* Difficulty breathing/shortness of breath
* A feeling of tightness in the chest
* Wheezing
* Coughing, particularly at night
* Hoarseness

An asthma attack may be brought on by **triggers** such as exercise, changes in air temperature or irritants in the air, e.g. pollen, dust or animal hair. Colds or chest infections can bring on attacks or worsen symptoms. Some people experience these symptoms regularly. It is estimated that children with asthma lose on average ten days from ELC/school each year (HSE 2021).

The main treatment for asthma is medication:

* **Preventers/controllers:** These are inhalers that help prevent the swelling and inflammation of the airways. This helps the airways to become less sensitive to irritants and reduces the risk of attacks. The effect of preventers/controllers builds up over time, so they need to be taken every day, usually once in the morning and once in the evening. It is important that the person with asthma takes their preventer/controller even when they are well, as this is what is keeping them well. Preventer inhalers usually contain a low dose of steroid, which reduces inflammation. For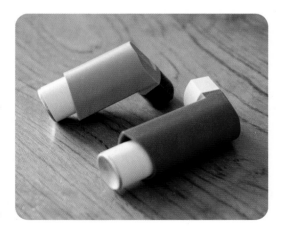
some people, preventers/controllers alone are not sufficient, and a combination inhaler may be prescribed. This inhaler will contain a steroid plus a long-acting reliever (see page 176).

* **Relievers:** Everyone with asthma will have a reliever. Relievers are taken immediately when the symptoms of asthma occur. Relievers work by quickly relaxing the muscles around the airways, allowing them to widen and helping the person to breathe more easily. Unlike preventers/controllers, they do not reduce swelling and inflammation. If relievers are taken before exercise, they reduce the chances of an attack. Relievers normally come in a blue inhaler. Examples include Salbutamol (e.g. Ventolin) and Terbutaline (e.g. Bricanyl). Individuals should not have to use relievers too often (more than once or twice a week), as this would indicate that their asthma is not well controlled. If this is happening, the individual's preventer/controller medication may have to be reviewed or other 'add-on' therapies used.

* **Add-on therapies:** One of the first add-on therapies that is usually tried is called a leukotriene receptor antagonist (LRA). This works by blocking the action of a group of naturally occurring chemicals in the lungs that cause inflammation, called leukotrienes. A long-acting reliever is usually prescribed with an LRA.

* **Steroids**: If an individual's asthma gets particularly bad at a particular time, a short course of steroid tablets may be prescribed, usually over 3–14 days. A small number of people with asthma may have to take longer courses. The type of steroids given to people with asthma are corticosteroids. They mimic those naturally produced in the body and are very unlike the anabolic steroids used by body builders, etc. Doctors generally prescribe the lowest effective dose.

Asthma is usually chronic, meaning that it does not go away. It may go into long periods of remission (where the individual does not get symptoms), and the degree of severity varies. Many children with mild to moderate asthma seem to grow out of it, becoming symptom-free adults. Prognosis is generally improved when asthma is treated early and effectively, before damage has been done to the airways. Unfortunately, in a minority of cases lungs become permanently damaged and the individual may experience problems throughout their life. Death from asthma is relatively uncommon and most deaths are preventable. It is rare for a person receiving proper treatment to die of asthma. Asthma that is not properly controlled can interfere with aspects of the individual's life, e.g. attendance at school and participation in sports or other activities.

REFLECTIVE PRACTICE

Download the 'Asthma Action Plan' from the Irish Asthma Societies website (www.asthma.ie). Print off a copy of the plan. In the ELC setting this is the type of information that should be available to staff for each child with an asthma diagnosis. If there are any children with asthma in your work placement setting, ask to see their care plan when you are next on placement there.

Please note that end of chapter questions have been incorporated into the Show You Know questions on page 192.

General and Specific Learning Disability

A general learning disability can range from borderline mild, to mild, to moderate, to severe/profound. Children with a general learning disability find it more difficult to learn, understand and do things than other children of the same age. With quality care and education, children with a general learning disability will continue to learn and make progress all through their lives, just at a slower pace than a child without this disability. Children with general learning disabilities can sometimes have additional conditions such as Down syndrome or autism. A psychologist will carry out several assessments with the child to determine if a child has a general learning disability. In general, children with a borderline mild or mild general learning disability will attend mainstream school; those with a moderate or severe/profound disability will generally attend a special school.

There are many possible causes of learning disability including genetic factors, infection before birth, brain injury at birth, brain infections or damage after birth. Intellectual ability, like many other traits, has a genetic component. Parents who have a general learning disability (not caused by infection, brain injury or other trauma) are more likely to have children who also have a general learning disability. When working with a child with a general learning disability, remember to:

* Choose high-interest materials and activities
* Spend more time on tasks and activities
* Introduce tasks one step at a time
* Make sure that tasks have a clear beginning, middle and end
* Repeat tasks – repetition can aid learning
* Ensure that you use language that the child can understand
* Be patient and give lots of encouragement and praise

11.1 SPECIFIC LEARNING DISABILITIES

Children with specific learning disabilities (SLDs) will have average or above average intelligence but, as the name suggests, have a specific difficulty in one area. SLDs have a genetic component in that a child is more likely to have one if a parent also has one. However, as with many other conditions detailed in this chapter, the cause can be multifactorial. Children can present with more than one specific learning disability. The following SLDs will be detailed here.

* **Dyslexia:** difficulty with reading, writing and spelling

* **Dyscalculia:** difficulty with mathematics

* **Dyspraxia**: difficulty with motor co-ordination

* **Dysgraphia:** difficulty with handwriting

DYSLEXIA

'One Spooky and Creepy night the lights turned off in the whole country. It was dark and there was an enormous and ferocious storm. Suddenly some shining lightning flashes in the air and every single person was shivering of fright'

There are many definitions of dyslexia. A very simple one would be that dyslexia is a specific learning difficulty that makes it harder for the individual to learn to read, write and spell and that these difficulties are unexplained in relation to their other abilities and educational experiences.

There is debate among professionals as to how prevalent dyslexia is. Approximately 20% of children in Irish schools have literacy difficulties (10% are judged to have serious difficulties). This figure rises to 50% in areas of poverty and social disadvantage, with 25–30% of children in these areas having serious reading difficulties. How many of these children have dyslexia and how many of them have literacy difficulties because of other reasons? Estimates of the prevalence of dyslexia (both mild and more severe) vary widely at between 4% and 10%.

Advocates of programmes such as the Reading Recovery programme (developed in New Zealand by Dr Marie Clay) believe that if more children were targeted at a younger age, before the child develops negative beliefs and attitudes about their own literacy ability, figures for literacy problems and indeed dyslexia would decrease. Some professionals believe that dyslexia is actually quite rare and that many children with a diagnosis of dyslexia do not actually have the condition, but rather got off to a bad start with reading, which has escalated into a severe literacy problem over the subsequent years.

Extend your learning

Reading Recovery is an early intervention for children (5–6 years) who have made very little progress in reading and writing during their first year at school. It involves a 30-minute daily one-to-one lesson with a specially trained teacher for a period of between 12 and 20 weeks. At the end of this time, most children have caught up with their classmates and can read and write at a level within the average band for their age. In Ireland, Reading Recovery training is offered to primary school teachers only. There is an example of a full Reading Recovery lesson (the clip is roughly half an hour long) on YouTube – the quality of the recording is not excellent, but it does demonstrate the techniques used in the programme.

Children in an ELC setting will obviously not yet have a diagnosis of dyslexia. However, the presence of a number of characteristics in children aged 3–5 may indicate that a child is at risk and should be closely monitored and allowed to learn at their own pace. This is important as it is vital that a child is not given a negative early experience of pre-literacy. When considering these characteristics, it is important to be mindful that no child will have all of them; some are more common than others, and all children will have some of them and not be at risk at all.

Speaking and listening:
* Learns to speak later than most children
* Has difficulty pronouncing some words, especially monosyllabic words
* Has difficulty separating spoken words into sounds and blending sounds to make words
* Confuses some language sounds, e.g. fan and van
* Is prone to spoonerisms e.g. chish and fips for fish and chips
* Has difficulty with rhyming
* Is unable to recall the correct word for something known to them
* Is slow to add new vocabulary
* May have difficulty telling or retelling a story in the correct sequence

Early literacy:
* Exhibits delays in acquiring emergent literacy skills, e.g. understanding that written language progresses from left to right and discriminating between letters
* Experiences problems learning the alphabet
* Has difficulty learning to write and spell their own name

Memory:
* Has difficulty learning numbers, days of the week, colours and shapes
* Has difficulty following multi-step directions or routines

Motor co-ordination:
* Has difficulty maintaining rhythm
* Delay in developing fine motor skills

(National Council for Special Education 2021)

Please see page 224 for ideas for promoting pre-literacy in children under six.

DYSCALCULIA

A child (or adult) with dyscalculia has an innate difficulty in learning or comprehending mathematics. In some ways, dyscalculia is to mathematics what dyslexia is to reading, writing and spelling.

Current estimates suggest that dyscalculia may affect about 5% of the population. However, some psychologists suspect that at least some children diagnosed with dyscalculia may not have the disability at all, and instead their difficulties with mathematics are due to environmental factors resulting in an intense dislike and/or fear of mathematics, leading them to avoid the subject if possible. As a result, the child gets little practice and falls further behind, continuing the cycle of dislike and avoidance.

As with dyslexia, a child under six will not yet have been assessed for dyscalculia. However, some of the following indicators may be present in children aged 3–5 years.

* Difficulty recognising numbers
* Delayed learning to count
* Struggles to connect numerical symbols to words, e.g. 5 and five
* May have difficulty recognising patterns
* May have difficulty placing things in order, e.g. smallest to largest
* Loses track when counting
* Difficulty classifying, i.e. grouping similar items together
* Difficulty matching similar items and sets of items, e.g. if a child is shown a place setting (knife, fork, dessertspoon and cup) they might have difficulty copying it
* Difficulty understanding position, e.g. over, under, up, down, on, in, beside and between
* Difficulty with concepts connected to time, e.g. morning/evening, night/day, days of the week, etc.

Please see page 259 for ideas for promoting pre-numeracy in children under six.

DYSPRAXIA

Developmental co-ordination disorder (DCD), also known as dyspraxia in Ireland and the UK, is a relatively common disorder affecting up to 6% of children with a ratio of 3:1 among boys and girls (Dyspraxia Ireland 2021). Dyspraxia affects fine and/or gross motor skills co-ordination. Children under six will generally not be yet diagnosed with dyspraxia but some of the following indicators may be present in younger children.

* Poor balance – may frequently fall over
* Difficulty throwing or catching a ball
* Poor awareness of body position in space, e.g. frequently bumps into things
* Poor sense of direction
* Difficulty hopping, skipping or pedalling a tricycle or bike
* Sensitive to touch, e.g. dislikes the 'feel' of certain clothing
* Confused about right and left
* Intolerant of having hair/teeth brushed, or nails/hair cut
* Slow to learn self-care skills, e.g. dressing or feeding

* Difficulty with pre-writing skills, e.g. learning to hold a pencil properly, using a pair of scissors
* Slow learning to speak
* May have phobias, obsessive behaviours and be impatient
* Disorganisation
* Difficulty staying still for any length of time

Strategies that can be used to support a child presenting with these difficulties include the following:

* Give instructions one at a time
* Repeat instructions and discreetly check that the child has understoo
* Use tick-off lists – these can be in picture form for a younger child
* Never compare the child with others
* Praise every effort and accomplishment
* Give plenty of one-to-one support in a group setting
* Prepare the child in advance for changes to routines

DYSGRAPHIA

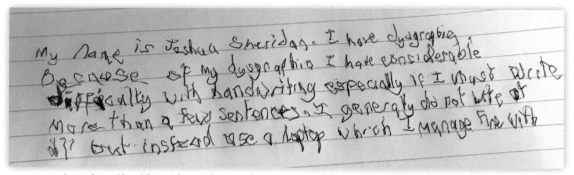

my name is Joshua Sheridan. I have dysgraphia. Because of my dysgraphia I have considerable difficulty with handwriting especially if I must write more than a few sentences. I generally do not write at all but instead use a laptop which I manage fine with.

Dysgraphia affects a child's ability to write legibly, regardless of their ability to read. There are three main types of dysgraphia.

1. **Dyslexia dysgraphia:** Written work created spontaneously is illegible, but copied work is good, and spelling is poor. A child with dyslexia dysgraphia does not necessarily have dyslexia.

2. **Motor dysgraphia:** Caused by poor fine motor skills, poor dexterity and/or poor muscle tone. Generally written work is poor to illegible, even when copied. Spelling skills are not impaired.

3. **Spatial dysgraphia:** Caused by a defect in spatial awareness; children may produce illegible spontaneous written work as well as illegible copied work. Spelling skills are generally not impaired.

In general, written work is presented with a mixture of upper/lower case letters, irregular letter sizes and shapes, and unfinished letters. Children may find it difficult to write on the lines and keep within the margins of the page. Children find writing an ineffective communication tool. Because the child must put so much effort into physically writing, it is difficult for them to think about the content of what they are writing. Children may have unusual writing grips, odd wrist, body and paper positioning, and often suffer discomfort while writing. Students may also poorly organise writing on a page.

There are some strategies that early years staff and teachers can use to help a child with dysgraphia.

* Activities that help children 'feel' how letters are made can help them learn letter formation, e.g. ask the child to close their eyes and trace the letter on the palm of their hand. Practise this and then have the child try to trace the letter onto a page.
* Have the child 'write' letters in sand or add sand to finger paint and have them form letters on a page.
* Roll clay into ropes and practise making letters, or flatten out some clay and have the child etch letters into it.
* Children with dysgraphia often have difficulty with correct pencil grip. Spread some balled-up pieces of paper on the table and have the child pick them up with tweezers.
* Activities that encourage co-ordinated movement can be beneficial before writing, e.g. arm windmills, jumping jacks, touching alternate toes or doing mountain climbers.
* Children with dysgraphia can have difficulty organising their thoughts. Practise reading stories to the child and having them retell the story in the correct sequence.
* As children get older, it helps if the child speaks what they want to say before they write. Use a smartphone or other device for recording.
* As children move through school, an application can be submitted to the National Council for Special Education (NCSE) for assistive technologies, e.g. a laptop.

11.2 VISUAL IMPAIRMENT

According to the CSO (2016), 2,379 children under the age of nine have a serious visual impairment or are legally blind. While visual impairment can be caused by a number of different factors, e.g. maternal rubella, oxygen deprivation at birth or head injuries after birth, there are some forms of visual impairment that are genetically inherited.

The following strategies may be used when working with a child with a visual impairment in an ELC setting.

* It is thought that sight is involved in 80% of a child's learning. It is therefore vital that a visually impaired child is encouraged and facilitated to develop their other senses, e.g. with sand and water play.
* For a partially sighted child, ensure that the ELC setting is well lit.
* Always describe to the child what is going on.
* Encourage self-help skills, e.g. putting on coats and shoes, washing hands, feeding. Be patient and allow the child as much time as they need.

* Tell the child before you touch him or her, e.g. 'I am going to change your nappy now, Ella.' The child cannot see you, so they could get a fright if they are suddenly whooshed up and laid down on a changing mat.

* Ensure the environment is safe and secure. Parents will be invaluable here, as they will have had experience with their child and should be involved in the safety audit carried out before the child starts the crèche, pre-school or school.

* Use storytelling, rhymes and action songs.

* Speak clearly, but not patronisingly. When someone speaks to us, we use many visual clues to figure out what they are saying. Visually impaired children rely only on auditory information and it is therefore more difficult for them to hear what has been said, especially in a noisy setting.

* Assist the child so that he or she can take part in all activities.

* Encourage the other children to name themselves while speaking to the visually impaired child. This will only have to be done initially, as the child will quickly be able to differentiate voices.

* Some children will have insufficient sight to read print (even enlarged print) and will need to learn Braille. Develop the child's abilities to discriminate by touch in preparation for learning Braille by playing games that require him or her to differentiate subtle differences in objects.

Extend your learning

Go to the National Braille Production Centre (www.braille.ie) to find out more about Braille.

11.3 DEVELOPMENTAL LANGUAGE DISORDER

Children with developmental language disorder (DLD) have difficulties with language development with no other associated conditions. If a child experiences difficulty with language and has another diagnosis this will be referred to as 'language disorder associated with', for example, autism. DLD often runs in families so frequently has a strong genetic link. Having said that, other environmental factors, such as premature birth, can also play a role. It is estimated that approximately 70,000 children and young people in Ireland have some degree of DLD.

Typically, children with DLD are slow to speak. Until the age of five or six children with DLD typically use sentences that are short and not grammatically correct, e.g. 'Car go', 'Me happy', 'She not going', etc. They have difficulty following instructions that are not embedded in a very familiar routine, have difficulty understanding what is being said (especially if it is said to a group and not just to them), and have difficulty finding the words to ask questions or express thoughts. The child may, as a result of these difficulties, be very quiet and avoid interactions.

Several areas of a child's development can be impacted by DLD. It may affect their literacy skills and thus their progress in ELC or school. They may find it more difficult to make friends, due to how DLD affects their social interaction skills. This can cause feelings of isolation, which can negatively impact on emotional development and wellbeing.

In the ELC setting the following strategies can be used by early years practitioners to support children with DLD.

* Always use the child's name before asking questions or giving instructions so they know when to listen.

* Ensure the child can see your face to make it easier for them to pick up on facial expression, which will aid understanding.

* Use simple language and repeat when necessary. Provide as many opportunities as possible for them to hear, see and use words, e.g. circle time.

* Talk calmly and slowly to allow time for the child to process what is being said.

* Give the child plenty of time to respond so that they can process what they wish to say.

* Use pictures and gestures when introducing new words, as these visual aids will help the child process them.

* Help the child learn skills needed to join in with other children, e.g. play games that require turn-taking and listening to others.

Extend your learning

Watch the short YouTube clip, 'Living with Developmental Language Disorder', which features a young man who has only been recently diagnosed with language disorder, and discuss the effects that the disorder has had on his life.

11.4 ATTENTION DEFICIT HYPERACTIVITY DISORDER (ADHD)

Attention deficit hyperactivity disorder (ADHD) is one of the most common childhood disorders and it can continue into adolescence and adulthood. ADHD will be diagnosed by a psychologist. Symptoms include difficulty staying focused and paying attention, difficulty controlling behaviour, and hyperactivity (overactivity). Parents, early years practitioners, teachers and others who work and live with children know that all children:

* Sometimes have difficulty controlling their behaviour

* Sometimes have difficulty paying attention

* Can be hyperactive and noisy from time to time

* Can be impulsive

The difference with children with ADHD, however, is that these behaviours occur much of the time and in all settings. It is estimated that up to 5–7% of children may have the condition, and three to four times more boys than girls.

While the precise cause of ADHD is not completely clear, it is now known that it is a predominantly genetically inherited condition. In terms of biological causes, magnetic resonance imaging (MRI) scans of the brain show that in people with ADHD, the right side of the brain is often smaller. Another type of brain scan, positron emission tomography (PET), has been used to obtain pictures of brain activity during tasks requiring concentration. Again, these show differences between those with ADHD and others. ADHD can also be influenced by environmental factors such as alcohol, drug use or smoking during pregnancy, which causes toxins to build up, thus harming the baby's brain.

The three main symptoms of ADHD are inattention, hyperactivity and impulsivity. As a result of these behaviours, children with ADHD can often develop social and emotional problems and can often feel depressed and angry. Many find it difficult to make friends because of their frequent disruptive and socially inappropriate behaviour. Based on the types of symptoms experienced, ADHD can be divided into three subtypes.

1. **ADHD mainly inattentive:** Children have significant difficulty with concentration and often have a poor working memory. This condition is sometimes called ADD, but this is nowadays considered an out-of-date term.

2. **ADHD mainly hyperactive-impulsive:** Children with this have a constant need for movement and action.

3. **ADHD combined:** Children have a mixture of both.

The following strategies are useful in an ELC setting to work successfully with a child with ADHD.

* Create very good structures and routines and have the child stick to these routines each day. Pictorial timetables of the daily routine can be helpful.

* Observe patterns of when the child finds it difficult to manage and change the routine accordingly, e.g. take a break outside for some free play at these times. Build this into the child's routine.

* Break tasks into small manageable steps and offer praise and encouragement after completion of each step.

* Stay calm, positive and consistent in your approach to avoid escalation of behaviours.

* Provide as much one-to-one attention to the child as you can; this will help the child stay calm and on task.

* Some computer games for children are very helpful for children with ADHD as they break tasks up into small sections, rewarding the child after each.

Extend your learning

Investigate a range of educational computer games for young children. Some are free online.

ADHD is usually treated with a combination of stimulant medication and behavioural therapy. Ritalin is perhaps the best-known ADHD medication and has been widely used since 1954.

Behavioural therapy can be used alone or with medication. Basically, behaviour therapy is designed to teach or train children to control their hyperactivity, impulsiveness and lack of attention. Based on the work of B.F. Skinner (see pages 84–5), desirable behaviour is rewarded (positively reinforced) and undesirable behaviour is not reinforced (ignored) or is punished (e.g. the child is asked to sit on a thinking chair) in the hope that this will discourage its repetition. Many ELC settings, however, do not agree with punishing behaviours.

Many children with ADHD have to be actively and directly taught social skills, e.g. through the use of role play and social stories. They tend to experience great difficulty picking up others' social cues, act impulsively, have limited self-awareness of their effect on others, display delayed turn-taking ability and over-personalise others' actions as being criticism. This can alienate them from their peers and cause emotional and social problems for them. Children with ADHD can find that much of the time, their environment is very negative. While they know that a lot of the negative feedback they get from adults and peers is caused by their own behaviour, because of their condition they are unable to effectively change this. Thus, low self-esteem, poor self-image and negative self-talk are very common in children with ADHD. It is vital that ELC practitioners are acutely aware of this and closely monitor the type of message they give to the child.

Collaborate

In groups, read the case study below about four-year-old Evan. Research and suggest some strategies that could be tried to help better manage his behaviour in the setting.

CASE STUDY

Evan is four years old and the elder child in his family. He has a younger sister who has just turned two. Three mornings a week Evan attends an ELC setting close to where he lives. Staff in the setting can certainly tell the difference between when Evan is in attendance and when he is not. When he arrives, staff try to get him to follow the normal arrival routine of taking his coat off, hanging it up and then sitting in his seat to wait for breakfast. Sometimes he does this, but at other times he will run straight in and begin to disrupt the children already there by taking whatever they are playing with away from them and running around the room. This causes the other children to get upset and the day gets off to a bad start. Throughout the day, a lot of the time Evan has trouble waiting and taking his turn. He sometimes gets angry and frustrated, at times pushing or hitting the other children. If engaged in activities such as story time, he finds it hard to sit still, and gets up off his bean bag and runs around the room. Staff find working with him difficult and very tiring and find that they spend a lot of their time trying to correct his behaviour.

11.5 CHROMOSOMAL DISORDERS

As you learned in Chapter 9, all of an individual's body cells, except for the ova (eggs) and sperm cells, contain 23 pairs of chromosomes – one set of 23 from their mother and one set of 23 from their father. Chromosomal disorders can be either **numerical** or **structural**. In a numerical disorder, the individual has either an extra chromosome or is missing a full chromosome. In a structural disorder, only part of the chromosome is missing or duplicated.

NUMERICAL CHROMOSOMAL DISORDERS

DOWN SYNDROME

While it is believed that Down syndrome has always existed, it was not until 1966 that the English doctor John Langdon Down first described the condition, which subsequently took his name. It was first understood as a chromosomal abnormality in 1959 when Professor Jérôme Lejeune, a Parisian geneticist, discovered that Down syndrome occurred as a result of a trisomy of chromosome 21. This means that instead of the usual 46 chromosomes in the cells of the body,

there is an extra chromosome 21, making 47 chromosomes in all.

Since then, other forms of the condition, which are much rarer, have been discovered, such as translocation (where one parent passes on an abnormal rather than an extra chromosome 21, which contains extra material) and mosaicism (where some cells in the body have the normal 46 chromosomes, while others have 47).

Approximately 94% of people with Down syndrome have standard trisomy 21, 4% have a translocation and 2% have mosaic Down syndrome. Individuals with mosaic Down syndrome may show fewer or less severe symptoms of the condition, depending on what percentage of their body cells have 47 chromosomes.

Individuals with Down syndrome have several distinctive physical characteristics, such as a small mouth, which is often kept open because of their large tongue and high arched palate. They have a flat nasal bridge, low hairline and small, low-set ears. Their eyes characteristically slant upwards and outwards, with extra skin folds on the upper and lower lids. The child will generally be short in stature and their hands will be characteristically broad, with short fingers, and there may be only one palm crease. Their feet will be broad and short with a deep cleft between the first and second toe.

Individuals will also have varying levels of intellectual disability and may have other health-related problems, such as frequent ear and chest infections due to a weaker immune system, poor vision and heart problems.

On average, Down syndrome appears approximately once in every 700 live births but more frequently as maternal age progresses (see table below). It is not known why this is the case. Some women, particularly those over the age of 35, opt to have prenatal diagnostic tests to detect Down syndrome and other genetic abnormalities; this practice is understandably controversial.

Since the 1930s the link between maternal age and the risk of having a baby with Down syndrome has been well documented. In 1997, however, a large-scale study by Columbia University Medical Centre of 3,419 babies with Down syndrome found that increased paternal age and maternal age increases the risk.

MATERNAL AGE	RISK
15–19	1 in 1,950
20–25	1 in 1,400
26–30	1 in 900
31–35	1 in 390
36–40	1 in 190
41–45	1 in 110
45+	1 in 30

Did you know?

John Langdon Down was born in 1929 in an upstairs room above his father's grocery shop in Torpoint, Cornwall, England. His father, Thomas, had failed in business on three occasions, but he prospered in Torpoint. John was taken out of school at the age of 14 and he spent the next four years behind the counter of his father's shop. He had no higher education. At the age of 19 he had what he described as a life-changing experience. A heavy summer shower drove the family to take shelter in a cottage. 'I was brought into contact with a feeble-minded girl, who waited on our party and for whom the question haunted me – could nothing for her be done? I had then not entered on a medical student's career but ever and anon ... the remembrance of that hapless girl presented itself to me and I longed to do something for her kind' (Down 1979).

Even though his language is of its day and would not be acceptable today, John spent his career working to understand and assist children and adults with intellectual disabilities. He worked tirelessly in both Earlswood and Normanfield hospitals in England setting up training systems based on physical exercise, sensory stimulation, and role-playing in such social activities as shopping. This involved training and encouraging a team of carers who would now be classified as play therapists, occupational therapists, speech therapists and specialist teachers.

Collaborate

Patrick is 2½ years old and has Down syndrome (Trisomy 21). He is a very sociable child, and makes good use of his non-verbal skills such as smiling and pointing. He has not yet begun to speak any words clearly. Jessica and Alan, his parents, have begun to research Lámh sign language to help Patrick with his communication skills. In groups, research Lámh sign language. Find out what it is and how it can be used to help children with Down syndrome develop their communication skills.

KLINEFELTER'S SYNDROME

Klinefelter's syndrome occurs when males have an extra X chromosome, making them XXY rather than XY. It is estimated that while one in every 500 males has the syndrome, only one in every 1,000 exhibits symptoms. Males with this condition are usually very tall, have an underdeveloped penis and testes, resulting in infertility, and may have increased breast tissue. In addition, there is frequently language and intellectual impairment, with poor motor co-ordination. Females with trisomy X (XXX), which occurs in approximately one in 1,000 live births, are healthy and have no unusual physical features other than being slightly taller than average. Triple X females may have learning disabilities, but their fertility is not affected.

XYY SYNDROME

XYY syndrome (sometimes called Jacob's syndrome) occurs in approximately one in every 1,000 males. Males with the condition have an additional Y chromosome, resulting in 47 chromosomes in each body cell. XYY males tend to be taller than expected (taking parents' height into consideration) and some studies show reduced IQ levels when compared with non-XYY siblings. This condition has for many years been associated with an aggressive criminal personality. Many of these studies have since, however, been criticised due to their method of studying height-selected institutionalised males.

TURNER SYNDROME

Turner syndrome occurs approximately in one in every 2,500 females. The condition occurs when there is only one full X chromosome present. The X chromosome may not be absent from all cells, so there can be degrees of Turner syndrome. Common symptoms include short stature, oedema (swelling) of the hands and feet, a broad chest (shield chest) and widely spaced nipples, low hairline, low-set ears, infertility due to underdeveloped ovaries, absence of a menstrual period, obesity, shortened fourth finger, small fingernails, webbed neck, heart defects, poor breast development, kidney problems, visual impairment, ear infections and hearing loss. Girls with Turner syndrome are usually provided with oestrogen therapy in order to develop secondary sexual characteristics. Most have normal intellectual ability.

STRUCTURAL CHROMOSOMAL DISORDERS

Disorders can occur not only from an abnormal number of chromosomes but as a result of changes to the structure of chromosomes – genes may be added or deleted. Such disorders are called structural chromosomal disorders.

WILLIAMS SYNDROME

Williams syndrome is a rare neurodevelopmental genetic disorder that features mild learning or developmental challenges with high levels of calcium in the blood and urine. Williams syndrome, or Williams-Beuren syndrome, occurs because approximately 20 genes are deleted from chromosome 7. Williams syndrome is very rare, occurring in approximately one in 10,000–20,000 births.

Children with Williams syndrome often have an unusual 'elfin' appearance. Facial characteristics include a small upturned nose, a wide mouth, a small chin and puffiness around the eyes. Unique personality traits include a high level of sociability and very good communication skills. They will frequently have an excellent memory for faces and names. For this reason, children with Williams syndrome are often very popular members of the pre-school, school and wider community. Their high level of verbal skills may mask other developmental issues and sometimes contributes to a late diagnosis. Challenges faced by children and adults with Williams syndrome include difficulties with spatial awareness, abstract reasoning and mathematical reasoning. Some health issues can arise, particularly cardiovascular problems and other issues related to high levels of calcium in the blood.

Most children with Williams syndrome are very keen to communicate with others, especially adults, and generally do not fear strangers. Many children have very sensitive hearing, which can cause a dislike of loud noises. Equally this can foster a love of listening to and making music; children with Williams syndrome have a very good memory for songs and have an excellent sense of rhythm (Bellugi 2006).

Collaborate

Read the following case study about Andrew, who has Williams syndrome. In groups, discuss how the environment he is growing up in has greatly helped his learning and holistic development.

CASE STUDY

Andrew was born weighing 1.9 kg (4 lb) at 39 weeks' gestation. During the first six months after his birth, Andrea, his mum, who is a qualified general nurse, began to suspect that Andrew could have some additional needs. From the beginning he did not feed well, he had reflux and frequently vomited up his small feeds. Andrea found it difficult to get him into any type of regular sleep pattern and this made him irritable and difficult to settle. At Andrew's six-month check-up it was noted that his motor development was not progressing normally. He had poor balance and could not sit, even when partially supported. He was referred to Temple Street Children's Hospital for further tests. At nine months old, just as Andrea would have been going back to work, Andrew was diagnosed with Williams syndrome. Andrea and her husband, Stephen, decided that it would be best if she took a career break for Andrew's pre-school years in order to give him the best chance that they could.

With hard work and determination, Andrea got Andrew into a very good routine of sleep, meals, rest and play. She spent lots of time talking to him, reading him stories and involving him in all her daily chores around the house. Andrea cooks all the family's meals from scratch using fresh ingredients and does not buy junk foods or drinks at all.

Both parents are very proud of their son and bring him everywhere – to the shops, restaurants, football matches and friends' houses. As a result, Andrew is very sociable and loves company. When Andrew was four, his parents decided that it was time that he joined a pre-school. He was not fully toilet trained, however, so this was a concern for them. He also displayed no fear of strangers or danger situations and often banged into objects and hurt himself.

Andrea visited several pre-schools and settled on one that she felt would suit his needs. The owner was a very experienced lady and spent a great deal of time understanding Andrew's additional needs and creating an individual plan for him. Andrea and Stephen have continued to work with their son on self-care tasks such as dressing and toileting, and he has recently become more independent in this regard. They continue to follow a well-organised routine with Andrew and encourage all aspects of his development by engaging him in everything that is happening in their house.

FRAGILE X SYNDROME

A newborn normally has either two X chromosomes (girl) or an X and a Y chromosome (boy). Fragile X syndrome occurs in approximately one in 2,000 males. While many girls (one in approximately 250) have an affected X chromosome, they rarely show symptoms of the condition because of their second X chromosome, which counteracts the effect. Fragile X occurs as a result of the X chromosome being constricted or broken. Boys with fragile X may show physically distinctive traits, e.g. long face, prominent ears, long fingers with double-jointed thumbs, flat feet, larger than normal testicles and poor muscle tone. Usually children will also have intellectual disabilities, a short attention span and poor memory and social skills.

Please note that the Show You Know questions on the following page relate to chapters 9, 10 and 11.

SHOW YOU KNOW

1. Show your understanding of the following basic concepts associated with genetics and heredity by writing a short paragraph on each:

    * Genotype and phenotype

    * Dominant-recessive gene principle

    * Sex-linked gene principle

    * Genetic imprinting

2. Differentiate between the following categories of genetically inherited developmental disorders by offering a brief definition and one example of each:

    * Single-gene inheritance disorders

    * Complex multifactorial disorders or polygenic inheritance disorders

    * Chromosomal disorders

3. Choose **three** of the genetically transmitted conditions listed below. Choose **one** classified as single-gene inheritance, **one** polygenic inheritance and **one** chromosomal.

    * *Single-gene inheritance:*
        * Cystic fibrosis
        * Duchenne muscular dystrophy
        * Hearing impairment
        * Sickle cell anaemia
        * Marfan syndrome
        * PKU

    * *Chromosomal:*
        * Down syndrome
        * Klinefelter's syndrome
        * XYY syndrome
        * Turner syndrome
        * Williams syndrome
        * Fragile X syndrome

    * *Complex multifactorial/polygenic:*
        * Autism
        * Asperger's syndrome
        * Spina bifida
        * Cleft lip and cleft palate
        * Epilepsy
        * Diabetes Mellitus
        * Psoriasis
        * Asthma
        * Dyslexia
        * Dyscalculia
        * Dyspraxia
        * Dysgraphia
        * Visual impairment
        * Developmental language disorder
        * Attention deficit hyperactivity disorder (ADHD)

4. Discuss the (a) causes; (b) symptoms; (c) treatments; (d) developmental challenges; and (e) supports required for children with each of the conditions you have chosen.

Section 4

Influence of Families and Other Adults on Child Development

Family Factors Influencing or Impacting on Children's Development (0–6 Years)

What I will learn

* The importance of the quality of parent–child interactions
* The significance of family-orchestrated child experiences
* What parental activities are relevant to ensuring the health and safety of the child

12.1 INTRODUCTION

As we saw in Chapters 1 and 3 in particular, children come into the world with a developmental potential influenced by their genes and uterine environment. Whether this potential can be realised or indeed enhanced is influenced by several environmental factors. The focus of this chapter is the influence of the family.

According to Guralnick (1998), three general types of family patterns have been clearly associated with child developmental outcomes.

* The quality of parent–child interactions

* Family-orchestrated child experiences

* Parental activities relevant to ensuring the health and safety of the child

Note: The term 'parent' is used here to include biological, non-biological (e.g. through surrogacy), foster and adoptive parents.

12.2 THE QUALITY OF PARENT–CHILD INTERACTIONS

With respect to fostering babies' and young children's development, the ability of parents to gauge their interactions to be consistent with their child's development level, mood and motivational state is crucial. The concept of 'sensitive responsiveness' is key (Ainsworth Blehar, Waters and Wall 1978) – see also attachment, page 115.

Parents with a highly developed sensitivity and understanding of the cues their children display are said to score highly on the 'sensitive-responsiveness' scale. These parents show an ability to respond to their child in a timely and predictable fashion and in a way that is relevant and appropriate. Their interactions are also warm, affectionate and enthusiastic. Such sensitive responsiveness gives the child a view of their world as being predictable and one in which their desires, interests and interactions make a difference. The child knows (often at a subconscious level) that they can exert an influence with respect to what happens next, e.g. a baby who is attended to quickly when they cry because they have a dirty nappy will not fret unnecessarily because they 'know' their parent will respond to their discomfort.

High levels of sensitive responsiveness also encourage social exchanges between parent and child to flourish, often creating a lively 'discourse' or 'conversation' between parents and young children, providing a context for elaborating on topics of mutual interest to both parent and child. This mutual discourse allows parents to 'scaffold' the child's language and information by gradually extending their language and knowledge or guiding their skilled actions just beyond the child's current level of development (Vygotsky 1978 – see also page 93).

PARENTING STYLES

The parenting styles commonly referenced in psychology today are based on the work of Diana Baumrind (1927–2018), a developmental and clinical psychologist at the University of California Berkeley. In the 1980s two other psychologists, Eleanor Maccoby and John Martin, refined Baumrind's model.

Baumrind is commonly considered a pioneer of research into parenting styles. She classified parenting styles into three categories to differentiate between normal parenting behaviours: authoritarian, authoritative and permissive. Baumrind suggested that authoritarian parents try to shape, control and evaluate their children's behaviour based on an absolute set of standards; permissive parents are warmer, grant more autonomy and are less controlling. An authoritative parenting style falls between those two extremes. Maccoby and Martin (1983) further developed Baumrind's work. Based on the combination of two dimensions – demandingness and responsiveness – they defined four parenting styles:

1. Authoritative (high demandingness and high responsiveness)

2. Authoritarian (high demandingness and low responsiveness)

3. Indulgent (low demandingness and high responsiveness)

4. Neglectful (low demandingness and low responsiveness)

Collaborate

Break up into four groups. Each group should take one of the parenting styles above. Write an imaginary case study of a child whose parents have that parenting style. Evaluate the effects that your chosen parenting style could have on that child.

12.3 FACTORS AFFECTING PARENT–CHILD INTERACTION

In all family units there will be times when parents are less sensitive or responsive to their child's needs, e.g. the death of a close relative may cause a temporary disruption to normal parent–child interaction patterns. Sometimes, however, longer-term factors affect a parent's ability to form a strong, sensitive and responsive relationship with their child. This can negatively impact on all aspects of a child's development. Such factors include:

* Post-natal depression and other mental illnesses

* Alcohol or drug misuse

* Relationship stress, separation and divorce

* Lone-parent families

* Financial stress and poverty (see Chapter 13)

* Poor work–life balance

* Children with additional needs

POST-NATAL DEPRESSION AND OTHER MENTAL ILLNESSES

POST-NATAL DEPRESSION

Post-natal depression (see also page 53) is the term used for the depression that some women experience in the first year after having a baby. Sometimes when a mother has post-natal depression it makes it more difficult for her to be sensitive and responsive to her baby's needs; sometimes mothers can display more negative behaviours towards their baby, e.g. raising their voice and less gentle handling. Some mothers, because they are dealing with their own difficult feelings, engage in fewer positive behaviours, e.g. talking to the baby or cuddling them. If this occurs over an extended period, without appropriate supports and interventions, it can have a negative impact on the child's development.

DEPRESSION

Depression is a very common mental health condition affecting approximately one in every ten people at any one time: 450,000 people in Ireland alone (Aware 2021). The main symptoms of depression are:

* Feeling sad, anxious or guilty

* Low energy, feeling tired or fatigued

* Too much or too little sleep

* Poor concentration, thoughts slowed down

* Loss of interest in hobbies, family or social life

* Low self-esteem

* Physical aches and pains with no physiological basis

* Loss of interest in living, thinking about death, suicidal thoughts

There are many ways in which the symptoms of depression can be effectively treated, including talk therapy, lifestyle changes, medication or a combination of these. Exercise can be very beneficial, as can eating a balanced diet. For people whose sleep is affected, the advice is not to drink tea or coffee late at night and to leave electronic devices out of the bedroom. Alcohol is a depressant and should be avoided. For some people, managing depression is very challenging, and it can make it much more difficult to be a sensitive and responsive parent. They may feel exhausted a lot of the time, sad and anxious. Caring for a child is both challenging and demanding; for a parent with depression, it can be quite overwhelming.

ANXIETY

While anxiety is a common feeling that most people experience at some stage, e.g. getting ready for an exam or worrying about an ill family member, if it becomes a persistent everyday feeling and there is no obvious reason for it, it can cause the individual significant difficulty. Symptoms of anxiety include:

* Dry mouth and/or difficulty swallowing

* Difficulty getting to or staying asleep

* Poor concentration

* Muscle tension, aches and pains without cause

* Rapid heart rate and breathing

* Sweating or trembling

* Diarrhoea

* Nightmares

* A flare-up in other problems e.g. psoriasis or asthma

* Sexual problems, e.g. loss of sexual feelings

The symptoms of anxiety can be treated in much the same way as depression. But, like depression, some people find it difficult to manage and because of this it can have a significant impact on their life. A parent who has ongoing anxiety can find it much more difficult to be sensitive and responsive to their child. They may also feel exhausted a lot of the time, but have difficulty sleeping. They may experience feelings of being overwhelmed and have fears of being unable to cope.

Collaborate

Research one of the mental illnesses listed below. Discuss in groups how you think having one of these conditions could impact on the parent–child relationship and thus the child's holistic development.

* Bipolar disorder

* Obsessive compulsive disorder

* Panic disorder

* Eating disorders

* Narcissistic personality disorder

* Borderline personality disorder

* Schizophrenia

ALCOHOL OR DRUG MISUSE

ALCOHOL USE DISORDER

Alcohol use disorder (which includes a level that's sometimes called alcoholism) is a pattern of alcohol use whereby the individual has problems controlling their drinking, is preoccupied with alcohol, continues to use alcohol even when it causes problems, has to drink more to get the same effect, or has withdrawal symptoms when they rapidly decrease or stop drinking.

There are an estimated 61,000 to 104,000 children in Ireland under the age of 15 living with parents who have problems with alcohol, whether they are alcohol-dependent/alcoholics, regular heavy drinkers or occasional binge drinkers (Alcohol Action Ireland 2021). This is approximately one in ten children.

Symptoms of alcohol use disorder include: being unable to limit the amount consumed; wanting to cut down but failing to do so; having strong urges or cravings to drink; continuing to drink even though it is causing physical, social and interpersonal problems; reducing social activities, work activities and hobbies; using alcohol when it is not safe to do so, e.g. while driving; developing a tolerance – needing more to get the same effect; and experiencing withdrawal symptoms. If one or both parents drink heavily or have alcohol use disorder, this can have very serious effects on all aspects of their child's development. Having said that, a child might have individual strengths, interests and supports outside the home and, most important, a stable adult in their lives who can make sure the child receives consistent care and that the normal family routines around school, mealtimes and bedtimes are followed.

Children who grow up in families where there is parental alcohol abuse may:

* Have little experience of what it is like to grow up in traditional, harmonious family. This can result in the child feeling conflicted, confused and self-conscious when they realise that drinking as their parent or parents drink is not considered normal in other families. They may hide their family's problems and are therefore often the invisible victims.

* Live in an environment where normal family routines become lost and so home life becomes disorganised and chaotic. This can affect the child's physical health and wellbeing, as they may not receive regular meals and have very irregular bedtime and other routines. This lack of predictability can have an adverse effect on self-confidence and self-esteem.

* Face an almost insurmountable range of challenges when there are additional issues in the family such as poverty, domestic abuse, mental health problems and the absence of a stable adult in their life who can ensure that the child's needs for care and love are being met.

* Experience fear and anxiety if their parents' drinking leads to unpredictable and changeable behaviour, particularly if that parent becomes aggressive, abusive or undermining of the child, a sibling or the other parent. This fear can lead the child to withdraw, further isolating themselves. Celebrations such as birthdays are dreaded, due to the unpredictability of what might happen.

* Witness family conflict and friction. This can be even more distressing than their parent's drinking in itself. Alcohol is a trigger in one in three of the most serious domestic abuse cases (Alcohol Action Ireland 2021). Alcohol is not the cause of domestic abuse, but it can remove control and inhibitions. Children are often the silent witnesses to domestic abuse, which in itself is emotional abuse.

* Be isolated by peers (particularly as they get older) because they are perceived as odd or different in some way; that difference can be compounded if there is poverty and/or neglect, e.g. children going to school unwashed with dirty uniforms.

* Have parents who are frequently unaware of their child's basic needs or, if they are aware, are unable to meet the daily requirements of parenting: getting children up for pre-school or school, giving them breakfast, making sure they have clean clothes to wear, or even that they should have been in bed hours ago. If there is no other adult to take on the caregiver role in the family, these roles can fall to a child, frequently the eldest.

* Be at an increased risk of suffering from a range of psychological and behavioural difficulties including conduct disorders, depression, withdrawal and social isolation, self-blame, low self-esteem and anxiety-related disorders.

* Be abused and/or neglected in their homes, if at the most extreme end of the spectrum of harm, and will have to be taken into the care of the state, e.g. a foster home.

DRUG MISUSE

Drug misuse is defined as the use of a substance for a purpose not consistent with legal or medical guidelines (WHO 2006). Problematic drug use is a condition that may cause an individual to experience social, psychological, physical or legal problems related to intoxication and/or regular excessive consumption and/or dependence. Substances used include cannabis, sedatives or tranquilisers, central nervous stimulants (e.g. MDMA, cocaine and crack cocaine) and opioids (e.g. heroin). The prevalence of drug misuse in Ireland varies between age groups. For example, during 2014/15 use of any illegal drugs among 15–34-year-olds was 15.7% as compared with 3.6% among 34–64-year-olds (Bates 2017). It is therefore likely that a significant number of children in Ireland are being reared in households where one or both parents misuse drugs.

For a variety of reasons, substance-abusing parents are considered less likely to provide high-quality parenting (Kelley 1998). Substance dependency can take over all aspects of the user's life. Parents who are substance dependent can also present with other issues such as depression and other problems such as antisocial and personality disorders. The needs of their children can easily become secondary to their addiction. The quality of care can be even more hampered if poverty and other negative social factors are also present. Substance-abusing parents tend to be either more authoritarian (more punitive and controlling) and less responsive, or neglectful.

Infants may be particularly vulnerable to disruptions in care between six and 24 months of age when they are in the process of establishing stable attachment relationships (Rutter 1987). Children of substance-abusing women are at increased risk of family disruption and frequent changes in carers (Zuravin 1992). International studies based on treatment data indicate that almost 50% of those who access treatment report having dependent children. Women are more likely to bear responsibility for their children and the majority of parents in treatment do not live with their children (Meirer *et al.* 2004). Substance-misusing parents are more likely to be involved in criminality and this can often lead to imprisonment, causing separation and a high risk of relationship breakdown (Beckerman 1998).

Child outcomes

It is important to note that children are very adaptive and that many children of substance misusers do not display significant developmental and psychological difficulties (Jacob and Leonard 1986). Among the most negative consequences of parental drug dependency are the psychosocial effects that this environment has on children. Children who live with an alcoholic or drug-dependent parent show increased tendencies towards internalising feelings (sadness and worry) and externalising feelings (increased aggression and other behaviour problems). Children of drug misusers are more likely to experience severe social and economic disadvantage and suffer more social isolation and higher stress levels.

In one American study by Wilens *et al.* (2002), 96 families and their children (32 families with alcohol dependence, 32 with opioid dependence and 32 with no dependence (control group)) were studied over a period. This study showed that while 88% of children from non-dependent families were living in intact families, only 32% (alcohol) and 18% (opioids) were. The study also showed that 59% of children with opioid-dependent parents had at least one major psychopathological condition compared with 41% (alcohol) and 28% (control group). These major psychopathological conditions included behavioural and attention disorders (ODD and ADHD), mood disorders such as depression, plus anxiety disorders. This same study found significant differences in cognitive functioning between the three groups, with the children living with opioid and alcohol abuse scoring lower than the control group in vocabulary, oral arithmetic and reading. Children living with opioid and alcohol users were more likely to have to repeat a year, be in a special class or require extra learning support.

The risk of substance abuse being transmissible between generations is high, due to both genetic and environmental mechanisms. Current data indicates that patterns of alcohol and drug use among children whose parents misuse raise the risk of alcohol and drug misuse during adolescence. In terms of next-generation parenting, studies such as Neppl *et al.* (2009) show that second-generation parents often emulate the child-rearing practices of their own parents, meaning that negative parenting practices are frequently repeated.

RELATIONSHIP STRESS AND CONFLICT

From as far back as the 1930s it has been recognised that parental conflict has a potentially debilitating effect on children's mental health and development (Towle 1931). Sometimes parental conflict results in overt violent verbal and physical exchanges; at other times it is much more subtle, e.g. interparental/partner withdrawal, i.e. the silent treatment or the use of sarcasm and humiliating put-downs. Until 24 November 1995, divorce was not permitted in Ireland, and while

Ireland's divorce rates are still comparatively low compared with other nations, it is likely that before separation and divorce became more acceptable in Ireland many families were living with ongoing relationship stress and conflict.

Ongoing parental conflict can put children more at risk of:

* Having problems with school and learning

* Negative peer relationships

* Physical health problems

* Smoking and substance misuse in adolescence

* Wellbeing challenges, i.e. internalising feelings (sadness and worry) or externalising feelings (anger and aggression)

* Mental health challenges, e.g. anxiety or depression

Relationship stress and conflict can be even more problematic if one or other parent confides in the child regarding the relationship problems and puts pressure them to take sides (see parental alienation, page 204).

SEPARATION AND DIVORCE

The number of couples deciding to separate or divorce in Ireland has steadily increased over the past 20 years. In 2016, for example, the total number of people who were separated or divorced was 222,073, an increase of 8.9% since 2011 (CSO). This means that a very significant number of children are living in families where their parents are separated or divorced.

Children thrive best in environments that are secure and where there is affection and continuity. Whatever changes are brought about by separation and divorce, children need to feel that they have a secure base. This means that parents must put aside their own differences and recognise and respond to the needs of their children. This can be very difficult to do, given the overwhelming feelings and emotions that separation and divorce bring for the couple themselves.

Children who have adapted well to separation and divorce will have been given a clear explanation from their parents about what was happening and why. During and after separation the children have good relationships with both parents as both parents have behaved in responsible and predictable ways.

Separation and divorce change the structure of the family unit for ever. This can cause a range of challenges for both parents themselves and their children.

* **Loss and grief:** Both children and parents grieve the loss of the family they had hoped for, and children grieve the daily presence and availability of both their parents. Feeling and mourning these losses is normal. Parents need to work through this grief and loss and at the same time help their child to do so. If this is done, an acceptance of the changed circumstances is achieved, and the family can function in a more harmonious way.

* **Family changes:** Separation and divorce can result in physical changes for the child. One parent will leave the family home, and the child may have to move to a new home, which can mean adjusting to a new pre-school or school and loss of friendships.

* **Family circumstances:** The culture, traditions and ethnic background of a separating family can influence how much support that family gets. In Ireland in the past, separating families would not have received the degree of acceptance or support that they get today.

EFFECTS OF PARENTAL SEPARATION AND DIVORCE ON CHILDREN'S DEVELOPMENT

Children's needs and emotional reactions to separation usually depend on their age and the circumstances of the separation. In the early stages, typical responses may be fear and worry about the future, anger, sadness, embarrassment, relief and guilt. These emotional responses, which may be expressed in the initial child's behaviours, will usually resolve over time. Children can, however, suffer long-term negative effects if the separation was acrimonious or if there is still ongoing conflict between parents.

Conflict, arguments and tension between parents before, during and after separation can affect children deeply and can leave them anxious, aggressive or withdrawn and more likely to develop behavioural problems. This can be more severe for children who go through several family changes, such as the breakdown of two or more parental relationships and adjusting to more than one new step-parent.

Separation is a cause of significant stress for parents, often affecting a person's self-esteem, health and personal wellbeing. It is important that separating parents take care of themselves and get help with their own painful feelings, so that they can be a good support for their child. It is also vital that parents do not make their child their confidante. When this happens, a child may feel that they must support or care for a distraught parent at their own emotional expense.

Parents who develop a working relationship with their former partner and can communicate effectively as parents are in a good position to help their child adjust to separation and divorce. This can be a difficult task in that parents have to separate their previous 'couple relationship' in order to work together for the benefit of their child. Parents who do this successfully:

* Develop a jointly agreed parenting plan and commit to making it work

* Are positive about their child's relationship with their former partner

* Communicate directly with their former partner when necessary – and do not send messages through their child

* Are respectful while interacting with their former partner

* Respect their former partner's right to privacy and do not try to find out details of their life

* Keep agreements and consult with each other before making important decisions about their child

PARENTAL ALIENATION

Parental alienation is a deliberate, unjustifiable attempt by one parent to distance his/her children from the other parent. It is not a case of parental alienation if one parent is protecting their child from the other – previously abusive – parent. It occurs when one parent decides to use a child to 'punish' the other parent. This can range from denying access to eradicating the other parent from the child's life. The child can be manipulated into this process and encouraged to say or think negative things about the other parent and their extended family. Parental alienation occurs when one parent fails to distinguish between their own feelings of betrayal and hurt and those of their children. It is very rare for a child who had a previously close and loving relationship with a parent to cease all contact with that parent; when this happens, it is likely that there has been deliberate parental alienation. This is very damaging for the long-term mental and emotional wellbeing of the child.

Studies have shown that adult children who endured parental alienation suffer from low self-esteem, self-hatred, abandonment issues, lack of trust and depression, and are more likely to experience substance abuse or addictions. While family law practitioners in Ireland are familiar with the term 'parental alienation', and the World Health Organization recognises and classifies it, Irish law does not recognise it.

In time, when the acute feelings following separation have settled, parents usually come to see clearly the emotional distinctions between themselves and their children. As a result, the situation often resolves itself. But in some cases, it does not.

It is widely suspected that people who engage in parental alienation, i.e. deliberately and systematically destroy a previously loving relationship between a parent and child, are people with personality disorders. A personality disorder combined with being a persuasive blamer seems to be the most common personality type for people who cause parental alienation (Baker, 2007).

REFLECTIVE PRACTICE

Sinéad is four years old and her parents have recently separated. The separation was not amicable – it occurred as the result of Sinéad's mum having a number of extramarital affairs. Sinéad lives with her father, Simon, during the week and goes to stay with her mum, Karen, every Saturday and Sunday. The ELC practitioners have noticed that Sinéad is having difficulty coping with the changes in her life. Discuss ways in which the ELC setting can support Sinéad during this upsetting time for her.

LONE-PARENT FAMILIES

National and international studies indicate that the children of lone-parent families experience poorer developmental outcomes than children living with two parents (Growing Up in Ireland, 2016). Five factors are thought to contribute to this.

1. **Economic hardship:** Poverty is the most profound and pervasive factor underlying children's development (McLanahan and Booth 1986). Approximately 30% of families headed by lone parents (mostly women) are at risk of living in poverty (Nieuwenhuis, 2020).

2. **Loss of parental support and supervision:** Because lone parents are in effect doing the job of two people, they can have less time to become involved in their child's educational and recreational activities and as the child gets older can find it more difficult to monitor their children's whereabouts as closely.

3. **Lack of family and community resources:** Children who are brought up in lone-parent families where there is a lack of extended family and community supports are most at risk. Where extended family and community supports are good, children's developmental outcomes are much more positive (Bronfenbrener 1991 – see also Chapter 8 page 138).

4. **Parental conflict:** There is considerable evidence that a conflict-ridden partnership or marriage jeopardises children's wellbeing (Wallerstein and Blakeslee 1989). Based on this, ending a conflict-ridden partnership or marriage may boost rather than undermine children's wellbeing. Recent evidence suggests that children in divorced single-parent families do better than children in high-conflict intact families (Amato 1993).

5. **Life stress and instability:** A single stressful life event is not as detrimental to children's wellbeing as many stressful events. Children in lone-parent families can experience a greater degree of stressful life events such as moving to a new house, changing schools, loss of contact with their non-custodial parent, increased risk of poverty (see above) and having to adjust to new parental figures. This can have an adverse effect on children's social and emotional wellbeing. Lone parents should endeavour to keep change to a minimum in their children's lives to help protect against stress, which can of course be challenging, e.g. lone parents are more likely to be living in rented accommodation.

POOR WORK–LIFE BALANCE

Over the past few decades a dramatic change has occurred in the labour market and demographic profiles of employees. Families have shifted from the traditional 'male breadwinner – stay-at-home mother' structure to dual-earner couples and lone-parent families. Organisations are demanding an increase in employee flexibility and productivity. Advances in information technology mean that some employees feel they are never fully off duty. As a result of these demographic and organisational trends, both men and women have experienced an increase in the demands from both their working and home lives.

Greenhaus *et al.* (2003: 510) define work–life balance as the 'extent to which an individual is equally engaged and equally satisfied with his or her work and family role'. Work–life balance consists of three elements:

1. **Time balance:** Equal time is given to both work and home.

2. **Involvement balance:** Equal psychological engagement is given to both roles.

3. **Satisfaction balance:** Equal satisfaction is taken in both roles.

In order to achieve good work–life balance, all three components must be considered. When parents struggle to satisfy the demands put on them by both work and home, an imbalance may occur, resulting in work–family conflict. This can occur in several ways. When a parent gives too much of themselves to work, they may have little time to spend with their family; or, when they do spend time with them, they are exhausted or still preoccupied with work. On the other hand, when a parent gets little or no satisfaction from their work, they may be in a low mood when they do spend time with their family.

Kotowska *et al.* (2010) found that more than 25% of Europeans suffer from some form of work–family conflict. This has serious implications for children's development and wellbeing. The children of parents experiencing work–family conflict are at a higher risk because of the impact this has on the parent's ability to be sensitive and responsive to their child's needs (see page 196), which negatively impacts on children's developmental outcomes.

CHILDREN WITH ADDITIONAL NEEDS

Parents of children with special needs are often faced with a continuous barrage of challenges, from societal isolation to financial strain, difficulty finding resources, outright exhaustion or feelings of burnout. This can negatively impact on the parent's ability to be sensitive and responsive to their child's needs (see page 196) and will thus have an impact on their child's developmental outcomes. Parents can experience enormous stress, which can over time result in more severe problems such physical ill-health and mental health problems such as anxiety and depression, which can further impact on themselves and their children. It is vital that parents have ready access to supports such as healthcare services, pre-schools and schools, and respite care where required.

12.4 FAMILY-ORCHESTRATED CHILD EXPERIENCES

As the primary educators of their children, parents are responsible for organising a variety of experiences for their children, both in the home and in the wider community, that provide developmentally enhancing opportunities for their child. This includes selecting and providing developmentally appropriate toys, materials and experiences for the child. Parents are also responsible for family routines such as bedtime reading and other home reading experiences. They are responsible for

involving children in family chores and activities such as meal preparation and laundry, which provide rich opportunities for quality parent–child interactions. Parents are responsible for selecting and supporting their children in pre-school and school and for supporting their child in their choices of recreational activities, whether football, dancing or music. Parents can influence their child's social competence, particularly in relation to their peers, by arranging and monitoring their experiences with peers (e.g. playdates) and by offering direct advice with respect to managing relationships with their peers, for example what to do if another child is not treating them kindly.

All the factors discussed above have relevance here. Parents who are under stress as a result of any of these factors may not be able to offer their child high-quality family-orchestrated experiences and this can have a negative impact on developmental outcomes. One significant factor that was not discussed above was the impact of parental education on children's developmental outcomes.

PARENTAL EDUCATION LEVELS

Parents who stay in school longer have children who also do better at school – from pre-school right through primary and post-primary level (Dubow *et al*, 2009). It is often difficult to know whether this is simply because the children of more educated parents inherit abilities that mean they also do well in school or whether it is the extra parental education itself that leads to their children also doing well. There may also be many other contributing factors.

Children of educated parents may:

* Live in more economically advantaged areas with better pre-school, primary and secondary school provision
* Live in homes where there is more disposable income to purchase educational materials such as books and engage in educational experiences such as international travel
* Live in environments where there are fewer stressors, e.g. financial worries
* Be better supported throughout their education, because their parents have the necessary knowledge and skills
* Grow up in an environment where progress in school is seen as the norm and is valued

Many people who left education and training early return at a later stage. This can have a very positive effect on the educational outcomes for their children. Often parents who for various reasons, e.g. financial, had to leave education and training early are incredibly supportive of their child's education and go to great lengths to ensure that their children are given the opportunities that they did not have.

12.4 HEALTH AND SAFETY PROVIDED BY THE FAMILY

The third family pattern of interaction focuses on the crucial ability of families to attend to their child's basic needs with respect to health and safety. Parents have a responsibility to maintain a child's good health, whether through preventive health (e.g. making sure a child receives all their immunisations), providing a nutritious balanced diet for their children or providing their child with opportunities to take exercise. When this is provided child can take advantage of many of the other development-enhancing aspects of family patterns of interaction described above. In terms of children's safety, children need to be supervised in a way that is appropriate for their age to keep them safe and to protect them from harm such as violence and abuse. Many of the factors described in Section 12.2 above are of relevance here. Parents who are under stress, e.g. as a result of alcohol or drug addiction, may not provide a healthy and safe environment for their children, which can have sometimes very serious consequences for the children's wellbeing.

14.1 INTRODUCTION

As we saw in Chapter 12, parents and guardians play a crucial role in their children's health and overall development. Throughout their framework documents, Aistear and Síolta acknowledge the fundamental importance of children's parents/guardians as the primary carers and educators of their children. Principle 5 of Aistear – Parents, Family and Community – states:

> *Parents are the most important people in children's lives. The care and education that children receive from their parents and family, especially during their early months and years, greatly influence their overall development. Extended family and community also have important roles to play.*

Principle 3 of Síolta – Parents, its associated standard (Standard 3) and the components of this standard are all concerned with how parents and ELC settings can work together in the best interests of the child. Principle 3 states:

> **Parents are the primary educators of the child and have a pre-eminent role in promoting her/ his well-being, learning and development.** *Quality early childhood care and education must value and support the role of parents. Open, honest and respectful partnership with parents is essential in promoting the best interests of the child. Mutual partnership contributes to establishing harmony and continuity between the diverse environments the child experiences in the early years. The development of connections and interactions between the early childhood setting, parents, the extended family and the wider community also adds to the enrichment of early childhood experiences by reflecting the environment in which the child lives and grows.*

Many children spend a large part of their day being cared for and educated by ELC practitioners in a variety of different settings. The focus of this chapter will be how parents/guardians can actively support ELC practitioners and settings who are caring for and educating their child.

14.2 PROMOTING ENGAGEMENT WITH PRACTITIONERS

Engagement between home and the ELC setting is a two-way process. The setting must be welcoming and respect and value the vital contribution that parents/guardians make to their children's lives. Likewise, for children to flourish and grow, parents/guardians must positively engage with the setting and value and respect the work being done there. To do this parents/ guardians can:

* Plan the beginning and end of the day so that there is time at drop-off and pick-up to talk to practitioners about their child. At drop-off give an account of how the child slept, what they had to eat that morning, any activities they were involved in the previous evening. At pick-up spend time finding out about their child's day, e.g. how the slept, how they ate and the activities they were involved in.

* Talk with their child about their day. Ask them about the activities they took part in, what they enjoyed, who they were playing with, what they had at snack time and lunchtime, etc.

* Get to know their child's key worker and refer to them by name while at home.

* Show appreciation of the work being done by ELC practitioners by offering positive feedback.

* Display around the home photographs and examples of the child's work completed in the setting.

* Where possible, contribute resources to the setting, for example:

  * Clothing for the dress-up box

  * Natural resources such as seashells, leaves, pinecones, feathers, seeds and pebbles

  * Kitchen items such as empty kitchen rolls, empty yoghurt pots and pasta shells

  * Items for imaginary play, e.g. old mobile phones

14.3 COMMUNICATING WITH PRACTITIONERS

Open and honest communication between parents/guardians and ELC practitioners is vital. As described in the previous section, parents/guardians should plan their day so that there is time at drop-off and pick-up to communicate with the setting. It is important to be on time at drop-off and pick-up so that these communications are not rushed.

Settings should have a daily observations notebook for each child in which practitioners record key information about the child's day, e.g. what they ate, how long they slept, the activities the child was engaged in and any other information that is important for the parent/guardian to know. Each evening parents/guardians should take time to read the information provided in this notebook, which can be used to talk to the child about their day. This helps the child to understand that there is a strong relationship between the setting and home.

Parents should arrange more formal meetings with the setting and their child's key worker to update them on any significant changes in the child's life, e.g. moving to a new house, death of a pet, parental separation. This can help the setting plan to meet the needs of the child during these times of transition (see Chapter 18).

14.4 ENCOURAGING CHILDREN'S EFFORTS IN LEARNING

Throughout a child's life it is vital that the efforts that they make with their learning is supported at home. The link with home is more obvious to parents/guardians when children reach schoolgoing age and are given homework to complete. However, parents of even very young children can support the work being done in ELC settings in many way, such as:

* Parents/guardians should meet with their child's key worker and other relevant staff members to discuss the curriculum being offered in the setting. Parents can then support and complement what is being done and, in this way, support their child's efforts in learning.

* Avoid 'structuring' children's activities too much at home. To encourage imaginative play, provide children with interesting resources, e.g. dress-up clothes, paints, paper and playdough, but allow the child to decide 'how' to play with them.

* Meet and discuss the daily routines followed in the setting and carry these through to the home. Examples include the following:

    * In ELC settings pre-school children are routinely asked to tidy away one activity before beginning another. Parents/guardians should continue this at home and not tidy up for their child.

    * Encouraging children's independence by allowing them to do things for themselves, e.g. if a child is putting on their coat and boots, ask 'Do you want me to help you or can you do it by yourself?' This is encouraging independence while at the same time letting the child know that you are there to help if needed.

    * If a child completes at task to the best of their ability, parents/guardians should not redo what they have done, e.g. refolding clothes 'properly' after a child has done their best. Doing this is essentially saying 'What you have done is not good enough.'

    * Assigning children age-appropriate manageable chores at home, e.g. watering plants or emptying the tumble dryer into the ironing basket. This encourages independence and builds self-confidence.

    * Predictable and well-thought-out routines are very much a part of quality ELC settings. Parents should support this by having good routines and structures at home, e.g. everyone gets dressed before breakfast, we wash our hands when coming in from outside, we put on our pyjamas and brush our teeth before story time, etc.

14.5 READING TO AND WITH CHILDREN

One of the most important ways parents/guardians can support their children's learning is by reading with them each day. As was explained in Chapter 6, children from homes where reading is a daily activity come to pre-school possessing many of the prerequisites for reading, e.g. knowing that reading progresses from left to right. More important, reading every day encourages confidence in the child and helps them develop a love of reading. In contrast, children from homes where there is little reading or limited access to reading materials are at a distinct disadvantage and frequently fall behind during the first two years of primary school, with many remaining behind for the rest of their schooling.

Reading and telling stories has many benefits, including:

* Helping children to get to know sounds, words and language, and develop early literacy skills

* Teaching children to value and enjoy books and stories

* Sparking children's imagination and stimulating curiosity

* Helping children to develop their ability to focus, concentrate and develop their communication skills

* Helping children learn the difference between 'real' and 'make-believe'

* Helping children understand new events, and the strong emotions that come with them, e.g. the birth of a new brother or sister

* Helping children to learn about the world, their own culture and other cultures

To encourage reading and storytelling, parents/guardians can:

* Build story time into the routine of each day. Allow the child to choose stories at bedtime. Parents/guardians should give their child their full attention during this very important part of the day. This gives the child positive associations with reading.

* Read with their child at other times of the day as children can sometimes be very tired if only read to at bedtime. Any time is a good time for reading or telling a story. Parents should bring a book with them everywhere and read to their child at every opportunity, e.g. while waiting for a bus.

* Reread stories to their child. Children often want the same stories over and over again. They often take comfort in their favourite stories.

* Include a visit to the local library as part of the child's weekly routine. Allow the child time to choose the books they would like to borrow. Using the local library makes books affordable for all families.

* Support the ELC setting's weekly request that a child to bring in their favourite story to be read at story time by ensuring that the child packs and brings a book in with them. This creates a link for the child with home and promotes the child's self-esteem.

* Provide writing materials at home for their child, e.g. pens, pencils, erasers, copies, notebooks, paper and colouring pencils.

* Encourage their child to make up their own stories or share family stories.

Reading isn't the only way parents/guardians can help their child's language and literacy skills. Telling made-up stories, singing songs and saying rhymes together are also important activities for language development and early literacy skills.

REFLECTIVE PRACTICE

Below is a list of top-selling children's books suitable for children aged 0–6 years. Choose one book to research. Why do you think your chosen book is so popular?

* *Not Now, Bernard* by David Mc Kee (interest level 4–5 years)
* *The Tiger who Came to Tea* by Judith Kerr (interest level 2+)
* *Where's Spot?* by Eric Hill (interest level 0–3 years)
* *Each Peach Pear Plum* by Allan Ahlberg (interest level 0–4 years)
* *The Very Hungry Caterpillar* by Eric Carle (interest level 2–5 years)
* *The Elephant and the Bad Baby* by Elfrinda Vipont (interest level 1–3 years)
* *Dogger* by Shirley Hughes (interest level 2–5 years)
* *Room on the Broom* by Julia Donaldson (interest level 3–6 years)
* *The Snowman* by Raymond Briggs (interest level 3+)
* *Hairy Maclary* by Lynley Dodd (interest level 2+)
* *The Gruffalo* by Julia Donaldson (interest level 2–4 years)
* *The Cat in the Hat* by Dr Seuss (interest level 3–6 years)
* *Meg and Mog* by Helen Nicholl (interest level 2+)
* *Would You Rather …* by John Burningham (interest level 3–6 years)
* *I Want my Potty* by Tony Ross (interest level 2+)
* *I Will Never Not Ever Eat a Tomato* by Lauren Child (interest level 4+)
* *Where the Wild Things Are* by Maurice Sendak (interest level 4–8 years)

Did you know?

Eric Carle, the author of *The Very Hungry Caterpillar*, died in 2021 aged 91. Carle's most famous book, which tells the story of a ravenous caterpillar, was published in 1969 and has sold more than 50 million copies. The simple but everlasting tale is just 224 words long and has been translated into 62 languages.

14.6 VOLUNTEERING TO PARTICIPATE IN SETTING ACTIVITIES

Component 3.2 of Síolta indicates that a quality ELC setting will provide 'a variety of opportunities for parents to be involved in activities within the setting, taking into account the range of parents' interests and time-constraints'.

Principle 5 of Aistear is concerned with promoting the role of parents/guardians as partners. Aistear explains from the child's perspective how this principle is realised: 'Remember that my parents and my family are the most important people in my life. Value their opinions and expertise.'

Parents/guardians have a wealth of knowledge and experience that they can bring to the ELC setting. Having a child's parent or guardian come into the setting to share this knowledge and experience can be hugely beneficial for the child's self-confidence and self-esteem. Such events must be planned well in advance as parents/guardians must complete Garda vetting beforehand and this can take several weeks. Here are some examples of when parents/guardians may be asked to volunteer to participate in setting activities.

* Accompany children on special trips away, e.g. to Dublin Zoo.

* Talk about their occupation, e.g. garda, nurse, builder, firefighter, farmer.

* Arrange a trip for children to their workplace, e.g. fire station.

* As part of cultural diversity activities, present cultural artefacts and speak about their culture or cook food from their culture for children to sample.

* Provide expertise to the setting, e.g. a parent/guardian with a keen interest in gardening could help children plant vegetables.

14.7 PARENTAL VOICE IN ADVISORY OR DECISION-MAKING ACTIVITIES

Parents/guardians are important stakeholders in ELC settings. It is therefore vital that their voice is heard in relation to setting policies and procedures. Some centres have a board of management with elected parent/ guardian members; others may have a parents' association. When an ELC setting creates a new setting policy or procedure it is very important that parents/guardians, as stakeholders, are asked for their input. Once a draft policy or procedure is agreed, the draft should be distributed to all parents/guardians for their comments and suggestions before it is finalised.

It is also very important that parents/guardians are empowered to communicate any concerns or suggestions they may have to the setting management. This can be done through a parents' association, via direct email or via a suggestion box.

SHOW YOU KNOW

1. Describe how parents/guardians can support their child's learning and development through engagement with ELC practitioners.

2. Explain why and how parents/guardians can communicate effectively with ELC practitioners.

3. Discuss how parents/guardians can encourage their child's efforts in learning.

4. Outline how parents/guardians can promote their child's language and literacy skills by reading to and with them.

5. Describe the benefits of parents/guardians volunteering to participate in setting activities. Give two examples of such volunteering activities.

6. Discuss how parents/guardians can be encouraged to have advisory and decision-making roles within the ELC setting.

Building Partnerships between Parents and Practitioners (Aistear and Síolta)

15

What I will learn

* How ELC practitioners can support families to feel welcome, valued and respected in ELC settings

* The importance of learning about different ethnic, cultural and socioeconomic backgrounds of children in ELC settings

* How to communicate effectively with families from diverse backgrounds

* The ways in which information may be shared with parents/guardians about the curriculum and children's learning and development

* How ELC practitioners can help parents/guardians to support their children's learning and development at home

* The importance of consulting with parents/guardians and how this can be accomplished

* The range of CPD opportunities available to ELC practitioners in the area of parental involvement

15.1 INTRODUCTION

Aistear's *Guidelines for Good Practice*, 'Building Partnerships between Parents and Practitioners' explains that 'Partnership involves parents, families and practitioners working together to benefit children. Each recognises, respects and values what the other does and says. Partnership involves responsibility on both sides' (NCCA 2009: 7). Increasingly, the early care and education of babies, toddlers and young children is shared by parents, families and ELC practitioners. A partnership approach between home and ELC setting is therefore vital and has huge benefits for parents, practitioners and for the children themselves.

15.2 SUPPORTING FAMILIES TO FEEL WELCOME, VALUED AND RESPECTED

Many new parents may have quite limited knowledge and experience of early years care and education. If they started their own education at primary school they will never have been to pre-school themselves. Supporting families to feel welcome, valued and respected is the most fundamental step in building strong partnerships with parents/guardians. Practitioners can do this in many ways.

* Ensure that the welcoming area of the setting is warm, colourful and inviting for parents/guardians. It is useful to have a 'parent/guardian zone' near reception where informal meetings can be held with parents/guardians at short notice.

* Many settings have an open-door policy – parents/guardians are welcome to call in at any time.

* Larger settings will appoint a member of staff to meet and greet parents/guardians at drop-off and pick-up. It is important that this person has a friendly disposition and knows all parents'/guardians' names.

* Noticeboards can be used in the welcoming area to display information, and photographs and examples of children's work.

* The word 'welcome' could be displayed in a variety of languages at reception. Ensure that the mother tongues of all parents/guardians in the setting are represented.

* Before a child starts in the setting, time should be set aside to meet with parents/guardians and allow them to meet all members of the staff team. At this meeting a parent/guardian handbook is useful to ensure that they have all key information. Time should be allowed for any questions the parent/guardian may have.

* Children's registration forms should capture important information about the child and their family. The registration form should include:

    * The child's full name and preferred familiar name and date of birth

    * Parents'/guardians' names

  * Parents'/guardians' address(es) (remember, parents may have separate addresses, so allow space for this)

  * Names of any people permitted to collect the child

  * Contact details, i.e. mobile numbers, work numbers and email addresses for parents/guardians

  * Daytime emergency contact details

  * Health information: GP details, special health requirements, known allergies, special dietary requirements, vaccination schedule

  * Consent for outings, holding of personal information, photography, first aid and medical emergency treatment

  * Other information, e.g. other languages used at home, ethnic origins, festivals celebrated at home, details of any other agencies working with the child

* Space should be given on the application form for details of any other information that could help practitioners assist the child when they are settling in, e.g. child's likes and dislikes, any fears, special words they use, comforters they have and when they may need them.

* Before a child starts fully in the setting, they should be given several short settling-in sessions beforehand. Parents/guardians may like to remain on the premises in the parent/guardian zone during this time.

15.3 LEARNING ABOUT DIFFERENT ETHNIC, CULTURAL AND SOCIOECONOMIC BACKGROUNDS

Principle 6 of Síolta is Diversity. Under this principle, 'Quality early childhood settings acknowledge and respect diversity and ensure that all children and families have their individual, personal, cultural and linguistic identity validated' (Síolta 2010: 7). Diversity is a term used to 'describe differences in individuals by virtue of gender, age, skin colour, language, sexual orientation, ethnicity, ability, religion, race or other background factors such as family structure and economic circumstance' (Síolta 2010: 7).

Several of Aistear's principles are also very applicable to this section. Principle 1, The Child's Uniqueness, states that:

> Each child has his/her own set of experiences and a unique life-story. He/she is an active learner growing up as a member of a family and a community with particular traditions and ways of life.
>
> (Aistear 2009: 7)

As with all Aistear's principles, it is then explained from the child's perspective as follows:

- I need you, my parents and practitioners, to share what you know about me with each other. By doing this, you can get to know me better and plan things for me to do that will help me to learn in an enjoyable and meaningful way.

- In order for you to understand and support me you need to understand my family background and community. This is especially important if I come from a disadvantaged or marginalised community.

Principle 2 of Aistear is Equality and Diversity. This principle is presented as a short statement:

> Nurturing equality and diversity is important in early childhood. Promoting equality is about creating a fairer society in which everyone can participate equally with the opportunity to fulfil his/her potential. Diversity is about welcoming and valuing individual and group differences and understanding and celebrating difference as part of life.
>
> (Aistear 2009: 8)

As with all other principles, this is explained from the child's perspective, highlighting the adult's role:

- Support me to feel equal to everyone else and do not let me be excluded because of my ethnicity, culture, faith/no faith, home language, family background and type, special educational need, physical appearance, gender, or ability. Recognise, value and accept me and my family.

- You may have to treat me in a different way to other children, to ensure I feel equal. Thank you for respecting my cultural identity and that of my family. Remember too that I may need you to help me to integrate into life in Ireland.

- Help me to learn to value social and cultural difference and to recognise that I live in a diverse, multi-ethnic society. Help me to learn to recognise and challenge injustice and discrimination and to stand up for myself and others.

- Remember that learning is more meaningful, motivating and enjoyable for me when activities and experiences are based on my skills, strengths and interests and when they are linked to my home culture and language.

- Help me to be open to the ideas, stories and experiences of others, and to listen and learn from these.

Quality ELC settings should demonstrate an understanding and respect for the diversity of people living in Ireland today. They can do this by promoting a sense of belonging, by celebrating each child's ethnic and cultural background and by providing rich and varied learning experiences that promote children's values and understanding of social and cultural diversity. To do this, practitioners must first learn about different ethnic, cultural and socioeconomic backgrounds. This may require practitioners to undergo additional continuing professional development (CPD) training. Practitioners need also to reflect on and be aware of their own beliefs, values and attitudes to diversity. Parents/ guardians are a very important source of information about their own ethnic background and culture. Practitioners should take time to talk to parents/guardians about their culture and customs.

CELEBRATING EACH CHILD'S ETHNIC AND CULTURAL BACKGROUND

* Invite parents/guardians into the setting to speak about their ethnic and cultural background. Ask them to bring in cultural artefacts to show the children.

* Find out about different cultural festivals and celebrate these in the setting.

* Ensure that toys and books in the setting represent a wide variety of ethnicities and cultures and that there is no evidence of bias or stereotyping.

* Celebrate children's mother tongue, if different from the setting's, by introducing new words to all children in the setting.

* Ensure that all staff use the correct pronunciation for children's names and those of their parents/guardians.

PROVIDING RICH AND VARIED LEARNING EXPERIENCES

* Cook foods from around the world for children in the setting to taste. Parents/guardians can provide suitable recipes.

* Children can be educated about different cultural and ethnic backgrounds by providing, for example, different cooking utensils in the home corner, different types of clothing in the dress-up box.

* Small world toys should depict people from different backgrounds, e.g. the Fresh Dolls range features dolls with natural hair colour and skin tones with realistic facial features for a number of different ethnic groups.

* Crayons and colouring pencils that represent different skin tones should be used, e.g. Crayola multicultural crayons.

* Books such as the *Little Traveller's Library* allow young children to travel around the world learning about different countries and their culture. This particular box set is translated into eight languages, each with a pronunciation guide.

REFLECTIVE PRACTICE

Look at the following table, which shows the country of origin of Irish residents born outside Ireland as classified by number of persons (CSO 2016). Each member of the class should choose one country from the table and research the ethnic and cultural traditions of that country. Information and photographs could be pasted onto an A3 sheet of paper for display in the classroom.

COUNTRY OF ORIGIN OF NON-IRISH NATIONALS RESIDENT IN IRELAND CLASSIFIED BY NUMBER OF PERSONS, 2016, CSO

Number of nationals					
1–10	11–50	51–200	201–1,000	1,001–10,000	Over 10,000
Andorra	Azerbaijan	Armenia	Albania	Afghanistan	America
Anguilla	Bahrain	Bolivia	Algeria	Australia	Brazil
Antigua/Barbuda	Barbados	Burma	Angola	Bangladesh	France
Bahamas	Benin	Burundi	Argentina	Belgium	Germany
Belize	Bhutan	Cuba	Austria	Bulgaria	India
Bermuda	Brunei	Cyprus	Belarus	Canada	Italy
British Indian Ocean territory	Chad	Eritrea	Bosnia	China	Latvia
Burkina Faso	Costa Rica	Guinea	Botswana	Congo	Lithuania
Cambodia	Dominica	Hong Kong	Cameroon	Croatia	Poland
Cape Verde	Dominican Republic	Iceland	Chile	Czech Republic	Romania
Cayman Islands	East Timor	Indonesia	Colombia	Estonia	Spain
Central African Republic	Ecuador	Ivory Coast	Denmark	Hungary	UK
Faroe Islands	Equatorial Guinea	Jamaica	Egypt	Malaysia	
French Polynesia	Fiji	Jordan	Ethiopia	Mauritius	
Gibraltar	Gambia	Kazakhstan	Finland	Mexico	
Grenada	Guatemala	Lebanon	Georgia	Moldova	
Guadeloupe	Guyana	Lesotho	Ghana	Netherlands	
Guam	Honduras	Liberia	Greece	New Zealand	
Guinea-Bissau	Kyrgyzstan	Macedonia	Iran	Nigeria	
Haiti	Laos	Malta	Iraq	Pakistan	
Liechtenstein	Luxembourg	Palestine	Israel	Philippines	
Macau	Maldives	Peru	Japan	Portugal	
Madagascar	Mali	Rwanda	Kenya	Russian Federation	
Monaco	Mauritania	Sierra Leone	Kosovo	Saudi Arabia	
Montserrat	Montenegro	Tanzania	Kuwait	Slovakia	

COUNTRY OF ORIGIN OF NON-IRISH NATIONALS RESIDENT IN IRELAND CLASSIFIED BY NUMBER OF PERSONS, 2016, CSO

Number of nationals					
1–10	11–50	51–200	201–1,000	1,001–10,000	Over 10,000
Mozambique	Nicaragua	Togo	Libya	South Africa	
Namibia	Niger	Trinidad and Tobago	Malawi	South Korea	
North Korea	Panama	Tunisia	Mongolia	Sweden	
Papua New Guinea	Paraguay	Uganda	Morocco	Thailand	
Puerto Rico	Salvadoran Republic	United Arab Emirates	Nepal	Turkey	
Qatar	Samoa	Uruguay	Norway	Ukraine	
Réunion	Senegal	Zambia	Oman	Venezuela	
San Marino	Seychelles		Serbia		
Solomon Islands	South Sudan		Singapore		
St Kitts and Nevis	Swaziland		Slovenia		
St Lucia	Uzbekistan		Somalia		
St Vincent's and the Grenadines	Yemen		Sri Lanka		
Suriname			Sudan		
Tonga			Switzerland		
Turkmenistan			Syria		
Turks and Caicos Islands			Taiwan		
Vatican City			Vietnam		
Western Sahara			Zimbabwe		
Former Yugoslavia					
Number of countries					
44	37	32	43	32	12
Total number of persons					
201	949	3,398	22,721	105,341	393,959

15.4 COMMUNICATING WITH FAMILIES FROM DIVERSE BACKGROUNDS

In April 2016, there were 535,475 non-Irish nationals living in Ireland, a 1.6% decrease on the 2011 figure (544,357). The proportion of the population who were non-Irish nationals had also fallen, from 12.2% in 2011 to 11.6% in 2016. This fall can in part be explained by the rise in the number of those with dual Irish nationality, who are classified as Irish in the census.

Just 12 countries, each with over 10,000 residents, accounted for 73.6% of all non-Irish nationals in 2016. In the next category, 32 countries with between 1,001 and 10,000 residents accounted for a further 19.7%, with the remaining percentage made up of persons from 156 different countries.

Sometimes communicating with families from different cultures and backgrounds can be challenging when their language is different from that of the setting and they do not speak English or Irish. Other parents/guardians in the setting can be asked to assist if they are more proficient in the English or Irish language. They can also be asked to help with translating documents, e.g. the setting's application form and other essential information. Practitioners should try to learn some words and phrases in the home language of children in the setting. It is also important to provide story books in a variety of languages or ask children to bring in their favourite books from home.

Collaborate

In groups, think about the ethnic and cultural background of the children in your work experience ELC setting. Use the internet to translate the following commonly used phrases. When you are next in your work placement, try out your new phrases – I am sure the children will be happy to help you with your pronunciation!

* Hello. How are you?
* Nice to meet you.
* Where are you from?
* What age are you?

* My name is …
* What is your name?
* Thank you.
* Have a nice day.

15.5 SHARING INFORMATION ABOUT THE SETTING AND CURRICULUM

Aistear's guidelines for good practice gives examples of how practitioners in ELC settings can best share information about the setting and curriculum. Examples of good practice include the following:

* Use a noticeboard to let parents know what activities children do on a particular day. This noticeboard should be kept up to date and current. This gives parents/guardians a clear idea of what happens in the setting each day, which can help them support their child's learning at home.

* Hang information sheets up on clipboards – parents can easily take a copy.

* Use pictures for sharing information with parents who have little English or Irish.

* Regularly send home photographs of the children with captions describing what they have been doing and learning. Photos can be easily and cheaply printed using apps such as Photobox.

* Let parents know about topics that interest their children. Find out what their interests are at home and build on these.

* Invite parents to share information about their culture and traditions that might be useful in supporting their children's learning and development.

* Organise information sessions for parents. Some of these might be especially important before and/or after children join the setting. A session might focus on Aistear's four themes and what you do to support children's learning and development in these.

* Explain that Aistear and Síolta are the main frameworks informing the work being done in the settings and guide them to where they can find copies of these documents.

* Develop a regular newsletter that provides useful information such as the words of songs and rhymes that the children are learning, important dates, updates on policies and procedures, etc. The newsletter can also be used to explain interesting pieces of child development and learning theory.

* Have a website where information about the setting and the curriculum offered can be accessed by parents/guardians.

* Have a members-only Facebook page, which can be used as both a communication tool and information source.

15.6 SHARING INFORMATION ABOUT CHILDREN'S LEARNING AND DEVELOPMENT

Aistear provides guidelines for settings and practitioners about ways that information can be shared with parents/guardians about their children's learning and development.

* Where possible, talk informally to parents on a regular basis as well as at parent/practitioner meetings. Encourage them to come to you for information.

* Share examples of children's work with parents and families. For example, make portfolios of the children's work. Organise open days and exhibitions to display and celebrate these. Send the portfolios home at the end of a month, term or year. Display children's work and photographs in hallways and change these regularly.

* Make sure that displays reflect the diversity of the families who use the service, including family structure, disability, Traveller and new community.

* Provide information and feedback orally as well as in writing, and in children's home languages where possible. Use email as well as printed notices, handouts and newsletters.

Use text messages to remind parents about special events and leave details on voicemail or answering machines that can be accessed at weekends and holidays.

* Share records with parents, in addition to the statutory minimum requirements under the Child Care (Pre-School Services) Regulations (Department of Health and Children 2006). For example, a practitioner might keep a daily notebook recording the baby's or toddler's physical care (bottles, meals, nappies) and achievements such as smiles, new words, friendships, and so on.

* It is important that practitioners are honest with parents and let them know about problems and issues of concern, as well as progress and achievements, as early as possible. This needs to be done in person.

* Let parents know that there is a regular time when a staff member is available to talk on the phone, e.g. during the half hour after the setting closes. This might be especially helpful for parents who are at work during the day or have difficulty in coming into the setting. However, it is generally better to have face-to-face discussions, especially if there is a problem.

15.7 HELPING PARENTS/GUARDIANS TO SUPPORT LEARNING AND DEVELOPMENT

There are many ways in which practitioners can help parents/guardians to support their children's learning and development.

* Hold workshops on children's learning and development, for example on learning through play. Give parents hands-on experience of some of the activities.

* Organise a variety of activities for parents at different times of the day and week to include as many parents as possible. For example, organise a crèche to allow parents of younger children to attend a meeting or another event. Ensure that people with mobility problems, literacy problems and sensory impairment can take part.

* Make a special effort to include dads. Building a relationship with them as they drop off and/or collect their children might help to encourage them to get more involved in their children's learning and development, and to come along to activities and meetings in the setting. Providing a crèche facility might encourage and enable both parents to attend a meeting or social event.

* Arrange social events for parents to help them to meet and build support networks with other parents as well as with practitioners.

* Collaborate with local adult education groups and encourage parents to participate in adult learning initiatives which can help to build their confidence in their own literacy and numeracy skills and in using the home as a learning environment.

* Ensure that parents/guardians are aware of the activities that their child is engaged in while attending the setting. In this way parents/guardians can be encouraged to extend these activities at home, e.g. if children are engaging in a cooking activity, the recipe for this activity could be shared with parents/guardians to be cooked at home.

15.8 CONSULTING WITH PARENTS/GUARDIANS

Standard 4 of Síolta considers the area of consultation. This standard states:

Ensuring inclusive decision making requires consultation that promotes participation and seeks out, listens to and acts upon the views and opinions of children, parents and staff, and other stakeholders, as appropriate.

It is very important that settings consult with parents/guardians in relation to decisions that impact on their children. This can be done in a variety of ways.

* Parents'/guardians' opinions and ideas can be gathered in simple ways. They can be encouraged to email the setting, a suggestion box could be placed in the reception area or they could be invited to evaluation meetings to get their opinions on the setting's curriculum and other setting practices and procedures.

* Parents/guardians should be consulted when the setting's policies and procedures are being created or updated. A parent/guardian focus group can be formed to work with staff on policies and procedures and when a draft is completed this can be distributed to all parents/guardians for feedback before the final policy or procedure is ratified.

* It is good practice to conduct an annual review. During this review all stakeholders, including parents/guardians, are invited to evaluate the setting in terms of what it is doing well and areas for improvement. When this process is completed, a plan for improvement can be agreed upon.

REFLECTIVE PRACTICE

The following is a list of common ELC policies and procedures. Interview the manager of your ELC setting to see which of those listed below they have in place or are planning.

* Care, learning and development policy

* Parents as partners policy

* Inclusion and diversity policy

* Healthy eating policy

* Procedures for children with special dietary requirements

* Behaviour management policy and procedures

* Rest and sleep policy and procedures

* Child protection and safeguarding policy

* Special education needs policy

* Complaints procedures

* Health and safety policy and procedures

* Late collection policy and procedures

* Data protection policy and procedures

15.9 SEEKING OPPORTUNITIES FOR CPD TRAINING IN PARENTAL INVOLVEMENT

There are several useful documents that provide additional information on the topic of parental involvement. Two Irish-based documents are:

1. *Parental Involvement: A Handbook for Childcare Providers*, Barnardos 2006. This is available to download from: www.barnardos.ie/media/1495/parental_involvement.pdf

2. Síolta also provides additional information on how to promote parental involvement in their Research Digest for Standard 3: Parents and Families. This is available to download from: https://siolta.ie/media/pdfs/Research%20Digest%20-%20Parents%20and%20Family.pdf

Each county has a County Childcare Committee. Search for your local committee and visit its website to find out what continuing professional development (CPD) courses they have on offer. Contact them to inquire if they have any courses on the topic of parental involvement.

SHOW YOU KNOW

1. Describe some of the ways ELC practitioners can make families feel welcome, valued and respected in ELC settings.

2. Explain the importance of learning about different ethnic, cultural and socioeconomic backgrounds of children in ELC settings.

3. Discuss how to effectively communicate with families from diverse backgrounds.

4. Outline some of the ways in which information may be shared with parents/guardians about the curriculum and children's learning and development.

5. Describe how ELC practitioners can help parents/guardians to support their children's learning and development at home.

6. Discuss the importance of consulting with parents/guardians and the ways in which this can be accomplished.

16

Nurturing and Extending Interactions (Aistear and Síolta)

What I will learn

* What characteristics of ELC settings place great importance on building positive relationships with children
* How highly effective practitioners:
    * Encourage children to help each other
    * Support children to resolve conflict
    * Model positive social behaviours
    * How highly effective ELC practitioners encourage children to play co-operatively
    * Promote children's thinking and meta-cognitive skills
* What adult-led activities are, the benefits of such activities and how these activities are best planned and implemented

16.1 INTRODUCTION

As you are aware, 'nurturing and extending interactions' is one of the six interconnected curriculum pillars of Aistear and Síolta. Aistear and Síolta both emphasise the importance of interactions to children's learning and development during the early years. Both frameworks offer guidance on how to nurture and extend interactions in order to build quality relationships. ELC practitioners play a very important role in this process. Babies, toddlers and young children need a secure attachment to at least one of the adults in their setting to make them feel secure and confident in their learning. Strong relationships allow children to feel socially and emotionally secure, creating an environment in which babies and toddlers feel safe and confident to interact, take risks, explore, participate in challenging experiences, and direct and co-direct their own learning.

16.2 BUILDING RELATIONSHIPS IN ELC SETTINGS

Building relationships is about supporting babies, toddlers and young children to be comfortable with and enjoy being with other people (both adults and other children) in the setting. When this happens, the baby, toddler or young child will enjoy coming into the setting and fully participate in all that is being offered there. Settings that place great importance on positive relationships will have the following characteristics:

* A low staff turnover so that children are cared for by the same people consistently.

* A key worker system where each practitioner works with the same small group of children daily. This allows them to get to know the children's personalities, dispositions, likes and dislikes.

* Where children have a key worker, this person will get to know children's non-verbal cues such as facial expressions, cries, body movements, gestures, sounds, touch and eye contact.

* Babies are cared for by one person with whom they have lots of one-to-one interaction.

* Effective practitioners know how to interact with young children – they ask open-ended questions, use comments to stimulate children's conversation, e.g. 'I love your pink coat!', physically get down to the child's level and give children time.

* Ensure that babies and toddlers spend most of their time with familiar groups of children so that they can build strong relationships and friendships with these children. Children will get to know their peers' personalities, dispositions, likes and dislikes very well, enabling them to get along harmoniously.

* Practitioners show babies and toddlers that they enjoy being with them by interacting in a warm, caring, playful and patient manner. Practitioners must always use a gentle tone of voice and use welcoming body language, e.g. smile and laugh.

* Practitioners maintain eye contact with babies, toddlers and young children while interacting with them. Be aware that some cultures do not do this.

* Practitioners know and understand the temperament of each child in their care and tailor how they interact with them, e.g. some children enjoy tickles; others are more reserved and do not.

* ELC settings foster positive interactions between babies and toddlers by supporting them to interact with peers and with children of different ages, including siblings, in pairs, small groups and sometimes in large groups, e.g. while playing outside on a warm day.

* Babies and toddlers usually play alone or alongside others up until about the age of 3–3½. ELC settings begin to encourage older toddlers to begin to play with each other by organising some activities that require co-operation and group work.

* Recognise and respect that while some children can successfully play with others they may still prefer to play alone at times.

* Involve babies, toddlers and young children in daily decisions that affect them, e.g. activities they want to engage in, what they would like to eat or drink.

* Interact with babies and toddlers during daily routines and care routines, e.g. sing to a baby while bottle feeding or talk to a toddler while nappy changing.

* ELC practitioners learn and use some words from the child's home environment to provide comfort and familiarity. For example, if a child calls the soft toy they bring to bed 'Wiggy', the practitioner should do so also. For children who use another language at home, they learn some frequently used words from this language to use while talking to the child.

* ELC practitioners support babies, toddlers and young children when upset by comforting them with soothing words and positive touch, e.g. a cuddle.

* ELC practitioners help children to develop resilience when things go wrong. They comfort them and talk through what happened, even with younger children, in a calm reassuring voice.

REFLECTIVE PRACTICE

Read through the characteristics listed above. Think about the setting where you are on work placement and the ways you interact with the children there. Reflect on practices in the setting and your own practices.

Extend your learning

Watch Wendy Lee's video 'The importance of relationships in building social competence' (2.43), available on the Aistear–Síolta Practice Guide website. Write down the key points that she makes about interactions.

Watch the video 'Developing a consistent interaction style in your setting (0–6 years)'. This video is just under four minutes long and explains how one setting got staff to observe and agree on the best ways to interact effectively with young children. Write down what they discovered.

16.3 ENCOURAGING CHILDREN TO HELP EACH OTHER

Jean Piaget believed that children up to about the age of seven are egocentric; they have difficulty seeing things from another person's perspective. Piaget would contend that children in that age group would find it difficult to appreciate that another child is in need and requires help. Whether young children are naturally able to see the needs of others and have a desire to help is not fully understood. What is understood is that adults can help children to understand that helping others is a very good and rewarding thing to do.

> If you want happiness for an hour, take a nap.
>
> If you want happiness for a day, go fishing.
>
> If you want happiness for a year, inherit a fortune.
>
> If you want happiness for a lifetime, help somebody.
>
> Chinese proverb

Did you know?

Aistear defines **dispositions** as 'enduring habits of mind and action. A disposition is the tendency to respond to situations in characteristic ways' (Aistear 2009: 54).

* Help children to develop positive dispositions such as kindness, co-operation, collaboration and being social. Give children opportunities to help each other and give praise for working and helping, e.g. 'You and Billy worked really well together in the sand tray – would you like to sit together for your lunch?'

* Have positive expectations. Say things like 'Mike is a very kind boy and likes to share his toys with his friends.'

* Be a positive role model. Involve the children in acts of kindness, e.g. if a co-worker has been out sick, encourage the children to help you make some cookies to help welcome her back. You are showing them **you** being kind. This is not the same as, for example, having them all make a get-well card. If you do this, you are not modelling kind behaviour, i.e. you are not showing kindness, you are telling them to be kind, which is not the same thing.

* Treat all adults in the setting and children in your care with kindness, gentleness and respect. This will encourage them to model this way of treating others.

* Help children to learn how to read other people's feelings, e.g. if a child falls down in the mud, say 'Sally is not laughing at what happened – look at her face. She looks sad and her clothes are all dirty and wet now.'

* Catch children being nice to others and acknowledge what they are doing, e.g. 'That was very kind of you, Sarah, to share your blocks with Thomas.'

* Read books to children that show kindness and compassion – see page 245 for some ideas.

* Avoid using comparisons or introducing competition – this only sets children up as rivals and goes against encouraging co-operation, compassion and sharing.

Thinking through what to say ahead of time can help children resolve conflict more easily. This also gives them confidence.

Role-playing with an adult can help. Having a safe space to practise difficult conversations can be very beneficial.

6 MODEL BEHAVIOURS

One of the most powerful things that adults can do to help children learn conflict resolution is to show them how it's done. When you experience a conflict, e.g. with a child who is acting out, put the techniques described here into practice.

16.5 MODELLING SOCIAL BEHAVIOUR

In Chapter 8 of this book we looked at Albert Bandura's social modelling or social learning theory, which shows that children are very influenced by what they see and hear around them. Social modelling teaches by example. Where children have good social models around them this is a very positive thing, but this is not always the case. Adults should be very mindful of the language, behaviours, values and attitudes that they display around children as children very often imitate what they see and hear.

Below are three examples from Aistear's *Guidelines for Good Practice* of adults modelling to support children's learning and development.

Effective ELC practitioners:

* Support toddlers by modelling and giving clear and consistent messages about socially accepted behaviour while having realistic expectations reflecting their developmental stage.

* Model respectful language for babies, toddlers and young children when interacting with them, their parents and other adults by saying please, thank you, sorry and excuse me.

* Model and give clear and consistent messages about appropriate behaviour and give immediate feedback to children, reinforcing, in a positive way, their actions and words, for example, instead of saying good job, we say, you did a great job helping to tidy the home corner.

REFLECTIVE PRACTICE

When you are next on work placement, listen and watch two or three children carefully. Can you spot any examples (positive or negative) of the children modelling the behaviours of adults in their home or ELC environment?

16.6 ENCOURAGING CHILDREN TO PLAY CO-OPERATIVELY

Co-operative play involves children playing together in a shared activity. It is the only type of play in Parten's six stages of play (see below) where children share common goals and objectives during play. During co-operative play children can be observed sharing resources, sharing ideas, assigning roles and coming together to agree on the rules of the play scenario. They learn important social skills such as negotiating, compromising

and working together for the good of the group. Lev Vygotsky and Jerome Burner believed that this type of play is incredibly important for learning and development. Co-operative play helps children to see things from others' perspectives and to incorporate other people's ideas into their own thinking on a topic. Children can learn from more knowledgeable peers during co-operative play. When children are required to work on a common play task with other children, they need to self-regulate. They cannot do whatever they want. Sometimes they must absorb disappointment, such as when they lose at a board game; delay gratification, such as waiting their turn; or allow other children to take on roles they would prefer so that the game can proceed.

Young babies learn very early how to co-operate, e.g. raising their arms so that their top can be removed. As children get older, they further develop these skills, beginning to play co-operatively with other children at approximately five years of age. To encourage co-operative skills, parents/guardians and practitioners should:

1. **Practise taking turns:** Babies begin to engage in back-and-forth interactions from about 6–9 months. These back-and-forth interactions are the building blocks of co-operation. Take opportunities to encourage turn-taking while playing with young children. Play back-and-forth games such as peek-a-boo with young babies. As the child gets older, practise turn-taking in everyday life, e.g. 'It is my turn to watch the TV now; I like to watch the news.'

2. **Practise working together:** Show children the importance of co-operation by giving them small tasks around the home and ELC setting. This helps children learn how to be responsible and co-operative. Do chores together, such as clearing up toys or setting the table. Once children are old enough, have them pick tasks that they want to be responsible for on a weekly or daily basis, and make them solely their responsibility.

3. **Teach empathy:** Empathy involves feeling compassion and understanding the feelings of others. Teach children to express empathy and act on this feeling. Talk to children about how they think about other people and their feelings, and model positive behaviour for them.

4. **Give plenty of opportunities for free play:** A good way for a child to learn co-operative play is to have plenty of opportunity to participate in free play with other children. Give children unstructured toys, e.g. cardboard boxes, which they can use to make things with and let co-operative play emerge organically. Also, give them their space. Let them work out problems, and don't over-manage. Children learn the value of co-operation with other children by playing freely, without adult-imposed restrictions and rules.

5. **Encourage co-operative activities:** Children can be encouraged to play co-operatively with fun activities and educational games. One example is putting a very large piece of paper up on the fence in the garden area and asking a group of children to paint it together. Sports and board games with rules help children to play co-operatively.

16.7 ASSISTING CHILDREN'S THINKING

Effective ELC practitioners help children to think about why and how things happen. This helps them to develop their own thinking and learning, which are **meta-cognitive skills**. Encouraging plenty of conversations in the setting with individual children, pairs of children or small groups provides excellent opportunities for children to think and talk about their learning. An effective practitioner will give the child or children they are talking to their full attention. They will listen attentively to what the children are saying through their gestures, behaviour or language. Display positive body language such as good eye contact, smiling and nodding to show you are listening.

The effective practitioner encourages children to describe and explain what they are doing, e.g. 'I am mixing blue and yellow paint.' The effective practitioner will encourage children to hypothesise and speculate, e.g. 'If I mix blue and yellow paint, I think it will make green.'

Practitioners can encourage and assist children's thinking by asking open rather than closed questions. Open questions encourage the child to think more deeply, whereas closed questions require only short or yes/no answers that require little thought.

Aistear offers some excellent examples of how adults can assist children's thinking.

* Help children develop language, listening and thinking skills by using the strategy of 'expanding' to extend their vocabulary by adding words or ideas to what they have said; for example, when a child says ball, we respond with 'Yes, that is a big, shiny ball.'

* Establish an atmosphere that encourages talk and discussion.

* Listen carefully to understand what children are thinking and feeling.

* Build on children's contributions, ideas and interests to extend conversations.

* Help children to use their full range of thinking skills.

* Pose appropriate, challenging questions.

* Help children to recognise their own progress and achievements and to build on these.

The adult may:

* Offer their own experiences, for example 'When I was young we ...'

* Think aloud, for example 'I believe that ...'

* Reflect back, for example 'You mentioned that ...'

* Make open-ended comments, for example 'I love it when ...'

* Speculate, for example 'I wonder why ...'

* Tell a joke or a funny story

* Ask for and act on children's opinions and ideas

* Use conversation 'door openers', for example 'I see', 'Hmmm', 'Really?', 'Tell me more', 'Can you ...?'

* Ask open-ended questions, for example 'What might happen if ...?', 'How would you feel if ...?', 'Why do you think that ...?', 'How did you learn that?'

By extending children's conversations and thinking in these ways the adult gathers information about their theories, ideas and feelings, and uses this to plan for future learning (NCCA 2009: 30–1).

16.8 LEADING, LABELLING AND DESCRIBING

Sometimes interactions can be nurtured and extended with adult-led activities. These are activities that adults initiate. These activities are not play, and children are not likely to see them as play, but they should be play*ful*. Activities presented to children should be as open-ended as possible and include elements of active exploration and imagination to increase and maintain interest and motivation for the children. As well as focused activities with groups of children, adult-led activities can include greeting times, story times, circle time, songs and tidy-up routines.

Adult-led activities should build on what children know and can do and should draw on children's known interests and themes observed in child-initiated activities. As with child-initiated activities, the practitioner actively uses a range of effective interaction strategies to support learning in the adult-led context.

The adult:

* Carefully **plans** and **leads** adult-initiated learning experiences

* **Describes** to children what they will be doing and learning and outlines how things work and what the 'rules' are

* **Explains** the reasons and clarifies why things are being done the way they are

* **Tells**, **interprets**, **hypothesises** and **thinks aloud**

* **Labels** items to extend children's vocabulary and understandings, e.g. 'We use a microscope to see things that are really small.'

SHOW YOU KNOW

1. Identify **eight** characteristics of ELC settings that place great importance on building positive relationships with children.

2. Describe **six** ways in which highly effective ELC practitioners encourage children to help each other.

3. Explain **four** ways highly effective ELC practitioners support children to resolve conflict.

4. Outline how highly effective ELC practitioners model positive social behaviours.

5. Explain how highly effective ELC practitioners encourage children to play co-operatively.

6. Describe how highly effective ELC practitioners promote children's thinking and meta-cognitive skills.

7. (a) Explain what is meant by 'adult-led activities'; (b) outline the benefits of such activities; and (c) offer some guidelines on how these activities are best planned and implemented.

17

Creating an Enriching and Inclusive Environment (Aistear and Síolta)

What I will learn

* The characteristics of a quality ELC environment in terms of:
    * Indoor physical layout
    * Indoor displays
    * Indoor resources
    * Outdoor physical layout
    * Outdoor resources
* What is meant by the term 'developmentally appropriate experiences'
* The importance of offering choice to young children in ELC settings
* Why it is important to provide an inviting, calm and homelike atmosphere to children in ELC settings
* Why having a key worker system is important in ELC settings where there are large numbers of children

17.1 INTRODUCTION

Síolta's Standard 2, Environments, states that quality ELC settings provide 'enriching environments both indoor and outdoor (including materials and equipment) that are well maintained, safe, available, accessible, adaptable, developmentally appropriate and offer a variety of challenging and stimulating experiences' (Síolta 2010: 19).

The environment provided for babies, toddlers and young children in ELC settings includes both the physical environment itself and the experiences that children have in that environment. The physical environment should be safe, accessible, available, adaptable, rich and diverse. The experiences provided for the children in that environment should be developmentally appropriate, children should be given choices, and all of this should be provided in an inviting, calm and homelike atmosphere.

This chapter will first look at the physical environment provided for babies and toddlers and children aged 3–6 years. It will then consider the learning experiences provided for in that environment. Finally, it will consider the importance of having a key worker system as a means of promoting feelings of security for children in the setting.

17.2 QUALITY ELC ENVIRONMENT FOR BABIES AND TODDLERS (0–3 YEARS) AND CHILDREN (3–6 YEARS)

As a part of the Aistear/Síolta good practice guide, practitioners are given two self-evaluation tools to help reflect on the quality of the learning environment, both indoor and outdoor, provided for (a) babies and toddlers aged 0–3 years and (b) children aged 3–6 years. These tools are very useful for seeing what a quality environment looks like and can be used by practitioners to assess the quality of their own setting and identify areas for improvement. For you as a student, working through this section will give you an understanding of how a quality ELC setting provides a physical environment for babies and toddlers that is safe, accessible, available, adaptable, rich and diverse. The self-evaluation tools break down the physical environment into five elements:

1. Indoor physical layout
2. Indoor displays
3. Indoor resources
4. Outdoor physical layout
5. Outdoor resources

As there is considerable overlap between what is provided for babies and toddlers (0–3 years) and young children (3–6 years), both will be listed here together. The material specific to the older age group is highlighted in blue.

INDOOR PHYSICAL LAYOUT

A number of considerations are relevant to the indoor area:

* It is divided into labelled play areas such as building area, messy play area, cosy area, construction area, pretend play area. For children aged 3–6 there will be a quiet area, library, mark-making and writing area. All areas should be labelled using pictures and words.

* Areas with similar activities are beside each other, e.g. the messy play area is near the sink.

* Babies' and toddlers' current interests are incorporated into it.

* There is enough space for young children to move around comfortably and to move materials, e.g. to move trucks from the pretend area to the sand area.

* The room layout enables young children to play alone, with an adult, or in pairs or small groups.

* It has cosy spaces where young children can relax on their own or with a key person with comfortable seating, for example to bottle feed, read stories or provide comfort. This area can be made more cosy by using fairy lights and curtains to corner it off

* There is a hidey-hole or den space where toddlers think they can't be seen. Toddlers enjoy crawling into this type of space; it can make them feel safe and it also appeals to their sense of fun – they can 'surprise' the adults by popping their heads out!

* It has mirrors at child height and accessible handheld mirrors.

* Toys, equipment and materials (natural where possible) are accessible to all young children, including those with disabilities.

* There are safe spaces for babies to roll, crawl and walk, with non-slip mats.

* There are rails, grab-bars and sturdy furniture that babies can safely pull themselves up on.

* There are slides, tunnels, boxes, steps and ramps for climbing up, though, over and into.

* The walls are painted in a neutral colour with no murals or strong colours.

* The area is well lit with as much natural light as possible and has a variety of indoor lighting – dimmers, lamps and fairy lights.

* There is good ventilation, for example windows that can open and fans or air conditioning for hot weather.

* There is limited background noise.

* It has a child-level sink.
* There is easy access to the outdoors so that children can choose to play inside or outside.
* Floor coverings have a variety of surfaces, such as cosy and smooth.
* There are soft furnishings such as rugs, cushions and tablecloths, and plants and fresh flowers.
* There are sleep rooms with observation panels, monitors, soft lighting and storage for mats and bedding.
* It has an appropriately equipped nappy-changing area.
* Low-level windows enable young children to look out.
* There is storage space with a name and photo for each baby's and toddler's belongings.

INDOOR DISPLAYS

Good indoor displays should reflect the families, communities, cultures and languages of all babies and toddlers in the setting. These displays help to make a connection between home and the setting. Displays can include photos from home and of children's experiences in the setting. This demonstrates to babies and toddlers that their experiences are valued. They can revisit them and enjoy these experiences whenever they wish. Displays can be wall mounted (at a low enough level for babies and toddlers to view), in scrapbooks or learning journals or displayed as part of learning stories. Displays can stimulate conversations and prompt information-sharing between children, practitioners and parents.

Quality indoor displays include:

* Photos of babies' and toddlers' families and others who have special significance for them, and their pets, displayed low on a wall, on 'cubes' or in albums.
* Paintings, drawings and photos of young children at play, displayed where they can see them. These should be dated, named and updated regularly.
* An information area for parents.
* Documentation noticeboards or display areas showing learning experiences, babies' and toddlers' backgrounds, cultures and languages and the local community. Children's artworks and constructions should be displayed here.
* Labels for materials, storage and facilities such as toilets, using pictures and words.

INDOOR RESOURCES

A good variety of materials and resources for children to explore, interact and play with helps babies and toddlers make choices about what interests them. These opportunities help them to develop into competent and confident learners. Aistear and Síolta recommend limiting the use of plastic and using resources made from natural materials where possible. Open-ended materials that can be used in different ways and for different purposes encourage young children to explore and to think. (Open-ended materials are items with no directions and can be used by themselves or with other materials.) They can be carried, lined up, redesigned, taken apart, moved and put back together in multiple ways. The child determines what materials are used and how to use them.

Aistear and Síolta outline that a quality setting will provide:

* A variety of equipment, toys and other items using as much natural material and as many open-ended materials as possible to support different types of play – creative, language, physical and pretend.

* Equipment and materials that reflect diversity, including ability, gender, ethnicity and family structure.

* Equipment for promoting Irish language, culture and heritage, e.g. CDs and traditional musical instruments.

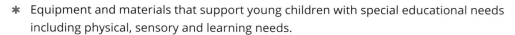

* Equipment and materials that support young children with special educational needs including physical, sensory and learning needs.

* Real-life items such as cups, plates, teapots, spoons, saucepans, dustpans and brushes, telephones, steering wheels, hard hats and props such as bags, shawls and shoes for young children to use.

* A range of play props for different topics, e.g. the mart, hairdresser, travel agent, café, North Pole, hospital and supermarket.

* Labelled storage for equipment and resources in a variety of textures, e.g. baskets and tins for young children to access. Storage in a variety of textures, e.g. baskets, tins and wooden boxes, so that children can independently find, use and return them.

* Treasure baskets containing items with a variety of textures such as toothbrushes, bath ducks, a soft ball, hair comb, pinecones, pastry brush.

* A range of paper, card, crayons, chalk, chalk boards, paints, easels, chubby pencils, paper, magazines and puppets to support babies' and toddlers' emerging literacy.

* A large selection of books suitable for young children, including nursery rhyme, pop-up, lift the flap, sturdy books that are accessible on low shelves, in baskets or boxes.

* A variety of literacy items such as:

  * Paper, cardboard, pencils, chalk, crayons, paint, notebooks, magazines, newspapers, leaflets

  * Wooden, magnetic and sandpaper letters

  * A large selection of books, including nursery rhyme, pop-up, lift-the-flap and factual books related to children's interests and current topics

  * Children's own created story books

  * Puppets, story sacks and other props to bring stories to life

Extend your learning

Aistear and Síolta have created a video called 'Supporting Emergent Literacy (3–6 Years): The Writing Table'. Watch the video and discuss how a writing table can excite children about writing and promote their emerging literacy and pre-writing skills.

* A range of clocks; wooden, magnetic and sandpaper numbers; blocks of different sizes; soft balls; and boxes to stack, sort, empty and refill, to support babies' and toddlers' emerging numeracy.

* A variety of additional numeracy items such as:

    * Weighing scales, measuring tapes, rulers, calculators, jugs, clocks

    * Blocks of different sizes and a range of boxes

    * Items to count, sort, pair, stack, order in a variety of colours, shapes, sizes and textures

    * Stories with maths-related ideas

* Instruments, CDs, wind chimes and shakers for exploring sound and music.

* Stable and slow-moving trolleys and push-along cars to support babies as they learn to walk.

* Push-and-pull wheeled toys such as hand-held cars and tractors, trailers and trucks for transporting objects.

* Natural materials such as sand, water, paint, playdough and gloop with accessories such as jugs, bowls, measuring spoons.

* Open-ended materials such as tubes, CDs, fabrics, switches, Velcro, padlocks, stones, corks and shells in a variety of textures, e.g. rough, smooth, soft and hard.

* A variety of materials to make indoor dens and hide-outs, such as fabric, sticks, pegs and cardboard boxes.

* Opportunities for children to use technology, including digital cameras and computers.

* A wide selection of materials and experiences to ensure challenge and progression in learning.

* Equipment and materials that are well maintained and safe.

OUTDOOR PHYSICAL LAYOUT

In order to promote babies' and toddler's health and wellbeing they should be permitted to play outside as often as possible. Some ELC providers have completely embraced what the outdoors has to offer, spending large parts of the day outside. Being outside gives young children opportunities to connect with nature and to experience different types of weather and the different seasons. Playing outdoors allows children to be noisier and messier, to play and build on a bigger scale and to practise their gross motor skills such as running and jumping, climbing and riding push toys.

Aistear and Síolta recommend the following in terms of outdoor physical layout for babies and toddlers.

* It is used daily by babies, toddlers, young children and practitioners.

* It enables toddlers and young children to play alone, in pairs and in small groups or with practitioners.

* There is easy access from the indoor playroom as well as from the nappy-changing areas and toilets.

* There is a tap or other source of water nearby.

* It has adequate storage for outside resources. Equipment, toys and resources are accessible so that children can independently find, use and return them.

* It provides protection from the weather, such as an awning or cover to provide shade in summer and shelter in winter.

* There are different interest areas, e.g. messy area, areas for wheeled toys, for climbing, building, planting, digging, with places to hide, to be quiet, to paint, to pretend; and it facilitates the movement of materials from one area to another.

* It has a safe space where babies can sit on rugs or mats and watch other children.

* It provides a variety of surfaces, including grass, and has an open space for toddlers and young children to run.

OUTDOOR RESOURCES

Nature is a great resource and babies and toddlers should be given opportunities to play outside to experience nature, rain, sun, wind and snow; and to handle natural materials such as grass, stones, sand and soil. Materials used indoors can be brought outside and used in areas such as sandpits and water trays. These resources will provide challenge for young children and support their developing skills, dispositions, values and attitudes, and knowledge and understanding.

Aistear and Síolta recommend that resources for outdoor play should include:

* Suitable outdoor clothes for babies, toddlers and practitioners – wellies, waterproof coats, pull-ups, hats, scarves, gloves, sunhats – with suitable storage for them

* A variety and sufficient amount of equipment, materials and toys (natural materials predominantly, and limiting the use of plastic) to support different types of play such as pretend, creative, language and physical

* Equipment and materials that reflect diversity, including ability, gender, ethnic diversity and family structure

* Equipment and materials that support young children with special educational needs including physical, sensory and learning needs

* Tunnels and boxes that toddlers can climb and crawl into and out of, as well as tricycles for pedalling and bicycles without pedals for balance

* A variety of materials to make dens such as fabric, sticks, pegs and cardboard boxes

* A variety of open-ended natural materials such as water, paint, blocks and stones, as well as sand and soil for digging and planting

* Wind-chimes, shakers and other materials to explore sound and music

* A texture wall or herb garden or space where young children can use their senses to explore

* Materials and items such as jugs, buckets, rulers, scales and mark-making equipment and books to support emerging numeracy and literacy skills

* A variety of literacy items, such as:

  * Paper, pencils, chalk, blackboards, cardboard, paint, crayons

  * Wooden, magnetic and sandpaper letters

  * Magazines, picture books, books about trees, plants, growing vegetables, birds and animals

  * Props to bring stories to life.

* A variety of numeracy items such as:

  * piping, jugs, measuring tapes, rulers, clocks

  * wooden, magnetic and sandpaper numbers

  * a variety of different-sized blocks and boxes

  * items to sort, count, pair, stack and order in different colours, shapes, sizes and textures

* Safety mirrors at the level of young children

* A space where adults and young children can sit comfortably to read a book or observe

* Equipment and materials that provide challenge and progression in learning

* Materials and equipment that are well maintained and safe

Extend your learning

As a class, watch the Aistear/Síolta Practice Guide video 'Creating Outdoor Environments for Babies and Toddlers (Birth–3 Years)'. Take note of all the ideas and suggestions given to enhance the outdoor space provided for children aged 0–3 years.

Watch the Aistear/Síolta Practice Guide video 'Creating Challenging Environments for 3–6-year-olds'. Take note of all the ideas and suggestions given to enhance the outdoor space provided for children aged 3–6 years.

17.3 DEVELOPMENTALLY APPROPRIATE EXPERIENCES

Principle 10 of Aistear is Relevant and meaningful experiences. As with all of Aistear's principles, this principle is presented using a short statement. This is followed by an explanation of the principle from the child's perspective. This explanation highlights the adult's role in supporting children's early learning and development.

Relevant and meaningful experiences make learning more enjoyable and positive for children. On-going assessment of what children do, say and make, and reflection on these experiences helps practitioners to plan more developmentally appropriate and meaningful learning experiences for children. This also enables them to improve their practice. Assessment is about building a picture of children's individual strengths, interests, abilities, and needs and using this to support and plan for their future learning and development.

This principle is explained from the child's perspective:

- Look at what I am doing, talk to me and listen to what I am saying. When I master something for the first time, take a picture of me or make a note of it and add it to my learning portfolio.

- Notice what I am interested in and what I can do. Record my progress and achievement in developing dispositions, attitudes and values, skills, knowledge, and understanding. This will help you to support my identity, respond to my changing abilities, interests and needs, and plan experiences which will enhance my learning and development.

- My parents and family have lots of information about me and they are interested in finding out what I do when I am not at home. They like to know how I get on with adults and other children, what I am interested in, what I can do, and how they can help me to learn and develop further. I need you, my parents and my practitioner, to make time to discuss how I am getting on. Sometimes I will need you, my practitioner, to show my parents what they can do to support my learning at home.

(Aistear 2009: 11)

To make this principle a reality, ELC practitioners must provide a rich and diverse indoor and outdoor environment (as described in the previous section) and observe and listen to children closely to determine what they are interested in and what their emerging needs are. In this way practitioners can build upon and extend the learning experiences being offered to the children in a developmentally appropriate way.

17.4 CHOICE

Síolta's Standard 1 is concerned with the rights of the child. To ensure that this standard is met, ELC settings and practitioners must ensure that children are enabled to exercise choice and to use their initiative as an active participant and partner in their own learning. Children must be allowed to take the lead, partake in activities that they personally are interested in, be permitted to problem-solve and be appropriately independent. Children should be encouraged by the adults in the setting to participate actively in daily routines, activities and conversations and must be considered as a partner in learning by the adult.

17.5 AN INVITING, CALM AND HOMELIKE ATMOSPHERE

The ELC learning environment, as described in section 17.2 above, can positively influence what and how children learn. An inviting and stimulating environment encourages and helps children to explore and to take advantage of opportunities presented for fun, choice, freedom, adventure and challenge. However, children also need to feel confident and secure in this environment. Therefore, it is important that the environment has a calm and homelike atmosphere.

17.6 THE KEY WORKER SYSTEM

Creating and developing positive relationships and attachments with carers outside the home in ELC settings is best achieved when children have a main caregiver. In ELC settings, this caregiver is usually called a key person or a key worker. Continuity and consistency of care in an ELC setting is critical in helping young children adjust to the separation from their parents and in helping them feel secure. Having a key person is one of the best ways to make sure that this happens, especially in settings where there are large numbers of children.

SHOW YOU KNOW

1. Choose one of the areas listed below and identify the characteristics of a quality ELC environment for children aged either 0–3 or 3–6 years.
   * Indoor physical layout
   * Indoor displays
   * Indoor resources
   * Outdoor physical layout
   * Outdoor resources
2. Describe what is meant by the term 'developmentally appropriate experiences'.
3. Explain the importance of offering choice to young children in ELC settings.
4. Describe why it is important to provide an inviting, calm and homelike atmosphere to children in ELC settings.
5. Explain why having a key worker system is important in ELC settings where there are large numbers of children.

18

Supporting and Meeting Children's Needs During Transitions (Aistear and Síolta)

What I will learn

* What is meant by a transition or significant event
* The types of transitions and significant events that children can experience
* The potential effects of transitions and significant events on the child
* Strategies that ELC practitioners can use to prepare children for planned transitions
* What is meant by the term 'reflective practice'
* Gibbs' reflective cycle (1988)

18.1 INTRODUCTION

A **transition** is a period of change from one stage or state to another. Babies and young children naturally pass through several stages as they grow and develop. They will be expected to cope with changes such as going from home to crèche, from crèche to pre-school and onwards to primary school. All of you reading this book have gone through these transitions. Recently you have started in college. Along with the excitement of starting a new course, meeting new teachers and making new friends you probably felt some degree of apprehension about this change in your life: What if I don't like the course? What if I don't know anybody? What if I find the assignments too difficult? Changes such as this are likely to affect you more if you haven't experienced many changes during your childhood and early adult life.

18.2 TRANSITIONS AND SIGNIFICANT EVENTS THAT CHILDREN CAN EXPERIENCE

TYPES OF TRANSITION

Transitions can affect all areas of development and they can be both expected and unexpected. Unexpected transitions are often called significant events and can sometimes impact negatively on children's behaviour and development.

* **Physical transitions:** Moving to a new setting, e.g. a new home, ELC setting or school
* **Physiological transitions:** Developing a long-term medical condition, e.g. a child who develops type 1 diabetes
* **Intellectual transitions:** Moving from pre-school to primary school or from primary to secondary
* **Emotional transitions:** Personal experiences such as parental separation, bereavement, entering foster care

Transitions can be either expected or unexpected.

EXPECTED TRANSITIONS

Expected transitions are experienced by most people and can usually be anticipated or expected. Even though they are expected they can still cause upset, albeit temporary. Examples of expected transitions for babies and children are:

* Being weaned on to solid foods
* Being cared for by someone other than their mother or father
* Progressing from crawling to walking
* Progressing from nappies to potty training
* Going to pre-school
* Going from pre-school to primary school
* Moving from primary school to secondary school

UNEXPECTED TRANSITIONS

Some transitions are not experienced by every child and not all can be anticipated. Examples of unexpected transition are:

* The birth of a new baby in the family; this is very common, but young children don't always fully understand it and therefore don't anticipate it
* Moving to a new house
* An unexpected change of school or childcare provider
* A change of key worker in the ELC setting
* Living in temporary accommodation, homelessness
* Parental separation and divorce
* A new step-parent and possibly step-family
* Violence or abuse in the home
* Serious illness or accidents
* Bereavement

18.3 POTENTIAL EFFECTS OF TRANSITIONS AND SIGNIFICANT EVENTS ON THE CHILD

How transitions and significant events affect the child depends on the nature of the transition and the event that has caused it. The effect will also depend on the child themselves and the support networks that surround them.

When a child is experiencing a transition, their focus is often on coping with their feelings in whatever way they can. Some children will enjoy the change and it will have little impact on their behaviour or development. Other children are less able to cope with change and may exhibit behaviours such as:

* Showing signs of frustration and confusion through their behaviour, e.g. a child may begin hitting or biting other children
* Regressing in their development, e.g. they may begin bedwetting or asking for a bottle again even though they no longer use one
* Withdrawing and becoming less involved in learning and play
* Withdrawing emotionally from new relationships, as they may fear that separation will happen again
* Clinging to and become more dependent on parents and/or practitioners

Some transitions and significant events, however, will have a profound effect on all children because of their serious and upsetting nature.

SEPARATION AND DIVORCE

Separation and divorce can leave the child with a huge sense of loss akin to a bereavement. When one parent moves out, they may feel as if they have lost one of their parents. This can be particularly acute if the separation or divorce has been acrimonious. Sometimes one parent tries to alienate the other (see page 204 for more detail on parental alienation). Some children feel as if they are somehow to blame for what has happened and experience feelings of guilt, e.g. if I hadn't been so messy/if I had worked harder at school then mum and dad would not have been fighting as much. These negative emotions may lead to emotional withdrawal, regressive behaviours (e.g. bedwetting) or negative behaviours (e.g. becoming aggressive). When children must move to a new house or area as a result of separation and divorce, this can cause further worry. They may grieve for their old life, miss their friends and can feel angry and resentful as a result of having to leave.

In cases where family breakdown was due to violence or abuse, children can feel a sense of relief and it can be a positive transition for the child.

BEREAVEMENT

The loss of a loved one, e.g. a grandparent, sibling or parent, can cause a huge number of emotions in a child. They will feel intense sadness and may be fearful about what is going to happen to them or that someone else might die next. Sometimes this happens when it is not a close relative but someone the child knows, e.g. the parent of a child in their setting. They may fear the same thing is going to happen to them. The child is likely to feel very confused about what has happened and why it has happened. They may feel guilty and blame themselves for the loss. Sometimes children feel angry about what has happened. All these emotions can manifest themselves in behavioural changes and can have a very profound effect on the child's sense of security and wellbeing. The child may become withdrawn, stop eating and/or sleeping or can become aggressive and unreasonable.

LONG-TERM MEDICAL CONDITIONS

When children are diagnosed with a long-term medical condition this can have a profound effect on them. They can have huge change to cope with, e.g. frequent hospital visits and new care regimes to get accustomed to. They may have to restrict the activities that they once enjoyed. This can cause sadness in the child and they may experience intense feelings of anger – why me? Why did I have to get sick? I am a good person.

BEING TAKEN INTO CARE

Being taken into care or foster care can be a very traumatic experience for children. They are being moved from the familiar to an environment that is unknown. They may feel frightened and angry about being forced to leave their home (despite there being an important reason to move). They may feel sad because they miss their parents and sometimes siblings. This change can mean a physical transition too. Children may have to deal with having to move to a new pre-school or school, meeting new carers and friends all over again.

18.4 THE ROLE OF THE ELC PRACTITIONER

STRATEGIES TO PREPARE CHILDREN FOR EXPECTED TRANSITIONS

Expected transitions, e.g. a child attending a new ELC setting, can be prepared for in advance and supported on the first day.

* Parents can be encouraged to prepare their child for this transition by reading books about starting pre-school and involving the child in preparations, e.g. buying a new lunch bag, or new clothes.

* Parents should stay with the child until they have settled and make it very clear to the child when they will be back.

* The child should be allowed to bring a comfort object with them to the pre-school, e.g. teddy bear or comfort blanket.

* One practitioner in the pre-school or nursery should comfort the child. Most settings operate a key worker system for this very reason.

* Contact the parent/guardian if the child does not settle within 20 minutes.

Síolta's Standard 13, Transitions, requires that ELC settings ensure continuity of experiences for children by having policies, procedures and practices in place that promote sensitive management of transitions, consistency in key relationships, liaison within and between settings, the keeping and transfer of information (with parental consent), and the close involvement of parents and, where appropriate, relevant professionals.

18.5 THE REFLECTIVE PRACTITIONER

We do not learn from experience. We learn from reflection on experience. (Dewey 1916)

WHAT IS REFLECTIVE PRACTICE?

The term 'reflective practice' was first coined by the American philosopher, psychologist and educational reformer John Dewey in 1916. Being a reflective practitioner is a very important skill for ELC practitioners. It involves thinking about situations and experiences and learning from them. There are two types of reflection:

1. **Reflection on action** is a retrospective process. The ELC practitioner thinks back on both the positive and negative aspects of an event or experience to learn about what did and did not work effectively.

2. **Reflection in action** occurs during the situation or event. It involves thinking while acting. It requires good observation and problem-solving skills. This type of reflective practice takes time and experience to develop.

REFLECTIVE FRAMEWORKS

Several reflective frameworks have been developed by different disciplines over the years. The most common one used in childcare and healthcare sectors is Gibbs' reflective cycle (1988).

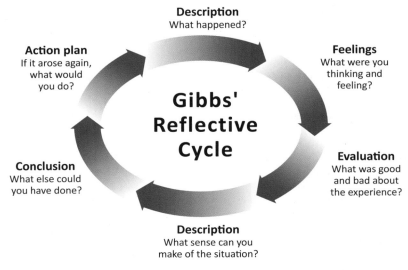

In order to use this cycle, think of a personal event or activity that you have been involved in and apply the above reflective steps.

Collaborate

Jenny is sick to the back teeth of her co-worker Sebastian. He arrives late, is frequently hungover and he hardly does any session planning, leaving it all to her. Jenny thinks it is so unfair. The centre manager, Justine, does not seem to notice or care. She seems to be charmed by Sebastian and doesn't say anything when he spends ages chatting to her in her office, while Jenny keeps everything going in the toddler room. Today she had enough and let fly at Sebastian, calling him out for the lazy good-for-nothing that he is. She raised her voice and frightened some of the children, plus got a severe telling off from Justine.

Imagine you are Jenny. Use Gibbs' reflective cycle to reflect on this experience.

Extend your learning

Investigate one of the following reflective frameworks. In what ways is it similar to Gibbs' cycle? In what ways is it different?

* Kolb's learning cycle

* Schön's framework

* Rolfe *et al.*'s framework

SHOW YOU KNOW

1. Explain what is meant by a transition or significant event.

2. Describe the types of transitions and significant events that children can experience.

3. Explain the potential effects of transitions and significant events on the child.

4. Outline the strategies that ELC practitioners can use to prepare children for planned transitions.

5. Describe what is meant by the term 'reflective practice'.

6. Outline the components of Gibbs' reflective cycle (1988).

Section 5

Child Observations

Child Observations and The Principles of Good Practice

What I will learn

* The purpose of child observation
* The five principles of good practice relevant to conducting child observations

19.1 INTRODUCTION

Section 4 of Aistear's *Guidelines for Good Practice* gives information on how ELC practitioners can support learning and development through assessment.

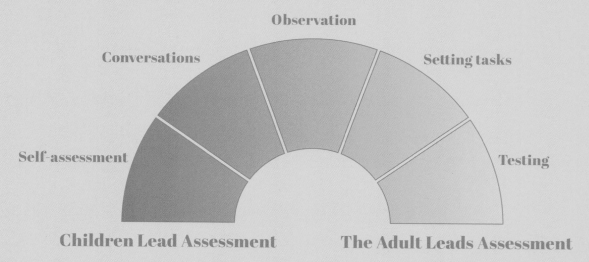

Child observation is one such assessment method. Observation 'involves watching and listening to children and using the information gathered through this to enhance their learning and development' (NCCA 2009: 87).

19.2 THE PURPOSE OF CHILD OBSERVATION

There are six main reasons why child observations are carried out in ELC settings.

1. To understand where children are in their physical, intellectual (cognitive), language and emotional development so that the activities planned are developmentally appropriate yet challenging for them.

2. To assess children's progress across Aistear's four themes – Wellbeing, Communicating, Exploring and Thinking, and Identity and Belonging – while paying attention to children's dispositions, skills, attitudes and values and knowledge and understanding.

3. To have a record of children's progress for parents or other professionals as may be required.

4. To be informed about individual children's developmental progress, perhaps identifying signs of developmental delay that may require further support and/or investigation.

5. For children exhibiting problem behaviour, to investigate frequency, possible triggers and how staff are responding to the behaviour.

6. To inform the layout and resource provision in the ELC setting, e.g. if you observe that boys are spending less time than girls in the book area, you might need to change the types of books offered to increase boys' levels of interest.

19.3 PRINCIPLES OF GOOD PRACTICE

There are five main principles of good practice when carrying out child observations: informed consent, confidentiality, objectivity accurate description and data protection.

INFORMED CONSENT

* Before you begin, you must ask for and get permission from the child's parent or primary carer to carry out the observation. Some settings require students to write formally to parents/guardians seeking consent (see sample letter on page 276).

* You should explain beforehand what the observation will involve and who will have access to the information gathered.

* If you are a student on placement, permission should be sought through your placement supervisor. They may then approach the child's parents.

* A parent or supervisor must sign at the end of each observation to show that you received permission.

* It is very important that everything that happens in the ELC setting is in the best interest of the children there. Children cannot give informed consent, but if for any reason you think your observation may be causing the child to become anxious or distressed you should stop. Look out for the following signals:

  * The child keeps watching you and seems inhibited from playing.

  * The child seems uncomfortable and looks or moves away if you get close.

  * The child says that they do not like you watching them.

* If the child asks what you are doing, say that you are watching them play and are very interested in what they are doing. Show the child your notebook and explain that you are writing things down. Patiently wait until the child returns to what they are doing before recommencing.

> ## REFLECTIVE PRACTICE
>
> Jacinta is under a bit of pressure to get her child observations done, as the deadline is fast approaching. She hopes to observe a little boy called Oisín today. As Oisín's mum is rushing out of the door to work after dropping him off, Jacinta asks her, 'Do you mind if I do an observation with Oisín today?' Is this informed consent?

CONFIDENTIALITY

As an acknowledgement of the rights of the child and their family, any information gathered while carrying out observations must be treated in the strictest confidence. In practice, this means:

* Never record the child's name or the name of the childcare facility where the observation was carried out. Instead, use the abbreviation TC (target child) and describe the childcare facility in general terms, e.g. a large crèche in an urban setting.

* Qualified ELC practitioners should not discuss observations outside the workplace setting.

* Students, however, may have to discuss aspects of their observations with their college tutor. If this happens, the child's anonymity should always be preserved.

OBJECTIVITY

The *Oxford English Dictionary* defines objectivity as a 'judgement based on observable phenomena and uninfluenced by emotions or personal prejudices'. For child observations to be accurate and worthwhile, they must be objective. As you get to know the children being observed, however, this can become more and more difficult. You must be aware of the following:

* Your previous knowledge of the child may lead you to interpret what you observe in an inaccurate way.

* Your own emotional response to the child, whether it is negative or positive, may lead you to observe in a biased fashion.

* The aim or purpose of the observation may distort your findings – you may begin interpreting things in a biased way in order to 'find what you were looking for'.

* It is not good practice to observe children when they are tired or hungry as this can influence what is observed.

Observers must make every effort not to allow the factors listed above to influence their observations. They must accurately record exactly what they see and hear. Some students ask tutors if they can carry out their observations for assessment on their own children. Tutors often advise against this on the grounds of objectivity. Can you see how a parent could have difficulty carrying out an objective observation with their own child?

ACCURATE DESCRIPTION

This principle of good practice is very closely related to objectivity. Everyday speech is full of inaccuracies and exaggerations – 'I nearly died laughing', 'She's driving me mad', 'He's a pain in the neck.' For child observations to be of worth, they must be as accurate as possible. Therefore, you should be very careful about how you record information, using only objective language. In particular, you should not record your own assumptions (what you think is going on), but only what is directly observable (exactly what you see and/or hear). Study the table below, which illustrates how observations should and should not be written.

SHOULD	SHOULD NOT
TC appears to be frustrated.	TC is frustrated.
TC appears to be looking at other children in the sand tray area.	TC is watching the other children playing in the sand tray. He would like to join in.
TC is holding a colouring pencil in his right hand using a mature tripod grasp. He is drawing small circles inside one big one.	TC is scribbling on a piece of paper. He can hold the pencil well.
TC pushes child B once with her right hand on child B's back. Child B is turning around, saying 'Stop, [TC]. Teacher, tell [TC] to stop.' Child B pushes TC once with his right hand on TC's chest.	TC is pushing child B because he is annoying her. Child B is well able for TC and pushes her back.

DATA PROTECTION

Two pieces of Irish legislation apply to the recording and storage of personal information such as child observations and assessments. They are the Data Protection Acts 1988, 1998, 2003 and 2018 and the Freedom of Information Acts 1997, 2003 and 2014. Both these Acts and their amendments concern personal data held on computer or in manual files by organisations, including ELC settings. In general, personal information must be:

* Obtained and processed fairly

* Kept for a specific purpose, e.g. applying for extra resources for a child with special educational needs (SEN)

* Used only for that specific purpose(s)

* Kept secure and safe

* Kept accurate and up to date

* Adequate, relevant and not excessive

* Not retained longer than necessary

Under the Freedom of Information Act individuals or the parents/guardians of children under 18 years have a right to access any personal information held.

19.4 SAMPLE CONSENT LETTER

Dear parent/guardian of [insert child's name]

My name is [your name] and I am on placement in [name of setting] for [dates of placement].

Among the things I will be learning about while on placement here is how children learn, develop and engage in social interactions with each other. To help with this, I am required to learn how to carry out child observations. I will be observing some individual children during the time I am here and would like to ask for your consent to observe your child. I would like to inform you that:

* You are free to give or withhold your consent.

* You can withdraw your consent at any time, without having to give a reason.

* You can see my observations of your child at any time and I would be very happy to speak to you about them.

* Your child's name will not be recorded on any observations. I will use codes, e.g. TC (target child) or child A, B, etc.

* I will keep my observations in a safe place where they cannot be read by other people. I will only share my observations with tutors on my course and with practitioners here in the setting.

Please sign below if you consent to allowing me observe your child.

Name: _____

Signature: _____

Date: _____

SHOW YOU KNOW

1. Outline six reasons for carrying out child observations.

2. Describe the five principles of good practice relevant to conducting child observations.

Observation Methods and Techniques

What I will learn

∗ A range of child observation techniques suitable for use in ELC settings

∗ Why certain types of observation are suitable for observing different areas of development and why some are used for specific purposes

∗ How to present observations for assessment purposes

20.1 INTRODUCTION

In the early education and care settings both Aistear and Síolta promote the use of observations as a method of assessment. There are many different observation methods. Which one you choose at any one time will usually be determined by the type of data you are trying to collect. In this chapter we shall outline some of the most common observation methods used in an ELC setting, explain the advantages and disadvantages of each and offer a sample observation to illustrate each method.

The methods described in this chapter are:

∗ Aistear's learning record

∗ Daily diaries or records of care

∗ Narrative

∗ Pre-coded method

∗ Checklist

∗ Time sample

∗ Event sample

∗ Movement or flow charts

∗ Tables, pie charts and bar charts

∗ Audio recordings used during observations

20.2 AISTEAR'S LEARNING RECORD

Aistear's learning record is used to record children while they are involved in daily activities and play. Usually a photograph is taken of the child or children while they are engaged in the activity. A brief description of what is happening is given and this is linked to the child's interests, dispositions, values and attitudes, skills, knowledge and understanding and also Aistear's themes, aims and learning goals. The learning record prompts the practitioner to think about how, based on what has been observed, they can help the child to learn more in ways that interest and excite them. Sample learning records like the one pictured below, and blank templates, are available to download at aistearsiolta.ie (click on Planning and Assessing).

SAMPLE OBSERVATION

1 **Look at what I'm doing** Include a short description and one or two photos of me as I learn and develop.	**Child/children** TC, aged 2.3	**Practitioner** Jenny	**Date**
	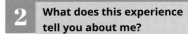		**Description** To add interest we added some spices to the resources for playdough, like peppercorns, cumin, cinnamon and crushed garlic. TC was really interested. She talked about the smells and the different foods they reminded her of.
2 **What does this experience tell you about me?** Think about my interests, dispositions, values and attitudes, skills, knowledge and understanding. Link to Aistear's themes, aims and learning goals.	TC loves food and smells. She talks about the smells and flavours at snack-time and dinner-time every day. We know her Mom works in a restaurant and she tells us about some of the dishes her Mom cooks at home. She shares her knowledge with the other children and in the home area especially, where she loves using pretend spices to serve wonderful dinners. C Aim 3, LG1; ET Aim 4, LG4; IB Aim 1, LG4 (C = Communicating; ET = Exploring and Thinking; IB = Identity and Belonging; LG = learning goals)		
3 **What will we do next to support my learning?** Think about how you can help me to learn more in ways that excite and interest me.	Extend the selection of herbs and spices we use with playdough. Add cookery magazines to the book area. See if we can visit the restaurant or have TC's mother visit us for a food-tasting session.		
4 **I want to show my family what I can do.** Let me bring my learning record home so I can share it with my family. They love to see and talk to me about what I'm learning.	**Parent's/guardian's signature:** _____ **Date:** _____ **Comment:**		

20.3 DAILY DIARIES OR RECORDS OF CARE

Daily diaries or records of care are normally used with babies, toddlers and children with special needs. They are used to record information about events during the baby's or child's day, e.g. feeding, naps, nappy changing, etc. They can also be used to record activities that the child was involved in during the day. Daily diaries or records of care are an important communication tool between home and the setting. They should be filled out accurately because the information in them sometimes needs to be used by parents/guardians; for example, if the child took ill during the night it would be important to know how the child was that day. Settings normally have a protocol for daily diaries or records of care, and these should be adhered to by practitioners. Below is an example of a record of care.

SAMPLE RECORD OF CARE

Daily Care Record – Baby Room
Little Rascals Crèche and Pre-school

What I enjoyed doing today   **Date:**

Key Achievement: _____

Nappy changes/	Time	Time	Time	Time	Time
Toilet visits	wet soiled ( ) ( )	wet soiled ( ) ( )	wet soiled ( ) ( )	wet soiled ( ) ( )	wet soiled ( ) ( )

Bottles	Time	Amount	Sleeps	From	To
	_____	_____		_____	_____
	_____	_____		_____	_____
	_____	_____		_____	_____

Meals

Breakfast _____

Lunch _____

Teatime _____

Snacks _____

Parent/guardian communication

Signature of ELC practitioner _____

20.4 NARRATIVE

In narrative records, the observer writes down exactly what the child is doing and saying while being observed. The child is usually observed for ten minutes or less, as it is quite difficult for the observer to record such detailed information over a more extended period. Codes are usually used to help speed up note-taking (see below). Observations should be written up properly from the notes as soon as possible afterwards.

CODES

In order to speed up note-taking while observing children, various coding systems may be used. One of the most commonly used is a system developed by Kathy Sylva and her colleagues (1980) as part of a pre-school research project. They developed a total of 30 different codes, some of which are listed below.

CODE	MEANING
TC	Target child (child being observed)
C	Other child
A	Adult (staff member, parent, student)
➔	Speaks to, e.g. TC➔A

SAMPLE OBSERVATION USING THE NARRATIVE METHOD

Date of observation: 29 November 2021

Time observation started and finished: 08.40–08.50

Number of children present: 1

Number of adults present: 1 staff member and 1 student (observer)

Permission obtained from: Supervisor

Description of setting: This observation took place in a registered childminder's home in a rural setting. While the childminder (and one co-worker) caters for children from six months to school-going age and also provides an after-school service, there are currently only one baby, two pre-schoolers and four after-school children attending daily. The facility is open from 8 a.m. to 6 p.m., Monday to Friday.

Immediate context: This observation took place in the playroom. It is a bright and airy room with a good variety of colourful toys available for the children. The observation began at 8.40 in the morning. TC is the only child in and has been there from 8.00, as his mother goes to work early. At the time of the observation, the ELC practitioner is sitting down on the floor sorting out jigsaw puzzles that have become mixed up while chatting with TC. TC is sitting on the floor playing with five small world figures: two Action Men (one dressed as an astronaut and one as a soldier), Gangrene (Action Man's arch-rival) and two figures from *The Lord of the Rings*, Gandalf and Frodo. At the start of the observation, TC is holding one Action Man figure (the astronaut) and Gangrene in his hands and has the rest at his feet.

Brief description of the child observed: TC is a male aged three years and one month. He has been with this childminder since he was six months old and is very used to the place, treating it like home. TC has two older brothers (aged 12 and eight) and one older sister (aged six). He is a very active, talkative child.

Aim of observation: The aim of this observation is to observe TC for a period of ten minutes in order to assess his cognitive development.

Rationale: It is important to observe children in order to plan developmentally appropriate activities for them.

Method: Narrative

Media used: Pen, refill pad

Observation

TC is sitting on the floor with his legs out in front of him holding a naked Action Man figure in his right hand and Gangrene in his left (earlier TC removed Action Man's space suit). He uses his whole hand to grasp the figures, as they are quite large. He is bashing one off the other as if they are fighting. TC appears to be giving a running commentary on the fight, saying, 'Gangrene, huh ah, Gangrene.' Adult says to TC, 'Ah, don't hit Gangrene.'

TC says, 'Is that, what, will you put this on him?' (Referring to silver astronaut suit.) Adult says, 'Yes, we can't have him going around with nothing on him,' but does not put the clothes on him – she continues sorting the jigsaw puzzles. TC repeats – holding the suit out to adult – 'Put this on him.' Adult says, 'You put Action Man's trousers on him.' TC holds out the suit again and says, 'I can't put this on him. This big style costume, this big one, I've got my suit on me.' (Seems to be referring to self.) Adult says, 'Yeah' and continues to sort jigsaws. TC bashes the action figures off each other again, saying, 'Oh buah, buah, buah, Gangrene, buah.' He asks again, 'Will you put his suit on him?' TC appears to be looking around for more clothes. Adult says, 'Will you help tidy?' TC says 'yeah' but makes no attempt to move. He begins to try to put on the action figure's suit. TC says again, 'Will you put this special suit on him?' When adult does not respond, TC says loudly, 'Do it, do it, do it … please.' (Seems to be getting frustrated.) The adult puts the suit on the action figure and hands it back to TC.

TC raises Gangrene and the Action Man with the space suit on him into the air over his head. He says, 'Gangrene can fly, whoosh, he can fly.' Adult says, 'Can he?' TC continues to play with action figures over his head, whooshing them over and back saying, 'De de ne, de de ne.' After a few seconds of doing this, TC drops the Action Man in the space suit and picks up the army Action Man and begins hitting him off Gangrene, again saying, 'Dah, dah.' He then begins walking around the room with the action figures still over his head, hitting them off each other and saying, 'Dah, dah, ooh.'

Adult asks TC, 'Which of them is your favourite?' TC says, 'This one.' (Appears to be looking at army Action Man in left hand.) Adult asks, 'Which one?' TC says, 'This one.' (Appears to be looking again at army Action Man in left hand.) Adult says, 'The one in your left hand?' TC answers, 'Yeah.'

Adult asks, 'Don't you like him?' (Referring to Gangrene.) TC says, 'No, he's bad.' Adult asks, 'Who is the other fellow in the silver suit?' TC replies, 'Superman, Superman!' (There is no Superman figure present.) Adult asks, 'So you prefer Superman to Action Man?' TC laughs and says, 'No, that's Superman and that's Superman.' (Referring to the two Action Man figures.) Adult says, 'Oh, right.'

TC jumps up and down, saying, 'De ne de ne de ne de.' TC goes quickly down on all fours on the ground and begins bashing the two action figures off each other again. TC says, 'Got you, got you, got you, Gangrene.' TC then drops the army Action Man and begins to twist Gangrene's arm (when you do this, Gangrene's head swivels – one side of the head is a smiling Gangrene and the other is ugly). TC swivels to the ugly side, saying, 'Gangrene yuck, Gangrene yuck.'

TC now picks up one of two *Lord of the Rings* characters lying on the floor and says, 'That's Lord of the Rings.' Adult appears to look towards TC and asks, 'What do you call that fella?' TC says, 'Gandalf.' TC examines Gandalf's white hair closely, saying, 'White man, he's a white man.' TC then removes Gandalf's hat using a pincer grasp, saying while he is doing so, 'Take off that hat.' TC then picks up Frodo (another *Lord of the Rings* character) with his right hand and begins to take off his top. While he is doing this, TC says, 'I'm going to take off their clothes.' Adult says, 'Will they not be cold?' TC says, 'No.' Adult says, 'Oh, I would say they might be cold.' TC says, 'No, they are fighting mans, they are fighting mans,' and continues to remove their clothes, saying, 'Now they are in their bare buff.' Adult laughs and says, 'Wrestlers, are they?' TC says, 'Yeah, in his bare buff, a wrestler.' TC then drops Frodo and picks up Gandalf again, saying, 'Gandalf, put your hat on.' TC puts Gandalf's hat on. TC then drops Gandalf and begins to get up, saying, 'Go outside, can I go outside?' TC runs towards adult, adult catches TC and begins tickling him. TC laughs. Adult says, 'Ah, TC's a great boy, isn't he?' TC laughs.

Observation ends

STRUCTURE OF EVALUATIONS

As with all reports, evaluations have a beginning, a middle and an end.

Beginning:

* State your aims.
* State whether you think each aim was achieved and why.
* Give a general statement of your findings.

Middle:

* Make three or four strong points.
* Describe what you found and back up each point with theory.

End:

* Restate your aim and summarise the points made in the middle section.

SAMPLE EVALUATION

The aim of this observation was to observe TC, a three-year-old boy, for ten minutes while engaged in free play in order to gain a better understanding of his cognitive development. I feel that I achieved this aim very well as I am satisfied that I observed TC very closely and recorded everything he said and did accurately and objectively. I found that generally TC's cognitive development appears to be within the normal range for his age.

Cognitive development includes the development of imagination, creativity, memory skills, concentration skills, problem-solving skills, sensory development and concept formation (Flood 2021). Some of these were evident in this observation. For much of the observation, TC used his imagination to act out or role play the battle between Action Man and Gangrene, his arch-rival. This observation illustrates Bandura's point (1977) about how children copy or reflect what they see, especially if it is violent. TC has two older brothers and it is therefore likely that he has seen the Action Man cartoons on TV, where Action Man and Gangrene do battle with each other.

TC's memory skills are in evidence in that he can remember the names of all the characters, i.e. Gangrene, Frodo and Gandalf. TC also shows good concentration skills in that he stayed at the same activity over the ten minutes and concentrated well when removing and putting on the action figures' clothes. TC was able to remove the astronaut's clothes but was not able to put them back on again. He made several attempts, but then realised that he could not succeed. He then asked the adult to help. This exchange was very interesting. The adult was preoccupied with sorting the jigsaws and was not really listening to TC. TC therefore had to solve the problem of getting the adult's attention so that she would put on the astronaut's suit. He tried to do this by changing the wording of his request each time. TC said, 'Will you put this on him', 'I can't put this on him … this big style costume, this big one', 'Will you put this special suit on him?' In the end, TC gets frustrated and says loudly, 'Do it, do it, do it … please.' He quickly says please because he seems to realise that he has been a bit forceful with his request. He shows that he understands that sometimes you must be persistent with adults in order to get their attention if they are distracted doing something else, but it is important not to be too demanding.

TC appears to have a good grasp of several different concepts. Gangrene is always the action figure on the receiving end of things, which indicates that TC understands the concept of good guy and evil villain. Also, when the adult asked him which figure he preferred, he chose Action Man, also indicating that he doesn't like Gangrene because he is bad. This indicates that TC understands that the villain is generally disliked.

TC also demonstrated that he knew what the concept 'wrestler' meant (a man stripped to the waist who fights), even though he could not think of the name. Vygotsky's concept of scaffolding was in evidence here in that the adult supplied the word 'wrestler', which TC used in the next sentence when he said, 'Yeah, in his bare buff, a wrestler.' TC's use of the words 'bare buff' again demonstrates how he listens to and copies other people.

Piaget's idea of animism, where children actually believe inanimate objects have feelings, may be in evidence in the observation in that TC acted as if there really was a fight going on between Action Man and Gangrene. Piaget believed that children under the age of four are not capable of seeing something from another's perspective, that they are not capable of imagining what another person is thinking, believing that everyone sees and thinks the same as they do. In this observation, the adult asks TC if the action figure (in his hand) is Action Man. TC seems to know that the adult already knows the answer to this question. Instead of answering, 'Yes, it is Action Man,' TC decides to play a trick and says instead, 'Superman and Superman,' laughing as he does so. It would seem as if TC knows that the adult knows it is Action Man but is asking anyway. While playing with Gandalf's hair (which is white), TC refers to Gandalf as 'White man, he's a white man'. TC seems to be able to recognise the colour white. Children begin to be able to name some colours from three years (Sheridan 1997).

In summary, TC's cognitive development in terms of imagination, memory, concentration, problem-solving and concept formation seems to be within the normal range for his age. The observation in particular demonstrated how children learn by copying what they see.

Personal learning gained:

* I learned a good deal more about children's cognitive development by observing imagination, memory, concentration, problem solving and concept formation. I observed how children can often understand a concept, e.g. wrestler, without having a name for it.

* I learned more about Piaget's pre-operational stage of development, but like many others, I question his finding that children under four are incapable of understanding a perspective other than their own.

* I saw the importance of Vygotsky's scaffolding in helping children in terms of cognitive and language development.

Recommendations:

* I recommend that adults should engage with children in conversations in order to fully support their learning.

* Perhaps this child should have less exposure to cartoons or films with a violent content.

References

* Bandura, A. (1977) *Social Learning Theory*. New York: General Learning Press.

* Flood, E. (2021) *Growth and Development in Early Childhood*. Ireland: Boru Press.

* Sheridan, M., revised and updated by A. Sharma and H. Cockerill (1997) *From Birth to Five Years* (3rd edn). UK: Routledge.

Signatures

Jenny O'Brien (student)   **Date:** 29 November 2021

Rita Shevlin (supervisor)   **Date:** 29 November 2021

Eric Falon (tutor)   **Date:** 9 December 2021

20.5 PRE-CODED METHOD

With language development observations, a pre-coded technique is often used. With this method, only what the child and those around them says is recorded. This makes this observation different from the narrative method described above, where everything the child does and says is recorded in detail. Codes (as described above) are used to enable the observer to accurately record everything that is said. A key to the codes is often given at the beginning of the observation. With permission, conversations may be taped for coding afterwards.

SAMPLE OBSERVATION

Date of observation: 15 November 2021

Time observation started and finished: 17.00–17.08

Number of children present: 2

Number of adults present: Parent and 1 student (observer)

Permission obtained from: Parent

Description of setting: This observation took place in the child's own home. The child's home is a detached house in a rural setting.

Immediate context: This observation took place in the kitchen. TC is seated at the kitchen table colouring a picture of *The Simpsons* cartoon characters. His mother is standing nearby, ironing. The observation took place at five in the evening three days after TC started school. TC's older brother is sitting on the floor nearby playing with Lego.

Brief description of the child observed: TC is a male aged four years and five months. He has been in an ELC setting since he was six months old and has just recently gone to primary school. He has one older brother (aged seven). Because both children attend a small country school, they are both in the same room at primary school. TC is a very active, talkative child.

Aim of observation: The aim of this observation is to observe TC for a period of eight minutes in order to assess his language development.

Rationale: It is important to observe children in order to plan developmentally appropriate activities for them.

Method: Pre-coded

Media used: Pen, refill pad

Observation Key:

A➜TC (adult speaks to target child)
A➜C (adult speaks to other child)
TC➜A (target child speaks to adult)
C➜A (other child speaks to adult)
M, N, O, P (other children)

CODE	LANGUAGE
A➜TC	Did you make any new friends at school?
TC➜A	Yeah, M and N and I play with them at lunchtime.
A➜TC	What sort of games do you play?
TC➜A	Mm, we play tag and duck, duck, goose.
A➜TC	What's duck, duck, goose?
TC➜A	Ya have to say duck and whoever you say goose to they're on and they have to try and catch ya and if you don't run quickly then they'll dus catch ya. I runned the fastest.
C➜A	And if you get into their place on time then they have to do duck, duck, goose.
A➜TC	I see.
TC➜A	Will I do this blue? (referring to shorts on Bart Simpson)
A➜TC	Yes, his shorts are blue, good man. And what else did you do? What's the best thing?
TC➜A	Eh, playing around at the yard.
A➜TC	And was there anything you liked doing in the classroom?
TC➜A	And we had to do a snake, I had to do little skirkles really tiny, I did them all big and messy. I thought you had to do them big.
A➜TC	Did you?
TC➜A	Yeah.
A➜TC	Did the teacher say it was messy?
TC➜A	Yeah.
C➜A	Yeah, it was the messiest.
A➜C	No, don't say that, C.
TC➜A	Yeah, she said she thought it was play school. (laughs)
A➜TC	What?
TC➜A	Play school.
A➜TC	And what about your friends in small school, little school?
TC➜A	O and P?
A➜TC	And do you miss them?
TC➜A	No.
A➜TC	Why?
TC➜A	Because they are going to my birthday, just ring up them.

A➔TC	Yeah.
TC➔A	Ring up them now.
A➔TC	But sure, your birthday is not for a while.
TC➔A	Tomorrow?
A➔TC	No.
TC➔A	When?
A➔TC	Not till March, pet, not for a long time.
TC➔A	Oh, can I go out now?
A➔TC	Yes, out you go, good man.
Observation ends	

SAMPLE EVALUATION

(See page 282 for a note on the structure of evaluations.)

The aim of this observation was to observe and record the language of TC, an almost four and a half-year-old boy, for eight minutes while he was sitting colouring a picture, in order to gain a better understanding of his language development. I feel that I achieved this aim very well because the conversation was taped and accurately transcribed. Generally, TC's language development appears to be within the normal range for his age.

By and large, TC's word pronunciation is accurate. He does make some errors, e.g. he says 'skirkles' for 'circles'. Other mispronunciations are more as a result of his accent, e.g. 'ya' instead of 'you' and 'dus' instead of 'just', rather than as a result of an inability to pronounce the words correctly. This is usual for his stage of development. While children between four and five years pronounce most words correctly, they 'may show some immature sound substitutions' (Flood 2021).

Children by and large master syntax, i.e. word order, in sentences by age four (Flood 2013). In this case, TC has managed to master syntax in that he makes only one syntactical error, saying 'Ring up them now' instead of 'Ring them up now'. All his other sentences, some of them quite complex, e.g. his account of how to play duck, duck, goose, are all syntactically correct. One of Noam Chomsky's key observations in support of his language acquisition device theory is children's use of what he calls virtuous errors. He believes that all on their own and very early on, children work out basic rules of grammar, such as adding 's' to pluralise a word and adding 'ed' to put a verb into the past tense. They then apply these rules even when they are not appropriate. TC uses one virtuous error during this observation when he says 'I runned the fastest', thus supporting Chomsky's theory.

TC shows a good understanding of the meaning of language, i.e. semantics, even when the speaker's exact meaning is not completely obvious. TC understood what his teacher meant when she criticised the messiness of his snake by saying 'she said she thought it was playschool'. He does not seem to be too upset by this criticism (he laughed). This is perhaps because he realises that he merely misunderstood what the teacher wanted, i.e. small circles, and therefore does not feel bad about his messiness. Or perhaps he is laughing because he is trying to cover up for his embarrassment?

In summary, TC's language development in terms of pronunciation, syntax and semantics seems to be within the normal range for his age. This observation also supports Chomsky's theory of language development in that TC used one virtuous error.

Personal learning gained:

* I learned a good deal more about children's language development. I now have a better understanding of the terms 'semantics' and 'syntax'.

* I learned more about Chomsky's theory of language development and have witnessed and recorded a child using a virtuous error.

* I have learned how difficult it is to accurately record speech and believe that in order to do so accurately, a tape recording with transcription is advisable.

Recommendations:

* I recommend that this child's parents continue to make time after each school day to sit down and discuss what happened that day. As Hart and Risley (1995) found, children who are engaged every day in conversation at home have an increased vocabulary and tend to succeed better in school.

* I recommend that this child's parents use open-ended questions when speaking to him. This will encourage him to elaborate on his answers and not just give short restricted answers.

References

Chomsky.info (website) <https://chomsky.info> accessed 2 December 2021.

Flood, E. (2013) *Child Development for Students in Ireland* (2nd edn.). Dublin: Gill & Macmillan.

Flood, E. (2021) *Growth and Development in Early Childhood*. Ireland: Boru Press.

Hart and Risley (1995) *Meaningful Differences in Everyday Experience of Young American Children*. New York: Brooks Publishing.

20.6 CHECKLIST

This type of observation uses a list of skills typical for the age group of the child you are observing. This method is most commonly used for physical and social development observations where behaviour and skills are easily seen. Suitable lists can be obtained from recognised developmental guides and textbooks. The source of the checklist should always be listed on the observation.

The observer observes the child, usually over an extended period of time, and ticks off skills as they are observed. If an item is ticked off, the observer should note why they ticked the item off, i.e. what evidence they observed that made them conclude the child could master the skill. If it is observed that a child has not yet mastered a skill on the list, then an X should be put beside that item, and again, evidence should be provided for this decision. If some items on the list are not observed, this too should be recorded (N/O).

SAMPLE OBSERVATION

Date of observation: 8 October 2021

Time observation started and finished: 09.30–12.30 (3 hours)

Number of children present: 3

Number of adults present: 1 staff member and 1 student (observer)

Permission obtained from: Supervisor

Description of setting: This observation took place in a large purpose-built community ELC setting. It caters for children from six months to school-going age and also provides an afterschool service. The setting is open from 8 a.m. to 6 p.m., Monday to Friday, and caters for up to 65 children at a time. Groups are divided according to age – babies, wobblers, toddlers, pre-school and after-school. Each group has their own purpose-built room. There is a large all-female staff.

Immediate context: This observation took place in the baby room. It is bright and airy with a separate sleep room attached. The room can accommodate a total of six babies, but today there are only three babies in. The room is supplied with a good variety of colourful toys.

Brief description of the child observed: TC is a female aged six months and one week. She is new to the crèche – this is her first full week in attendance. She is a large baby who eats and sleeps well. Her mother has her in a very good routine.

Aim of observation: The aim of this observation is to observe TC throughout the morning in order to assess her physical development.

Rationale: It is important to observe children in order to plan developmentally appropriate activities for them.

Method: Checklist.

Media used: Typed checklist (from Flood (2021)), pen

Observation

Directions:

Put a ✔ beside items you have observed and an ✘ beside those skills that you have observed TC cannot yet master. Put N/O beside items you have not had the opportunity to observe.

ITEM	OBSERVED?	EVIDENCE	DATE
Prone: can lift head and chest well clear of the floor, supporting with outstretched arms – hands flat on the floor.	✔	TC lifted head well clear of floor when she was placed on the play mat after nappy change.	8/10
Prone: can roll over from front to back and (usually) from back to front.	✔	Rolled from front to back when placed on a play mat – did not appear to try to roll back.	8/10
Prone: may pull knees up in an attempt to crawl but will slide backwards.	N/O		
Supine: will lift head to look at feet.	✔	Lifted head to look at feet during nappy change.	8/10
Supine: may lift arms in a request to be lifted.	✘	Does not yet do this despite staff member putting their arms out to TC to encourage her to do so on several occasions.	8/10
Supine: will kick strongly using alternate feet.	✔	Kicked strongly during nappy change and when sitting in baby bouncer.	8/10
Supine: may lift up legs and grasp one foot or both, attempting to put them in mouth.	✔	Does lift up legs but did not put foot in mouth while lying under play gym.	8/10
Sitting: held sitting, back will be straight and head firmly erect.	✔	After bottle, sits up with head held firmly erect.	8/10
Sitting: may sit alone momentarily, but is likely to topple and will not put hand out to break fall.	N/O		
Sitting: when hands grasped, will brace shoulders and pull themselves to sit.	N/O		
Standing: enjoys bearing weight and will bounce up and down.	✔	Bounced on carer's knee while looking towards the window.	8/10
Standing: may demonstrate the parachute reflex when held in the air and whooshed downwards.	N/O		
Uses palmar grasp to grab objects of interest.	✔	Used palmar grasp to hold small, flat, soft toy rabbit.	8/10
Transfers toys from hand to hand.	✔	Transferred toy rabbit jerkily from hand to hand.	8/10
Puts toys and other objects in their mouth to explore them.	✔	Sucked and bit down on toy rabbit.	8/10

SAMPLE EVALUATION

(See page 282 for a note on the structure of evaluations.)

The aim of this observation was to observe TC, a six-month-old baby girl, throughout the morning in order to assess her physical development. I feel that this aim was achieved very well because the observation was conducted over the entire morning and so allowed me to observe TC for a significant period. Generally, I found that TC's physical development was within the norms for her age.

In terms of gross motors skills, i.e. use of the large muscles of the body, TC can lift her head and chest up off the floor when lying in the prone position and did so when lying on the play mat after her nappy change. On the play mat she showed she was able to roll from front to back but did not roll from back to front. TC is making no attempt to crawl yet while in the prone position, which some babies of her age may do (Sheridan 1997). In the supine position, she does lift her head up to look at her feet and kicks strongly using alternate feet during her nappy change. While lying under the play gym, when she got tired of reaching for the dangling objects with her hands, she began playing with her own feet but did not attempt to put them in her mouth. This is not to say that she cannot do so, but rather that it was not observed at this time. TC does not lift arms in a request to be lifted, even when carer puts out their arms to her.

While sitting, TC's head is very erect and she likes to look around. I did not get the opportunity to observe whether she could sit alone or brace herself while being pulled to sit. TC does enjoy bearing weight on her legs and bouncing on the carer's knee while looking towards the window. Again, this is in line with developmental norms for a six-month-old, according to Flood (2013). I didn't observe TC demonstrating the parachute reflex. In terms of fine motor skills, TC used the palmar grasp to hold her soft toy rabbit. She transferred it from hand to hand using jerky movements and sucked and bit down on the toy to explore it. This is in line with the developmental norms as outlined by Minett (2005: 135).

At six months, the baby can now grasp an object without it having to be put in her hand, and she uses her whole hand to do so. At this age she picks up everything in her reach with one hand or two, passes it from hand to hand, turns it over and takes it to her mouth. In summary, TC's physical development in terms of both gross and fine motor skills seems to have reached most of the developmental milestones expected at her age.

Personal learning gained (make two points):

* I feel I learned a great deal from doing this observation. As this is the first one that I have done, I learned a lot about actually carrying out observations – how they are laid out, how you try to be as objective as possible and how you ensure confidentiality.
* I also learned a good deal about the physical development of a six-month-old. I would never have looked at this topic in such detail before.

Recommendations:

* Continue to provide plenty of toys that encourage TC's physical development, e.g. bricks to hold and bang together, nesting and stacking toys, paper to tear and rattle, objects to grasp that are safe to put in the mouth to explore.
* Offer finger foods – always under supervision – and allow babies to experiment with the texture of the food with their fingers.

✻ As long as babies are in a warm environment, give them time free from their nappy to kick their legs.

References

✻ Flood, E. (2021) *Growth and Development in Early Childhood*. Ireland: Boru Press.

✻ Minett, P. (2005) *Child Care and Development* (5th edn). UK: Hodder Arnold.

✻ Sheridan, M., revised and updated by A. Sharma and H. Cockerill (1997) *From Birth to Five Years* (3rd edn). UK: Routledge.

20.7 TIME SAMPLE

This method is used to get a general picture of a child's activities, social group and language interactions. It is sometimes used if staff are concerned that an individual child is having difficulty interacting with other children. The target child is observed at fixed time intervals, e.g. every five minutes over a 30-minute period or every 30 minutes over a three-hour period. For objectivity, time intervals must be decided in advance. It is a useful method in that the child does not have to be watched continuously. Observations are usually organised under predetermined headings, such as:

✻ Actions (what the child is doing)

✻ Social group (who the child is with)

✻ Language (what the child is saying).

SAMPLE OBSERVATION

Date of observation: 25 September 2021

Time observation started and finished: 15.30–14.00

Number of children present: 15

Number of adults present: 2 staff members, 1 student (observer)

Permission obtained from: Supervisor

Description of setting: This observation took place in the back garden of a large ELC setting. The setting provides an after-school service. All the children in the setting attend a primary school nearby and are collected from school and walked to the setting by ELC staff.

Immediate context: This observation took place just after the children's after-school snack. They have gone outside to play in the back garden of the setting. At the beginning of the observation, TC is standing alone at the side wall of the setting watching the other children play in the garden.

Brief description of the child observed: TC is a male aged five years and 10 months. He is currently in senior infants and is one of the oldest in his class. He is very shy and quiet and much smaller than many of the boys in his class. TC has learning difficulties and his speech is sometimes difficult to understand. TC does not often play with other children, and frequently comes to staff telling on other children, e.g. child X said a bad word.

Aim of observation: The aim of this observation is to observe TC for five-minute intervals over a period of 30 minutes in order to assess his social development.

Rationale: TC seems to be having difficulties joining in with other children, especially when an adult is not structuring the activities, e.g. during free play. TC frequently (every few minutes) reports to staff that other children have done something wrong, e.g. used bad language. TC also has several antisocial habits, e.g. picking his nose. It is important to observe TC interacting with other children in order to get a clear picture of what is happening so that a plan can be put in place to encourage TC to interact more effectively with his peers.

Method: Time sample

Media used: Pen, prepared time sample grid, clipboard

OBSERVATION			
Time	Action	Social group	Language
15.30	Standing at the side wall of the garden looking towards the other children playing in the garden.	On own	Not speaking.
15.35	Walking towards adult A, and then walking back to child A	Adult A, child A	'Teacher, child A (says name of child) has his roll, teacher, child A has his roll.' Adult says, 'Tell child A he shouldn't be eating his roll while running around, he'll choke on it.'
15.40	Standing watching a group of three girls making marks with chalk on the ground. TC is picking his nose constantly and putting it in his mouth.	On own near group of 3 girls	Girls are talking away among themselves but do not speak to TC, who is standing quite close to them. TC does not attempt to speak to them.
15.45	TC has joined a group of boys from his class who are running in a row up and down the garden.	TC is running in a row with four other boys from his class	TC is not speaking. The other boys are shouting to each other.
15.50	TC is walking up to adult A to tell on child A (same child as before). TC walks back to child A and tells him to go over to adult A.	Adult A	TC says, 'Teacher, child A said a bad word.' Adult says, 'Tell child A I want to talk to him.' Adult says to child A, 'No bad language, child A, now off you go.'
15.55	TC is walking around the perimeter of the garden, scraping the tops of his runners on the ground.	On own	Not speaking but is humming.
16.00	Children have lined up to go back inside. TC is towards the back of the line and is lightly kicking at the back of the legs of child B who is in front of him.	TC is in a line with another 15 children. There is a boy to the front of him and another boy behind him	Child B (in front of TC) turns around and says, 'Stop that TC, TC stop that.' TC smiles and kicks child B again. When child B turns around again, TC says, 'Sorry.' Child C, who is standing behind TC, says, 'TC, that's stupid.'

SAMPLE EVALUATION

(See page 282 for a note on the structure of evaluations.)

The aim of this observation was to observe TC over a 30-minute period (when the children had gone out to play in the garden after having their after-school snack) in order to assess his social development. TC seems to be having some difficulty interacting effectively with his peers, so it was therefore important to observe how he is interacting in a systematic way over a period of time so as to put a plan in place for him.

Social development essentially involves the development of three sets of skills: an ability to interact effectively with others, an understanding of the norms of society, and moral development (Flood 2021). Generally, TC seems to be having difficulty in all three of these areas.

At the beginning of this observation, TC is standing on his own along the side wall of the garden watching his peers playing together. He makes no attempt to join in. TC seems to have difficulty joining peer groups in play, especially if he has to interact or speak. TC was able to join his peers when they were just running up and down the garden. From about four years, children 'begin to try to work out how to integrate themselves smoothly into peer activities and to begin friendships with selected peers' (Flood 2021). TC is almost six years old and does not seem to be able to do this very successfully yet.

TC does understand the rules of the setting and frequently tells on others if they break them. He is very much at Piaget's heteronomous stage of morality, where everything is black and white and rules are handed down from on high, in this case from the practitioners in the setting. During this observation, he went to the teacher and told on another child twice. He reported the first time that a child was eating a roll while running in the garden and the second time that they had said a bad word. This is very usual behaviour for TC and makes him unpopular with his peers. Wentzel and Asher (1995), after interviewing large groups of schoolchildren, found that children can be categorised into five different peer group statuses – popular, average, neglected, rejected and controversial children. TC would probably fall into the 'rejected' category. This may be because he constantly tells on others and does not understand some social norms (see below). This would fit with Wentzel and Asher's (1995) description of rejected children. They found in general that rejected children find it difficult to consider things from someone else's perspective (TC does not consider what it is like to be told on), cannot process social information (TC acts inappropriately, kicking the child in front of him in the line and then smiling) and are not able to regulate their emotions. While TC did not cry or get angry during this observation, he often does.

Social norms 'are descriptions or "rules" about people's behaviour, beliefs, attitudes and values within a society or social group' (Flood 2021). Using a tissue to clean your nose is a social norm in our society. TC does not seem to understand this and picks his nose quite openly, much to the annoyance of his peers.

In general, TC's social development seems to be somewhat behind the norms for his age group. He seems to have difficulty interacting appropriately with his peers or joining in with games. He seems to try to get peer attention the wrong way, e.g. kicking them. He does not seem to understand some societal norms, e.g. cleaning your nose in a tissue. TC does understand rules, but sees them in a very black and white manner. Any time one of his peers breaks a rule, TC feels that he should report it to the adult on duty. This is making him unpopular with his peers.

Personal learning gained:

* I learned a good deal more about children's social development. I learned that social development is composed of three elements: interacting with others, understanding the norms of society, and moral development. Before this, I would have thought social development meant interacting with peers only.

* I learned about the importance of objectively observing children. Through observation, important issues can be highlighted more precisely, and a plan put in place to help the child develop the skills they need.

* I learned about Piaget's theory of moral development. He proposed that morality develops in two stages and that children under seven years are generally at stage one – heteronomous morality.

Recommendations:

* TC is almost six years of age but is not yet very good at integrating himself into peer activities. Perhaps TC could be taught this skill directly, e.g. using social stories.

* Practitioners should reinforce social norms with TC, e.g. telling him to use a tissue for his nose.

References

* Flood, E. (2021) *Growth and Development in Early Childhood*. Ireland: Boru Press.

* Santrock, J. (2009) *Child Development* (12th edn). New York: McGraw-Hill.

* Wentzel, K. and Asher, S. (1995) 'The academic lives of neglected, rejected, popular and controversial children', *Child Development* 66: 754–63.

20.8 EVENT SAMPLE

'That child is always pulling toys off other kids'; 'He is forever hitting the rest of them'; 'She spits at the others if she doesn't get her own way.' Sometimes children are described like this because they behave in an unacceptable way in the ELC setting. However, while general statements like this may frequently be made by staff, they are not helpful and can label children unfairly. Children whose behaviour is causing concern should be observed systematically and an accurate picture of what is actually going on arrived at. Event sampling is an observation method designed to do just this.

Event sample observations:

* Define the behaviour that is causing concern before the observation begins.
* Record the behaviour each time it occurs.
* Record whether the behaviour was provoked or unprovoked.
* Record what happened immediately before the behaviour occurred – this allows staff to investigate whether there is something triggering the behaviour. This is called the antecedent, but it may not always be known.
* Record what the consequences were for the child concerned – this can allow staff to assess how effectively they are dealing with the behaviour.

SAMPLE OBSERVATION

Date of observation: 13 January 2022

Time observation started and finished: 09.00–12.30

Number of children present: 10

Number of adults present: 3; 2 staff and 1 student (observer)

Permission obtained from: Supervisor

Description of setting: This observation took place during the morning session in a large, private, purpose-built ELC setting in an urban area. It caters for children from six months to school-going age and also provides an after-school service. The setting is open from 8 a.m. to 6 p.m., Monday to Friday, and caters for up to 65 children at a time. Groups are divided according to age – babies, wobblers, toddlers, pre-school and after-school. Each group has their own purpose-built room. There is a large all-female staff.

Immediate context: This observation took place during the morning session in the wobbler room. This is a large airy room with plenty of colourful toys. There is a separate sleep room attached. The room can accommodate a total of ten children and there are ten in today. This is generally the case – there are six children who are here every day and four others who rotate depending on what day it is.

Brief description of the child observed: TC is a female aged 28 months. She is large for her age and very active. TC's mother has recently had twin boys (they are now three months old). TC has continued in the setting during her mother's maternity leave. While TC's passive vocabulary is extensive, her active vocabulary is limited, and she uses only a few words at present. In recent weeks, TC has developed a tendency to be quite rough with the other children. She tends to push, grab and pull toys off them as well as hit and bite.

Aim of observation: The aim of this observation is to observe TC during the morning session in order to assess her emotional development.

Rationale: In recent weeks, TC has begun behaving in an unacceptable manner towards the other children in the room. She pushes other children, pulls toys off them, frequently hits out and sometimes bites. Staff members are concerned about this and wish to observe TC in order to assess what is triggering this behaviour and how it is being dealt with.

Method: Event sample

Media used: Pen, prepared event sample grid, clipboard.

OBSERVATION					
Date	Time	P/UP*	Antecedent	Description of behaviour	Consequence
13/1	9.22	UP	Child L is sitting alone playing with the shape sorter.	TC walks over to child L and pulls the shape sorter off her. Child L stands up and tries to resist. TC pushes her and she falls back to the floor. Child L begins to cry.	Adult A walks over and takes the shape sorter from TC, saying, 'Don't push. You have to wait until child L is finished, TC.' TC jumps up and down saying, 'No' and then lies face down on the floor, crying.
13/1	10.19	UP	Three children are playing with Duplo on the floor.	TC sits with the three children. Shortly after joining them, she begins to scatter and throw the Duplo.	A goes over and says, 'No, don't throw the bricks, TC, you could hit someone and hurt them.' A puts the Duplo back in a pile and takes TC with her by the hand. TC resists, saying, 'No.' A lets go of TC after a few minutes and she returns to the blocks.
13/1	10.21	P	Child M says, 'No, TC, go away' and pushes her away from the Duplo.	TC begins fighting with child M, pinching her face.	A walks quickly over and says, 'No, TC, that is not nice. You have to sit on the thinking chair.' TC says, 'No, no , no.' A takes TC to the bold mat and tries to get TC to sit on it. TC begins to cry and will not stay on the mat. A stays with TC until she has calmed down. A says, 'You can't pinch, you must not pinch, no, no.'
13/1	11.00	UP	The children are having their snack around a large round table. Ham sandwiches with juice.	TC begins sticking her fingers into child O's sandwich.	A says, 'No, TC, don't do that, child O wants to eat that.' A moves TC over beside her.
13/1	11.15	UP	Child N is playing with a doll and pram. She is pretending the doll is asleep.	TC walks up to child N and tries to pull the pram off her. Child N resists and TC bites her (lightly) on the arm where she is holding the pram. Child N cries loudly.	A immediately walks over to child N and begins to comfort her. A second adult (A2) comes over and speaks loudly to TC. 'That is very, very bold, TC, you have hurt child N, that is very bold, TC.' A2 walks away with TC while the other staff member continues to comfort child N.
13/1	12.06	UP	Two children and TC are at the water tray.	TC begins fighting over a blue plastic jug with child L. Child L resists, saying, 'No.' TC pulls harder and gets the jug off child L. TC then strikes child L on the arm with the jug.	A takes the jug off TC and says, 'That's not nice, TC, now come away from the water.' A takes TC away from the water. TC resists, crying. A persists and takes TC over to the bold mat, putting her back on it each time she tries to get off it. A explains to TC that we have to use nice words and kind hands.

* P/UP means provoked/unprovoked.

SAMPLE EVALUATION

(See page 282 for a note on the structure of evaluations.)

The aim of this observation was to observe TC over the course of the morning in order to assess her emotional development. I feel that this aim was achieved very well as TC was observed very closely over a full morning and all incidents accurately and objectively recorded. TC's behaviour of late has been causing some concern in that she seems to be frequently pushing other children, pulling toys off them, hitting out and sometimes even biting them. This observation seeks to observe how often this behaviour does actually occur, what, if anything, is triggering it and also how TC's behaviour is being dealt with by staff. Over the course of the morning, TC was engaged in a total of five incidents where she wanted something another child had and tried to take it by force. Piaget believed that children under the age of two are cognitively egocentric in that they find it difficult to see something from another person's perspective. TC is just over two years so this could explain why TC does not seem to take the feelings of her peers into account, e.g. pulling the shape sorter off child L, pinching child M, biting and pulling the pram off child N and taking the blue plastic jug off child L. Having said this, at the minute TC does seem to behave like this more than the other children in the room, who are all the same age. This could be TC's emotional response to her mother recently having twin boys, taking her emotional confusion out on the children in the setting.

Staff for the most part respond to TC's behaviour from a care perspective:

> In addition, it is important that pre-schools and schools advocate a care perspective for the promotion of moral development. Such a perspective concentrates on educating children about the importance of engaging in pro-social behaviours such as considering the feelings of others, being sensitive to the needs of others and helping each other. (Flood 2013)

Examples of where staff use a care perspective in this observation are when TC throws the bricks, the staff member says, 'No, don't throw bricks, TC, you could hit someone and hurt them'; and when TC bites child N and the staff member says, 'That is very, very bold, TC, you have hurt child N, that is very bold, TC.'

Having said this, the language staff use towards TC is somewhat negative, e.g. 'That's bold, you will have to go on the bold mat,' and so on. Perhaps staff could say something like 'No, TC, biting hurts, we never bite.' Settings sometimes use a thinking chair now instead of a bold mat or naughty mat or step.

Hoffman (1970) suggests that induction should be used as a discipline technique with children. This is where the adult reasons with the child and explains the consequences of their actions. Induction is similar to the care perspective described above. Induction, while it was used during this observation, was not always used. At times a more behaviourist approach (punishment) was used, such as when TC was made to sit on the bold mat or when the adult spoke loudly to TC after she bit child N. This could be because TC is quite young and perhaps staff felt she might not understand them if a short, simple message was not given. TC's language is quite limited. During this observation her responses were limited to single words, e.g. 'no'. This may be one of the reasons why TC is acting the way she is. If TC is angry, jealous or confused about the situation at home, she is not able to express her emotions through words and is therefore acting out instead. Of course, this may not be the reason for her actions. It is not possible to tell for sure because she cannot yet speak for herself.

In summary, TC does seem to be angry and frustrated at the minute. This could be as a result of the recent changes in her family structure and the inevitable reduction in the amount of attention she is getting there. Staff in the crèche are for the most part dealing with TC's behaviour from an appropriate care perspective and using induction as a discipline technique.

Personal learning:

 * I learned how important it is to objectively observe children to get an accurate picture of what is actually happening in the childcare setting.

 * I learned that when children act in a way that hurts or may hurt others, adults should adopt a care perspective and use induction as a discipline technique. This way, the child learns to consider things from someone else's point of view.

 * I learned that language helps emotional expression and that while their language skills are still developing, children may act out their emotions.

Recommendations:

 * Perhaps it is not a good idea to use negative language like 'That is bold' with young children. It might be better to word things in a positive way, e.g. 'You must be nice.' Although with something as serious as biting it is understandable that staff feel the need to be stern with TC.

 * Staff must watch TC carefully while she is going through this emotional time as it is not acceptable for her to hurt other children in the setting. Staff should, however, be careful not to treat TC in an overly negative way.

 * Perhaps staff could make time to spend on one-to-one activities with TC. The fact that her mother has just had twin boys probably means that TC is not now getting the attention she was used to at home and may be feeling a little left out.

References

* Flood, E. (2013) *Child Development for Students in Ireland* (2nd edn). Dublin: Gill & Macmillan.

 * Hoffman, M. (1970) 'Moral Development', in M. Bornstein (ed.), *Manual of Child Psychology* (3rd edn., Vol. 2). New York: Wiley.

20.9 MOVEMENT OR FLOW CHARTS

As the name suggests, movement or flow charts record a child's movements within the childcare setting over a specified period of time. They are generally used to track or monitor a child's use of equipment and resources. When complete, flow charts show at a glance how a child spent their day. Sometimes a number of flow charts are carried out with different children to discover what toys and activities are most and least preferred. It can also be used to observe children's concentration levels. Sometimes the findings of the flow chart are summarised (see right).

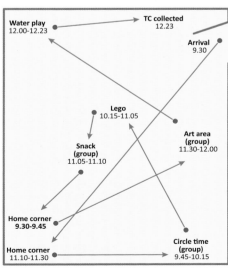

Excerpt from a flow chart observation

20.10 TABLES, PIE CHARTS AND BAR CHARTS

Strictly speaking, tables, pie charts and bar charts are not observation methods, but rather methods of representing information gathered about children in the workplace. They can be used to display information about virtually anything, but in the childcare setting they are usually used to display information about equipment usage.

CHILD	HOME CORNER	SAND	WATER	SMALL WORLD TOYS	BOOK AREA
Child A			✓	✓	
Child B	✓				✓
Child C	✓				✓
Child D	✓				
Child E		✓	✓	✓	✓
Child F					
Child G	✓	✓	✓	✓	
Child H	✓				

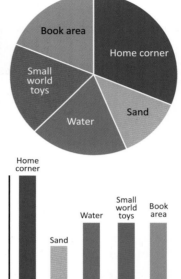

20.11 AUDIO RECORDINGS

It is advised that no video recording be carried out by students while doing observations. The reason for this is that the anonymity of the child cannot be preserved; they can be seen and their identities known. Audio recordings, on the other hand, can be used and are a useful way of recording language, especially when children get older and speak so quickly that it would be impossible to write down everything they say there and then. If you do decide to use an audio recording, e.g. recording on your phone, there are some points that you must consider.

* Permission should be sought from parents before recording the speech of any child.

* The child has the right to know that they are being recorded. Discuss it with them beforehand, answering any questions, e.g. 'Why are you recording me?'

* Proper transcription of taped conversation takes considerable time – make sure you allow for this.

* Recordings should be erased after transcription.

SHOW YOU KNOW

1. Describe three types of child observation techniques suitable for use in ELC settings.

2. 'Certain types of observation are suitable for observing different areas of development and some are used for specific purposes.' Discuss.

References

Ainsworth, M. (1979), 'Infant–mother attachment', *American Psychologist*, 34: 932–7.

Ainsworth, M.D., Blehar, M., Waters, E. and Wall, S. (1978), *Patterns of Attachment: A Psychological Study of the Strange Situation*. Hillsdale, NJ: Erlbaum.

Amato, P.R. (1993), 'Children's adjustment to divorce: Theories, hypotheses, and empirical support', *Journal of Marriage and the Family*, 55(1): 23–38.

Aspire (Asperger Syndrome Association of Ireland) (2009), *Development Plan 2007–2010*.

Aware (2021), 'Depression' <https://www.aware.ie/information/depression/> accessed 12 June 2021.

Baker, A.J. (2010), *Adult Children of Parental Alienation Syndrome: Breaking the Ties that Bind*. W.W. Norton & Co.

Bandura, A. (1977), *Social Learning Theory*. New York: General Learning Press.

Bates, G. (2017), 'The Drugs Situation in Ireland: An Overview of Trends from 2005 to 2015'. Liverpool: Centre for Public Health, Liverpool John Moores University.

Bauer, P. (2007), *Remembering the Times of Our Lives*. Mahwah, NJ: Erlbaum.

Beckerman, A., (1998), 'Charting a course: Meeting the challenge of permanency planning for children with incarcerated mothers', *Child Welfare*, 77(5): 513.

Bell, S. and Ainsworth, M. (1972), 'Infant crying and responsiveness', *Child Development*, 43: 1171–90.

Berko, J. (1958), 'The child's learning of English morphology', *Word*, 14: 145–69.

Blurton-Jones, N.G. and Konner, M.J. (1973), 'Sex differences in behaviour of London and Bushman children', in D.E. Papalia and S. Wendkos Olds, *Human Development* (7th edn). USA: McGraw-Hill.

Bouchard, T., Lykken, D., McGue, M., Segal, N. and Tellegen, A. (1990), 'Source of human psychological differences: The Minnesota Study of twins reared apart', *Science*, 250: 223–8.

Bowlby, J. (1958), 'The nature of the child's tie to his mother', *International Journal of Psychoanalysis*, 39: 350–73.

Bowlby, J. (1969), *Attachment and Loss* (Vol. 1). London: Hogarth Press.

Bronfenbrenner, U. (1991), 'What do families do?', *Family Affairs*, 4(1–2): 1–6.

Campbell (Reece, J.B., Urry, L.A., Cain, M.L., Wasserman, S.A., Minorsky, P.V. and Jackson, R.B.) (2015), *Campbell Biology* (10th edn). Melbourne, Victoria: Pearson.

Campbell, M. and Mottola, M. (2001), 'Recreational exercise and occupational safety during pregnancy and birth weight: A case control study', *American Journal of Obstetrics and Gynaecology*, 184: 403–8.

Clark, E. (1993), *The Lexicon in Acquisition*. New York: Cambridge University Press.

Collins, W. and van Dulmen, M. (2006), 'The Significance of Middle Childhood Peer Relationships in Early Adulthood', in A. Huston and M. Ripke (eds), *Developmental Contexts in Middle Childhood*. New York: Cambridge University Press.

Damon, W. (1988), *The Moral Child*. New York: Free Press.

de Onis, M., Blössner, M. and Borghi, E. (2012), 'Prevalence and trends of stunting among pre-school children', *Public Health Nutrition*, 15(1): 142–8, doi: 10.1017/S1368980011001315, accessed 15 June 2021.

DeCasper, A. and Spence, M. (1986), 'Prenatal maternal speech influences newborn's perception of speech sounds', *Infant Behaviour and Development*, 9, 133–50.

Deer, B. (2009), 'MMR doctor Andrew Wakefield fixed data on autism', *Sunday Post*, 8 February.

Department of Health (2010), *The Irish Health Behaviour in School-aged Children (HBSC) Study* <http://www.nuigalway.ie/hbsc/documents/nat_rep_hbsc_2010.pdf> accessed 21 June 2021.

Department of Health (2010), *National Standards for Pre-school Services* <https://www.gov.ie/en/publication/0308cf-national-standards-for-pre-school-services/> accessed 11 June 2021.

Diamond, A.D. (2007), 'Interrelated and interdependent', *Developmental Science*, 10: 152–8.

Donaldson, M. (1978), *Children's Minds*. London: Fontana.

Donaldson, M. and Hughes, M. (1978) in The Open University (2006) Media Kit, ED209: Child Development DVD-ROM (Media Kit Part 1, Video Band 1). Milton Keynes: Open University.

Dubow, E.F., Boxer, P. and Huesmann, L.R. (2009), 'Long-term effects of parents' education on children's educational and occupational success: Mediation by family interactions, child aggression, and teenage aspirations', *Merrill-Palmer Quarterly* (Wayne State University Press), 55(3): 224.

Dunn, J. (2007), 'Siblings and Socialisation', in J.E. Grusec and P.D. Hastings (eds), *Handbook of Socialization*. New York: Guilford.

Erikson, E. (1968), *Identity: Youth and Crisis*. London: Faber.

Fantz, R. (1963), 'Pattern vision in newborn infants', *Science*, 140: 296–7.

Farrell, C., McAvoy, H., Wilde, J. and Combat Poverty Agency (2008), *Tackling Health Inequalities – An All-Ireland Approach to Social Determinants*. Dublin: Combat Poverty Agency/Institute of Public Health in Ireland.

Fenson, L., Dale, P., Resnick, S., Bates, E., Thal, D. and Pethick, S.J. (1994), 'Variability in early communicative development', *Monographs of the Society for Research in Child Development*, 59: 74–5.

Fried, P.A. and Smith, A.M. (2001), 'A literature review of the consequences of prenatal marihuana exposure: An emerging theme of a deficiency in aspects of executive function', *Neurotoxicology and Teratology*, 23(1): 1–11.

Gesell, A. (1934), *Infancy and Human Growth*. New York: Macmillan.

Gibbons, J. and Ng, S. (2004), 'Acting bilingual and thinking bilingual', *Journal of Language and Social Psychology*, 23: 4–6.

Gibson, E. and Walk, R. (1960), 'The "visual cliff"', *Scientific American*, 202: 67–71.

Glover, V., Miles, R., Matta, S., Modi, N. and Stevenson, J. (2005), 'Glucocorticoid exposure in preterm babies predicts saliva cortisol response to immunization at 4 months', *Pediatric Research*, 58(6): 1233–7.

Greenhaus, J.H., Collins, K.M. and Shaw, J.D. (2003), 'The relation between work–family balance and quality of life', *Journal of Vocational Behavior*, 63(3): 510–31.

Guralnick, M.J. (1998), 'Effectiveness of early intervention for vulnerable children: A developmental perspective', *American Journal on Mental Retardation*, 102(4): 319–45.

Harlow, H. (1958), 'The nature of love', *American Psychologist*, 13: 673–85.

Harris, M., Jones, D. and Grant, J. (1983), 'The non-verbal context of mothers' speech to infants', *First Language*, 4: 21–30.

Hart, B. and Risley, T.R. (1995), *Meaningful Differences in the Everyday Experience of Young American Children*. New York: Brooks Publishing.

Harter, S. (1985), *Self-perception Profile for Children*. Denver: University of Denver, Department of Psychology.

Hoffman, M. (1970), 'Moral Development', in M. Bornstein (ed.), *Manual of Child Psychology* (3rd edn, Vol. 2). New York: Wiley.

Holt, J. (1983), *How Children Learn* (revised edn). London: Penguin Books.

HSE (Health Service Executive) (2020), *Vital Statistics Yearly Summary* Table 1a: Marriages, Civil Partnerships, Births, Deaths and Natural Increase by Number 2010–2021. CSO statistical information.

Irish Autism Action (2021), 'What is Autism?' <https://autism.ie/information/faq/what-is-autism/> accessed 15 June 2021.

Jacob, T. and Leonard, K. (1986), 'Psychosocial functioning in children of alcoholic fathers, depressed fathers and control fathers', *Journal of Studies on Alcohol*, 47(5): 373–80.

Kagan, J. (1987), 'Perspectives on Infancy', in J. Osofsky (ed.), *Handbook on Infant Development*. New York: Wiley.

Kelley, S.J. (1998), 'Stress and coping behaviors of substance-abusing mothers', *Journal for Specialists in Pediatric Nursing*, 3(3): 103–10.

Kohlberg, L. (1958), 'The Development of Modes of Thinking and Choices in Years 10 to 16', PhD dissertation, University of Chicago.

Kotowska, I.E., Matysiak, A. and Styrc, M. (2010), *Second European Quality of Life Survey: Family Life and Work*. European Foundation for the Improvement of Living and Working Conditions.

Kramer, L. and Radley, C. (1997), 'Improving sibling relationships among young children: a social skills training model', *Family Relations*, 46: 237–46.

Labov, W. (1969), *The Study of Nonstandard English*. Washington, DC: National Council of Teachers of English.

Layte, R. and McCrory, C. (2011), 'Growing Up in Ireland – Overweight and Obesity in 9-Year-Olds' <https://www.esri.ie/publications/growing-up-in-ireland-overweight-and-obesity-among-9-year-olds> accessed 17 June 2021.

Leslie, E.J., Carlson, J.C., Shaffer, J.R., Feingold, E., Wehby, G., Laurie, C.A., Jain, D., Laurie, C.C., Doheny, K.F., McHenry, T. and Resick, J. (2016), 'A multi-ethnic genome-wide association study identifies novel loci for non-syndromic cleft lip with or without cleft palate on 2p24. 2, 17q23 and 19q13', *Human Molecular Genetics*, 25(13): 2862–72.

Levinson, D. (1978), *The Seasons of a Man's Life*. New York: Knopf.

Levitin, D.J. and Bellugi, U. (2006), 'Rhythm, Timbre and Hyperacusis in Williams-Beuren Syndrome' in C. Morris, H. Lenhoff and P. Wang, *Williams-Beuren Syndrome: Research and Clinical Perspectives*, pp. 343–58.

Loomes, R., Hull, L. and Mandy, W.P.L. (2017), 'What is the male-to-female ratio in autism spectrum disorder? A systematic review and meta-analysis', *Journal of the American Academy of Child and Adolescent Psychiatry*, 56(6): 466–74.

McAvoy (2006), www.combatpoverty.ie.

Maccoby, E. (2007), 'Historical Overview of Socialisation Theory and Research', in J.E. Grusec and P.D. Hastings (eds), *Handbook of Socialization*. New York: Guilford.

Maccoby, E.E. and Martin, J.A. (1983), 'Socialization in the Context of the Family: Parent–Child interaction', in P.H. Mussen (ed.), *Handbook of Child Psychology*, Vol. 4.

McLanahan, S. and Booth, K. (1989), 'Mother-only families: Problems, prospects, and politics', *Journal of Marriage and the Family*, 557–80.

Meier, P.S., Donmall, M.C. and McElduff, P. (2004), 'Characteristics of drug users who do or do not have care of their children', *Addiction*, 99(8): 955–61.

Minett, P. (2005), *Child Care and Development* (5th edn). UK: Hodder Arnold.

Minsky, R. (1996), *Psychoanalysis and Gender*. London: Routledge.

NCCA (National Council for Curriculum and Assessment) (2009), *Aistear – The Early Childhood Curriculum Framework, Principles and Themes*. Dublin: NCCA.

NCCA (2009), *Aistear – The Early Childhood Curriculum Framework, Guidelines for Good Practice*. Dublin: NCCA.

Neppl, T.K., Conger, R.D., Scaramella, L.V. and Ontai, L.L. (2009), 'Intergenerational continuity in parenting behavior: Mediating pathways and child effects', *Developmental Psychology*, 45(5): 1241.

Nettle, D. (2003), 'Intelligence and class mobility in the British population', *British Journal of Psychology*, 94: 551–61.

Nieuwenhuis, R. (2020), *The Situation of Single Parents in the EU*. European Parliament, Policy Department for Citizens' Rights and Constitutional Affairs.

O'Moore, A.M. (1997), *Nationwide Study on Bullying Behaviour in Irish Schools*. Dublin: Trinity College.

O'Hara, M.W. and Swain, A.M. (1996), 'Rates and risk of postpartum depression: A meta-analysis', *International Review of Psychiatry*, 8(1): 37–54.

Piaget, J. (1932), *The Moral Judgement of the Child*. New York: Harcourt Brace Jovanovich.

Piaget, J. and Inhelder, B. (1969), *The Child's Conception of Space*. New York: W.W. Horton.

Pollard, I. (2007), 'Neuropharmacology of drugs and alcohol in mother and foetus', *Seminars in Foetal and Neonatal Medicine*, 12.

Pressley, M. (2007), 'Achieving Best Practices', in L. Gambrell, L. Morrow and M. Pressley (eds), *Best Practices in Literacy Instruction*. New York: Guilford.

Rolfe, G., Freshwater, D. and Jasper, M. (2001). *Critical Reflection for Nursing and the Helping Professions: A User's Guide*. UK: Palgrave Macmillan.

Rosenberg, M. (1965), *Society and the Adolescent Self-image*. Princeton, NJ: Princeton University Press.

Rutter, M. (1987), 'Psychosocial resilience and protective mechanisms', *American Journal of Orthopsychiatry*, 57(3): 316–31.

Santrock, J. (2009), *Child Development* (12th edn.). New York: McGraw-Hill.

Schaffer, H. (1996), *Social Development*. Cambridge: Houghton Mifflin.

Shayer, M. and Wylam, H. (1978), 'The distribution of Piagetian stages of thinking in British middle and secondary school children II', *British Journal of Educational Psychology*, 48: 62–70.

Sheridan, M., revised and updated by Sharma, A. and Cockerill, H. (1997), *From Birth to 5 Years* (3rd edn). UK: Routledge.

Síolta (The National Quality Framework for Early Childhood Education) (2010), *Síolta User Manual*. Dublin: Department of Education and Skills, Early Years Education Policy Unit.

Skinner, B.F. (1957), *Verbal Learning*. New York: Appleton-Century-Crofts.

Spohr, H.L., Williams, J. and Steinhausen, H.C. (2007), 'Foetal alcohol spectrum disorders in young adulthood', *Journal of Pediatrics*, 150.

Sweeney, M.R., Egan, E. and Kelly, F. (2021), 'Voluntary folic acid fortification levels of food staples in Ireland continue to decline: Further implications for passive folic acid intakes?', *Journal of Public Health*, 43(2): 281–6.

Sylva, K. and Lunt, I. (1980), *Child Development*. London: Blackwell Publishing.

Thelen, E. (2000), 'Perception and Motor Development', in A. Kazdin (ed.), *Encyclopedia of Psychology*. Washington, DC and New York: American Psychological Association and Oxford University Press.

Thomas, A. and Chess, S. (1977), *Temperament and Development*. New York: Brunner/Mazel.

Towle, C. (1931), 'The evaluation and management of marital situation in foster homes', *American Journal of Orthopsychiatry*, 1(3): 271.

Van Meurs, K. (1999), 'Cigarette smoking, pregnancy and the developing fetus', *Stanford Medical Review*, 1(1): 14–16.

Vygotsky, L.S. (1978), 'Socio-cultural theory', *Mind in Society*, 6: 52–8.

Wallerstein, J.S. and Blakeslee, S. (1989), *Second Chances: Men, Women, and Children a Decade After Divorce*. Boston, MA: Ticknor and Fields.

Wentzel, K. and Asher, S. (1995), 'The academic lives of neglected, rejected, popular and controversial children', *Child Development*, 66: 754–63.

WHO (World Health Organization) (2005), 'Sickle-cell Anaemia: Report by the Secretariat', 59th World Health Assembly.

WHO (2006), *Lexicon of Alcohol and Drug Terms* <http://www.who.int/substance_abuse/terminology/who_lexicon/en/> accessed 13 June 2021.

Wikipedia (online) 'Attention deficit hyperactivity disorder' <http://en.wikipedia.org/wiki/Attention-deficit_hyperactivity_disorder>.

Wilens, T.E., Biederman, J., Licsw, E.B., Hahesy, B.A., Anaabrantes, B.A., Deborahneft, A., Millstein, R. and Spencer, T.J. (2002), 'A family study of the high-risk children of opioid- and alcohol-dependent parents', *American Journal on Addictions*, 11(1): 41–51.

Winnicott, D.W. (1973), *The Child, the Family, and the Outside World*. Harmondsworth: Penguin Books.

World Nuclear Association (2020), 'Nuclear Power in the World Today', updated June 2021 <https://world-nuclear.org/information-library/current-and-future-generation/nuclear-power-in-the-world-today.aspx>.

Zuravin, S.J. and DiBlasio, F.A. (1992), 'Child-neglecting adolescent mothers: How do they differ from their nonmaltreating counterparts?', *Journal of Interpersonal Violence*, 7(4): 471–89.

Websites

Central Statistics Agency – www.cso.ie

HSE (information on crisis pregnancies) – www.crisispregnancy.ie

Irish Health (information for health professionals) – www.irishhealthpro.com

Oireachtas debates – https://www.oireachtas.ie/en/debates/find/

Organisation for Economic Co-operation and Development – www.oecd.org

Index

A

accommodation (cognitive development) 87

active learning 96–7

adaptation 87

additional needs *see also* special needs

children with 206

identifying 7

adult-led activities 252–3

AIDS 58, 156

Ainsworth, Mary 116

Aistear 34–5

assessment 272–3

building relationships 246

child's uniqueness 230

cognitive development 97–9

dispositions 244

diversity 230–1

emotional development 125

equality 231

equipment 257–8

information sharing 235–7

interactions 241

language development 110–11

learning environments 255

learning record 278

parents/guardians 221, 226, 229–30

physical development 74–5

relevant and meaningful experiences 262–3

social development 143–5

social modelling 249

themes 20–1, 273

thinking skills 252

alcohol 43, 55–6, 185, 197, 208

Alcohol Action Ireland 199–200

alcohol use disorder (alcoholism) 199–201, 217

allergies 175

alpha-fetoprotein (AFP) test 51

Amato 205

amnesia, infantile/childhood 77

amniocentesis 52

amniotic sac 44

analytical intelligence 94

animism 89

antenatal care 49–52

antisocial behaviour 141–2

anxiety 61, 198 *see also* separation anxiety; stranger anxiety

Apgar scale 53–4

Aristotle 3

Asher, S. 130

Asperger, Hans 164

Asperger's syndrome (AS) 164–5

Aspire 164

assimilation (cognitive development) 87

assisted delivery 46

asthma 174–6

inhalers 175–6

astigmatism 83

attachment 115

attachment behaviours 116

attachment theories 14, 115–18

evaluation 117–18

attention deficit hyperactivity disorder (ADHD) 184–6, 201

attention span 79

audio recordings 300

autistic spectrum disorder (ASD) 141

auditory learning style 96

auditory processing deficits 165

autism 162–4

autistic spectrum disorder (ASD) 162–5

autonomous morality 133

Aware 197

B

Babinski reflex 69

Bandura, Albert 131–2, 135, 249

bar charts (in observation) 300

Barlow's test 54

Barnardos 213, 239

Bates 200

Bauer, P. 77

Baumrind, Diana 196

Beckerman 201

Beckwith-Wiedemann syndrome 151

behaviour management 142–3

behaviour modification 85–6

behavioural therapy 186

behaviourist theories (child development) 8, 10, 84–6

of language development 109

bereavement 267–8

Bernstein, Basil 212

bilingualism 107

bioecological systems theory 138–9

biological maturation theory 67

birth weight 64

Blakeslee 205

blindness 83, 182 *see also* visual impairment

causes of 57–8

blood incompatibility 57

bobo doll experiment 132

Notes